★
**The Most
Idiosyncratic
Hotel Guide
in
the
World**

★ Cover illustration by Chloë Cheese
★ Cover design by Robert Updegraff
★ Illustrations by Natacha Ledwidge

THE
300 BEST HOTELS
IN THE WORLD

CHOSEN BY RENE LECLER

MACMILLAN

First edition 1975
Second edition 1978
Third edition 1980
Fourth edition reprinted 1983

This edition first published 1985 by
MACMILLAN LONDON LIMITED
4 Little Essex Street London WC2R 3LF
and Basingstoke

Associated companies in Auckland, Delhi, Dublin, Gaborone,
Hamburg, Harare, Hong Kong, Johannesburg, Kuala Lumpur, Lagos,
Manzini, Melbourne, Mexico City, Nairobi, New York, Singapore
and Tokyo

Typeset by Rowland Phototypesetting Ltd
Bury St Edmunds, Suffolk

Printed in Hong Kong

British Library Cataloguing in Publication Data

Lecler, René
　The 300 best hotels in the world.—5th ed
　1. Hotels, taverns, etc.—Directories
　I. Title
　647′.94　　　TX907

ISBN 0-333-37595-5

CONTENTS

FOREWORD

Welcome to the fifth edition of THE 300 BEST HOTELS IN THE WORLD.

The book is celebrating its tenth birthday and little did I know a decade ago that it would be on the market-place for ever and ever and become a true perennial. My only interest then, as it is now, was the pursuit of perfection in hotel-keeping plus a generous portion of personal preferences and prejudices and the feeling that a dash of *je ne sais quoi* can make a hotel memorable wherever it is. Obviously, I was not alone and over the years I have been truly amazed by the number of people around the world who felt as I did – that travel is a direct reflection of one's lifestyle.

What began almost as a labour of love has turned out to be a one-man industry – with a lot of help from others. My own hotel notes, which started life in a small cardboard box, have now become the jam-packed contents of three huge steel filing cabinets, and I do not believe that there are many potentially good hotels anywhere from Seattle to Sydney that I have not investigated either personally or by proxy.

This edition contains thirty-seven new names (and naturally thirty-seven casualties which I very much regret). With respect to this final judgment, readers of all nationalities have been my real friends in need. Each edition of THE 300 BEST HOTELS IN THE WORLD gives rise to between 1500 and 2000 letters from people who care about travel and the places in which they stay when travelling. Hundreds of them write exceedingly useful letters, both critical and eulogistic and, though it is not always easy to answer them all, every letter is carefully filed, cross-indexed and constantly referred to. I have met some of the writers of these letters at the oddest spots between Thailand and Brazil and it always feels like meeting old friends.

I am quite certain that it is this feed-back that has allowed this operation *not* to become a business. Who needs staff and inspectors when he has at his disposal the expertise of many discerning people who travel at their own expense and pass on their own comments? So, I say a sincere thank you to all of you.

The book has remained very much a *personal* affair – 'the most idiosyncratic hotel guide in the world' as we say on the cover, and it is my firm intention to keep it so. This is not a hotel directory or a credit-card compendium. It is a list of the hotels I like and admire, quite properly underlined by the feelings of readers and members of the staff of *Harpers & Queen*, the illustrious British magazine that it has been my privilege to serve for a quarter of a century. For these reasons, the book has happily remained *totally* uncommercial, though the temptations to the contrary have been great at times. It will remain so. We do not accept advertising of any kind, either officially or unofficially. There is no commercial connection and we are not indebted to anyone. *Entry in the book is free of charge* – no hotel has ever paid to be included and I believe that both readers and hotel people are well aware of that. When I visit a hotel for the first time I do so incognito as far as possible and hotel people whose establishments are listed never really know whether they are to be included in a new edition until it is published. By now, of course, having visited more than 3000 hotels in 103 countries, it is inevitable that people should know me and my easily recognizable name – there is nothing I can do about that – but the friendship and approval of real hotel experts is very precious to me.

Over the years the nature of THE 300 BEST HOTELS IN THE WORLD has moved slightly sideways. The number of great hotels in great cities has continued to grow but I have tried to move away from the obvious. Anyone who travels regularly to London, Paris or New York has his own favourite hostelry and nothing that I might say is likely to change his mind. Such hotels must be included simply because they are there. On the whole, I have tried to go further afield, to include hotels in unlikely places where one would not expect anything very special. I feel it is my duty as a professional traveller to open new windows, clear new paths and encourage people to go to places they may not have known about. In the last edition, when I first listed Karawari Lodge in Papua New Guinea, people thought I was mad. Three of them wrote and said so and several others implied it. I have news for them: in the past two years, just over 250 people who had read the book have stayed at Karawari Lodge (it's not exactly next door . . .) and loved it for what it is – a very unusual hotel in an extremely odd location. One American TV moghul wrote: 'Karawari Lodge was the experience of a lifetime for my wife and myself. We will never forget it!' That warms the cockles of my heart.

Yet there is a strange anomaly here. In no way could Karawari Lodge be compared with, for instance, the Oriental in Bangkok or the Pierre in New York. I feel it is my duty to spread the fame of all of them and I am never happier than when I discover a hotel in an offbeat location, run by a man who has staked his all on making a success of it in spite of hair-raising difficulties. In my opinion, that man deserves a medal.

So I try to give the book as wide a geographical context as possible. Some people object to the density of listed hotels in certain countries and say: 'How can you have nineteen hotels in France and thirty-three in the United States when everyone knows that French hotels are the best in the world?' Chauvinism? Ignorance? Possibly. In my view the United States, being so much larger than France, deserves more entries – so long as they are really remarkable places, and anyone who has stayed at the Remington in Dallas or the Stanford Court in San Francisco will, I believe, agree with me.

In many ways – with a few exceptions – bad hotels are getting worse and great hotels are getting greater. Last year, Hong Kong's Mandarin celebrated its twenty-first birthday and,

looking back, its birth was possibly the watershed when it came to really fine city hotels of a new generation. Anyone else could only imitate and they have done so. Most chain hotels are getting better all the time – they have realized that opening sixteen new hotels every year was not really the name of the game. The Gulf is a case in point – an area where many vast caravanserais were built quickly in a period of boom and where so many are falling apart now that the boom has gone bust. The survivors will inevitably be the good ones. Knowing my fondness for Eastern hotels, one famous London hotelier said to me: 'If I could have two staff for every guest I too could run a better hotel!' That is not my fault or his. Perhaps he ought to emigrate?

Yet, when it comes to individual excellence, it is hard to beat the smaller, personalized, family-run hotel – examples of this type are numerous in Britain, Germany and France. The personal touch rates very highly in hotels and there is no real substitute. For myself, above all, I admire professionalism – the professionalism of the man who has gone through the mill, learned and applied the right techniques to his own particular case. This is why, as I have stated in previous editions, I often follow general managers rather than hotels. If one GM leaves his post, I might leave with him and go where he is going. I have rarely been wrong.

Now, for those who are joining us for the first time, let us make a few things clear.

★ I do not award stars or grade hotels in any way. Long ago I decided that to give three stars to this hotel and two to that one was not only an expression of the selector's own judgment – not always perfect – but implied an element of comparison, which is inappropriate. One can compare hotels within one country or one city but not on a worldwide basis.

★ If a hotel is not in the book, it does not necessarily mean that it is no good – simply that I do not know it and have received no comments about it one way or another. Just one of those things.

★ I take great care not to go automatically for what is loosely called luxury, although at first glance luxury affects me just as it does everyone else. It is the second glance that counts. Absent from this edition, for instance, is one brand new hotel in Southern Asia billed by its promoters as 'the greatest thing since the Moghuls. . . .' It is indeed a beautiful hotel, with acres of marble, vistas of colourful seating and quite gorgeous carpets. There is also an incongruous and quite unnecessary escalator which only the local children appear to like and one gets the feeling that the management ought to provide each arriving guest with a bicycle to get to the reception desk. That is a show-off, a convention hotel, and it is not for me. Nor, I hope, for you.

★ Some people have accused me of choosing only expensive hotels. This is quite untrue. Some hotels in this book are perfectly reasonable in price. It is simply that in these inflationary days the best is rarely cheap.

★ The factual part of each entry gives me more trouble than my own comments! It is of course supplied by the hotel concerned and whilst one can tone down corporate exuberance it is not always possible for me to go and measure a bathroom in the South Pacific. Room standards also vary, sometimes considerably, within one hotel. The upgrading is continuous. The best way to insure yourself against disappointment is to ask to see your room *before* your luggage is delivered. If the hotel GM is a real professional he and his staff won't mind at all. Previous editions contained many hints on what to look for so it would be invidious to repeat them. But in general, make sure that the room is really what you want and expect for the price. In-spect the bedside lighting (often notoriously bad), the firmness of the mattress (on both sides of the bed . . .), look at the cleanliness or otherwise of the waste pipes in the bathroom. Make sure that there is enough space for you to open your luggage comfortably – this is often a weak point in hotel design. If noise is objectionable to you (as 'musak' in general is to me) look to see that your room is reasonably well insulated. Above all, don't hesitate to complain – *immediately* – and confine your complaints to specific points.

★ Keep abreast of changes in the world of hotels and one of the ways of doing this (besides making me a little richer . . .) is to make sure that you buy *every* edition of THE 300 BEST HOTELS IN THE WORLD. People often write to me about hotels that have been sent to the guillotine in the current edition. The book is published every two years, usually in the early spring.

Three final points for those who read this book.

Do write in, air your views and tell us where you think we are right or wrong. Your views are never, but *never*, ignored and they will help to make the next edition even better. THE 300 BEST HOTELS IN THE WORLD relies on your own experience.

For your interest, the Hotel Guide now has a companion volume: THE WORLD SHOPPING GUIDE (not a credit-card compendium but a serious book listing the things that are worth buying in seventy-eight countries). Do ask for it.

As I have stated, the book is totally non-commercial and it thrives on its sales alone. If you like it, tell your friends, talk about it, spread the word and help us to ensure that THE 300 BEST HOTELS IN THE WORLD is widely read by people of taste and discrimination and for all those who value quality in their travel.

HOTEL REPRESENTATION AND RESERVATION COMPANIES

ADDRESSES AND TELEPHONE NUMBERS CHANGE FREQUENTLY.
IN CASE OF DOUBT, READERS SHOULD CONSULT THEIR LOCAL
DIRECTORY AND/OR ACCREDITED TRAVEL AGENT.

ABERCROMBIE & KENT INT INC
LONDON: 42 Sloane Street, London, SW1X 9LV. 01-235-9761
U.S.A.: 100 Oak Brook Road, Oak Brook, Illinois 60521. (800) 323 3602

AER LINGUS
LONDON: Aer Lingus House, 52 Poland Street, London, W1V 4AA.
01-734-1212
NEW YORK: 122 East 42nd Street, New York, N.Y. 10017. (212) 557–1090
(Executive offices); (212) 557-1110 (Reservations)
and worldwide

AIR FRANCE
LONDON: 158 New Bond Street, London, W1Y OAY. 01-400-9511
NEW YORK: 666 Fifth Avenue, New York, N.Y. 10019. (212) 247-0100
and worldwide

AIRTOURS INTERNATIONAL
FRANKFURT: Gartnerweg 4–8, D-6 Frankfurt/m. 79-281

MARK ALLAN TRAVEL LTD
LONDON: 130 Mount Street, Berkeley Square, London, W1Y 5HH.
01-491-3200

AMERICAN WOLFE INTERNATIONAL
NEW YORK: 500 Fifth Avenue, New York, N.Y. 10036. (212) 730-8100

ASTIR HOTEL CO INC
LONDON: 204–208 Tottenham Court Road, London, W1P 9LA. 01-636-0818
BRUSSELS: 75 Defacqz Street, 1050 Brussels, Belgium. (02) 538-8112

ATESA
PARIS: 28 Rue Saint Marc, 75002 Paris, France. 073-3440

AUSTRIAN AIRLINES
LONDON: 50/51 Conduit Street, London, W1R ONP. 01-439-0741

BAHAMAS RESERVATION SERVICE
LONDON: 23 Old Bond Street, London, W1X 4PQ. 01-491-4800
U.S.A.: 255 Alhambra Circle, Coral Gables, Florida 33143. (305) 442-4860
FRANKFURT: Poststrasse 2–4, 6000 Frankfurt/m. (0611) 25 20 27

BEST OF GREECE
U.K.: Rock House, Boughton Monchelsea, Maidstone, Kent. 0622 46678

BEST WESTERN HOTELS
U.S.A.: PO Box 10203, Phoenix, Arizona, Arizona 85064. (2602) 957-4200 tollfree except Arizona (1-800) 528-1234

BRENDAN TOURS
U.S.A.: 510 West Sixth Street, Los Angeles, California 90014. (213) 488–9191

BRITISH AIRWAYS
LONDON: West London Terminal, Cromwell Road, London, SW7 4ED. 01-370-4255

BRITISH TRANSPORT HOTELS LTD
LONDON: St. Pancras Chambers, Euston Road, London, NW1 2TU. 01-387-2878
NEW YORK: 185 Madison Avenue, New York, N.Y. 10006. (212) 684-1820.

R.M. BROOKER LTD
UK: PO Box 90, 1 Old Hall Street, Liverpool, L69 3EP. (051) 236-9306/7

CANADIAN NATIONAL RAILWAYS
LONDON: 17 Cockspur Street, London, SW1Y 5BS. 01-930-2150
CANADA: CN Hotels, 4th Floor, 700 Dorchester Boulevard West, Montreal, Quebec. (514) 877-3643

CIGA – ITALIAN GRAND HOTELS LTD
LONDON: 67 Jermyn Street, London, SW1. 01-930-4147
NEW YORK: 745 Fifth Avenue, New York, N.Y. 10022. (212) 935-9540
FRANKFURT: Barckhausstrasse 4, D-6000 Frankfurt/m. (0611) 72 97 44
ROME: Via Piemonte 32, 00187 Rome. 475-7198
PARIS: 22 rue de L'Arcade, Paris 75008. 265-8434

JOYCE B. CLARKE ASSOC
MONTREAL: Suite 402, 1117 St. Catherine West, Montreal, Canada 43B 149. (514) 844-4421

COMFORT HOTELS INTERNATIONAL
WASHINGTON: 1735 Eye Street, NW Washington DC, DC 20006. (202) 872 0770

CUNARD
LONDON: see Windotel Ltd
NEW YORK: Cunard, 555 Fifth Avenue, New York, N.Y. 10017. (212) 880-7390

DAN HOTEL GROUP
LONDON: Roxburghe House, 273/287 Regent Street, London, W1R 7PB. 01-499-4597
NEW YORK: 120 East 56th Street, New York, N.Y. 10022. (212) 752-6120
TEL AVIV: 99 Hayarkon Street, Tel Aviv, Israel. 03-241141
ZURICH: Talstrasse 82, 8001 Zurich, Switzerland. 01-211-7302

CLAUDE L.C. DUTEIL
PARIS: 11 rue de Rome, Paris 75008. 522-1034

EXP-O-TEL (HOTEL RESERVATIONS) LTD
LONDON: Banda House, Cambridge Grove, London, W6 OLE. 01-568-8765

MURIEL FLEGER INTERNATIONAL
ONTARIO: 500 University Avenue, Toronto, Ontario, Canada, M5G 1V7

FOUR SEASONS HOTELS LTD
LONDON: Inn on the Park, Hamilton Place, London, W1A 1AZ. 01-499-0888
CANADA: 1100 Eglinton East Avenue, Toronto, Ontario M3C 1HB. (416) 444-2561
NEW YORK: Pierre Hotel, Fifth and 61st Street, New York, N.Y. 10021. (212) 838-8000

GERMAN NATIONAL TOURIST OFFICE
LONDON: 61 Conduit Street, London, W1R OEN. 01-734-2600
NEW YORK: 747 Third Avenue, New York, N.Y. 10017. (212) 308-3300

GOLDEN TULIP HOTELS RESERVATION SERVICE
See K.L.M. Royal Dutch Airlines

HILTON RESERVATION SERVICE
LONDON: 6 Bedford Avenue, London, WC1. 01-631-1767
NEW YORK: 401 Seventh Avenue, New York, N.Y. 10001. (212) 594-4500
and worldwide/any Hilton Hotel

IBERIAN SERVICES LTD
LONDON: 116 Judd Street, London, WC1H 9NS. 01-837-4325

IBEROTEL SYSTEM
FRANKFURT: M. Kirchnesstrasse 6–8, Frankfurt. (0611) 20971

INTER-CONTINENTAL HOTELS CORP
LONDON: Park Towers, Old Park Lane, London, W1. 01-491-7181
NEW YORK: 200 Park Avenue, New York, N.Y. 10166. (212) 973–3800
and worldwide/any Inter-Continental Hotel

IRISH TOURIST BOARD
LONDON: Ireland House, 150 New Bond Street, London, W1Y OAQ. 01-493-3201
NEW YORK: 590 Fifth Avenue, New York, N.Y. 10036. (212) 246-7400

ISRAEL HOTEL REPRESENTATIVE
NEW YORK: 120 East 56th Street, New York, N.Y. 10022. (212) 752-6120

JAPAN TRAVEL BUREAU INTERNATIONAL INC
NEW YORK: 45 Rockefeller Plaza, New York, N.Y. 10020. (212) 246-8030

HARRY JARVINEN & ASSOCIATES
NEW YORK: 25 West 43rd Street, New York, N.Y. 10036. (212) 354-2077
LOS ANGELES: 1717 North Highland Avenue, Los Angeles, California 90028.
(213) 462-6391 tollfree except California (1–800) 421-0767

K.L.M. ROYAL DUTCH AIRLINES (Golden Tulip Hotels Reservation Service)
LONDON: Time and Life Building, 153 New Bond Street, London, W1Y OAD. 01-568-9144
NEW YORK: 437 Madison Avenue, New York, N.Y. 10022. (212) 247-7950

KEYTEL INTERNATIONAL UK LTD
LONDON: Edgware Road, London, W2 1ED. 01-402-8182/3/4

KNIGHTSBRIDGE MARKETING SERVICE INC
FRAMINGHAM: 1661 Worcester Road, Massachusetts 01701, U.S.A. (800) 982-4770 (Massachusetts); (800) 255-2230 tollfree elsewhere

LANDMARK INTERNATIONAL HOTELS LTD
LONDON: Landmark House, 1 Great Scotland Yard, London, SW1A 2HJ. 01-930-1735

NICHOLAS LAWSON LTD
LONDON: 30 Old Bond Street, London, W1Y 3AD. 01-491-7431

RALPH LOCKE
NEW YORK: 315 East 72nd Street, New York, N.Y. 10021. (212) 628–8149. Outside New York (800) 223–1108

LOEWS REPRESENTATION INTERNATIONAL
LONDON: 30 Old Bond Street, London, W1X 3AD. 01-541-1199
NEW YORK: 666 Fifth Avenue, New York, N.Y. 10019. (212) 841-1111 and worldwide
LOS ANGELES: 8380 Melrose Avenue, Room 301–02, Los Angeles, California 90069. (213) 651-3134
FRANKFURT: Hans Regh Associates, Holbeinstrasse 25, 6000 Frankfurt/m. (0611) 612083
JAPAN: c/o Palace Hotel Arcade, 1-1-1 Marunouchi, Chiyoda-Ku, Tokyo. 215-5141

MANDARIN INTERNATIONAL HOTELS LTD
LONDON: 15 New Bridge Street, London, EC4V 6AU. 01-583-3411
NEW YORK: 747 Third Avenue, New York, N.Y. 10017. (212) 752-9710
LOS ANGELES: 6151 West Century Blvd, Los Angeles, California 90045. (213) 649-1634
HONG KONG: Connaught Centre, 2/F Hong Kong. 5-221142

MARKETING AHEAD INC
NEW YORK: 515 Madison Avenue, New York, N.Y. 10022. (212) 759-5170

MARRIOTT HOTELS INC
LONDON: 25 Southampton Street, London, WC2E 7JH. 01-836-8521
U.S.A.: Marriott Drive, Washington, DC 20058. (800) 228-9290 tollfree

McDONOUGH HOTELS
U.S.A.: PO Box 1825, Parkesburg, WV 26101. (800) 624-1921

MERIDIEN RESERVATION INTERNATIONAL
LONDON: Air France House, 158 New Bond Street, London, W1Y OAY. 01-491-3516
NEW YORK: 1350 Avenue of the Americas, New York, N.Y. 10019. (212) 841-7499
and any Air France office worldwide

JOHN MILLER
SYDNEY: Scottish House, 17/19 Bridge Street, Sydney, NSW 2000. 241-2727

DAVID B. MITCHELL & CO INC
NEW YORK: 200 Madison Avenue, New York, N.Y. 10016. (212) 371-1323

MORRIS ASSOCIATES LTD
LONDON: Chase Garden House, Chase Side, Enfield, Middlesex.
01-367-5175

RAY MORROW ASSOCIATES
U.S.A.: 360 Main Street, Ridgefield, Connecticut, Connecticut 06877. (203)
438-3793 tollfree except Connecticut (800) 243-9420

ERNEST J. NEWMAN INC
NEW YORK: 770 Broadway, New York, N.Y. 10003. (212) 420-0360

OBEROI HOTELS
LONDON: Loews Representation International, 30 Old Bond Street, London,
W1X 3AD. 01-541-1199
NEW YORK: 7th Floor, 300 East 42nd Street, New York, N.Y. 10017. (800)
223-1474
SYDNEY: 5th Floor, 50 Pitt Street, Sydney, WLNSW 2000. 276 061
JAKARTA: Hotel Kartika Plaza, 10 Jln Thamrin, Jakarta, Indonesia. 321108

PREFERRED HOTELS ASSOCIATION
TORONTO: Prince Hotel, 900 York Mills Road, Toronto, Canada M3B 3H2.
(800) 323 7500 (U.S.A. except Illinois), (800) 942 7400 (Illinois)

PRESTIGE HOTELS
LONDON: 13–14 Golden Square, London, W1R 3AG. 01-734-6446

PRINCESS RESERVATION SERVICE (SBM)
GERMANY: Butznickelstrasse 32, D-6246 Schlossborn/TS, Glasshutten 2.
06174 6904

PRINCESS HOTELS INTERNATIONAL
LONDON: Regent Arcade House, 252–260 Regent Street, London, W1R 5DA.
01-439-8027
NEW YORK: 805 Third Avenue, New York, N.Y. 10022. (212) 715-7000
SAN FRANCISCO: c/o Sir Francis Drake Hotel, Sutter & Powell Streets,
California 94101. (415) 392–7755

QANTAS AIRWAYS
LONDON: 500 Chiswick High Road, London, W4 5RW. 01-995-1344
NEW YORK: 542 Fifth Avenue, New York, N.Y. 10022. (800) 227-4500

REGENT INTERNATIONAL HOTELS
LONDON: 149 Sloane Street, London, SW1X 9BZ. 01-730-8687
NEW YORK: 122 East 55th Street, New York, N.Y. 10022. (212) 935-4950
LOS ANGELES: 8730 Wilshire Blvd. (213) 652 1454
SINGAPORE: Orchard Plaza, Orchard Road. 737-3555
TOKYO: Yurakucho Building, 1-10-1 Yurakucho Chiyoda-ku. (03) 211 4541

ROBERT REID ASSOCIATES
LONDON: Walmar House, 288 Regent Street, London W1R 5HE.
01-580-8313/4
NEW YORK: 1270 Avenue of the Americas, New York, N.Y. 10020. (212)
757-2444

RELAIS ET CHATEAUX
PARIS: Hotel de Crillon, 10 Place de la Concorde, 75008 Paris. 742-0020

RESINTER NOVOTEL
LONDON: 1 Shortlands, London, W6. 01-724-1000
PARIS: 2 rue de la Mare Neuve, 91019 Evry Cedex. (6) 077-2727

ROCKRESORTS RESERVATIONS INC
NEW YORK: 30 Rockefeller Plaza, New York, N.Y. 10019. (212) 765-5950

SBM/SOCIETY HOTELS
LONDON: 1 Sherwood Street, Piccadilly Circus, London, W1V 7RA.
01-439-9751
PARIS: 24 rue Marbeuf, Paris 75008. 256-13 82
NEW YORK: 505 Park Avenue, New York, N.Y. 10022. (212) 688 9890
COPENHAGEN: Enrumvej 2, 2942 Skodsborg, Copenhagen, Denmark.
20 89 40 93

SCOTT CALDER INTERNATIONAL
NEW YORK: 295 Madison Avenue, New York, N.Y. 10017. (212) 535 9530

SERGAT
PARIS: 9 rue Guenegaud, 75006 Paris. 325-3429

SHANGRI-LA INTERNATIONAL
LONDON: 45–47 Cheval Place, London, SW7 1EW. 01-581-1611
LOS ANGELES: Suite 404, 4/F 1801 Avenue of the Stars, California 90067.
(213) 551-1121
SYDNEY: PO Box N250, Grosvenor Street, Sydney 2000, Australia. 279 567

SHERATON RESERVATIONS
LONDON: 210 Kings Road, London, SW6. 01-636-6411
BOSTON: Sixty State Street, Massachusetts 02109, U.S.A. (617) 367-3600,
tollfree (800) 325-3535
and Sheraton Hotels/Sheraton Reservation offices worldwide

STEIGENBERGER RESERVATION SERVICE
LONDON: 123–125 Gloucester Place, London, W1H 3PJ. 01-486-5754
NEW YORK: 40 East 49th Street, New York, N.Y. 10017. (212) 593-2988

SUPEREPS INTERNATIONAL
LONDON: Suite 433, High Holborn House, 52 High Holborn, London, WC1V
6RL. 01-242-9964

SUPRANATIONAL RESERVATIONS SERVICE
LONDON: Thistle Hotels Reservations Centre, c/o Kensington Palace Hotel,
De Vere Gdns, London, W8 5AF. 01-937-8033

THE LEADING HOTELS OF THE WORLD
LONDON: 15 New Bridge Street, London, EC4V 6AU. 01-583-3050
NEW YORK: 747 Third Avenue, New York, N.Y. 10017. (212) 838-3110

THE TAJ GROUP OF HOTELS, INDIA
LONDON: Utell International, Banda House, Cambridge Grove, London,
W6 OLE. 01-741-1588
INDIA: Central Reservation Service, The Taj Mahal Inter-Continental, Apollo
Bunder, Bombay 400 039. 243 366

JOHN A. TETLEY CO INC
U.S.A.: 3075 Wilshire Blvd, Los Angeles, California 90010. (213) 388-1151,
tollfree (800) 421-0000 except California, (800) 252-0211 (California)

TRUST HOUSE FORTE
LONDON: 240 Bath Road, Hayes, Middlesex. 01-759-6311
NEW YORK: 810 Seventh Avenue, New York, N.Y. 10019. (212) 541 4400
and worldwide

UNITED TOURING INTERNATIONAL
LONDON: Blue Star House, Highgate Hill, London, N19 5UT. 01-263-8591

UTELL INTERNATIONAL
LONDON: Banda House, Cambridge Grove, London, W6 OLE. 01-741-1588
NEW YORK: 119 West 57th Street, New York, N.Y. 10019. (212) 757-2981
SYDNEY: 8th Floor, Network House, 84 Pitt Street, Sydney, NSW 2000.
235-1111
and worldwide

ROBERT F. WARNER
NEW YORK: 711 Third Avenue, New York, N.Y. 10017. (212) 687-5750
ALSO: Boston, Lausanne, Miami, Toronto and Washington

WESTIN HOTELS RESERVATION SERVICE
LONDON: 7/8 Conduit Street, London, W1R 8QT. 01-408-0636
U.S.A.: The Westin Building, Seattle, Washington 98121. (206) 447-5022
tollfree U.S.A. (800) 228-3000, tollfree Canada (800) 268-8383
or any Westin Hotel worldwide

WINDOTEL HOTEL REPRESENTATION
LONDON: 149 Sloane Street, London, SW1X 9BZ. 01-730-7144/5

ABOUT THE GUIDE

★ **CLASSIFICATION:** The countries covered are listed in alphabetical order and within these countries the cities in which the hotels are located. The only exceptions are the Caribbean islands which are all grouped under the headings Caribbean, South Pacific and South America.

★ **ENTRIES:** All entries are in two sections – a practical section giving the hotel's vital statistics and a personal comment. The vital statistics have been communicated by the hotels concerned and while it is likely that most of them are accurate, we cannot accept responsibility for those that are not – especially in such matters as the size of bedrooms etc. Every hotel has been visited personally and recently by the Editor or by our own correspondents and opinions have been double-checked against those of others. However, it is possible that changes have occurred in certain hotels due to the length of time taken in producing the Guide.

★ **PRICES:** Much as we would have liked to include prices, in practice this has not proved possible due to inflation, changes in currency rates, seasonal variations etc. Readers will find that worldwide reservations offices quote prices under three headings: CP (Continental Plan) which means room and breakfast; AP (American plan) which means room and all meals; and MAP (Modified American Plan) which means room, breakfast and either lunch or dinner. In holiday resort areas at the height of the season, hotels are often unwilling to quote for anything except AP.

Room prices also vary considerably with orientation and elevation and whether a room is classified as 'standard' or 'de luxe'. A suite is generally accepted to comprise a bedroom and a sitting room – but this is not always the case, especially in Mediterranean countries, and readers are advised to make proper inquiries. Although no rules apply to room service worldwide, it must be understood that this is charged for.

★ **MERIT:** As stated in the Foreword to the Guide, no stars or other emblems of merit are awarded. Hotels included in this Guide cannot therefore be compared one with the other but simply accepted as the best I know in the locality. Neither am I able to rate the standard of food except in a personal way. This Guide being produced by Europeans, naturally comments on hotels and food that would be best understood by the average, well-travelled European.

★ **RESERVATIONS:** Most hotels in the Guide are represented by booking agencies which are listed under each entry, with their latest addresses listed on the preceding pages. Booking agencies make no charge to the client for this service and will supply a confirmation notice.

★ **COMMENTS PLEASE:** As stated in the Foreword, no guide is ever perfect. THE 300 BEST HOTELS IN THE WORLD is not perfect either. The Guide is published every two years and future editions will be only as good and complete as readers of this edition can make it. If you have any complaints, remarks, additions or comments to make, please do so in writing to:

The Travel Editor (Hotel Guide)
HARPERS & QUEEN, NATIONAL MAGAZINE HOUSE,
72 BROADWICK STREET, LONDON W1V 2BP

THE
300 BEST HOTELS
IN THE WORLD

AUSTRALIA
Melbourne

HILTON INTERNATIONAL MELBOURNE, Cnr. Wellington Parade and Clarendon Streets, East Melbourne, Victoria 3002

- ★ TELEPHONE: 419-3311
- ★ CABLES: Hiltels Melbourne
- ★ TELEX: 33057/Himel AA
- ★ IN OPERATION: since December 1974
- ★ RESERVATIONS: Hilton International
- ★ ROOMS: 78 doubles 323 twins
- ★ SUITES: 22
- ★ RESTAURANTS: 4
- ★ BARS: 3
- ★ DISCOTHEQUE: yes and live piano music in Tapestry Lounge
- ★ SHOPS: 7 – beauty shop/hairdresser, barber, car rental, drugstore/news stand/souvenirs, liquor store, speciality shop, florist
- ★ CONFERENCE ROOMS: 12 (40 to 1200)
- ★ BANQUETING ROOMS: 12 (40 to 800)
- ★ STANDARD BEDROOM SIZE: 25 m^2
- ★ PRIVATE BALCONIES: no
- ★ SWIMMING POOL: yes – fresh water, 18 × 5 m
- ★ GARDENS: no, but overlooks Fitzroy Gardens
- ★ RECREATIONAL ACTIVITIES: health club with sauna and massage, golf and tennis nearby
- ★ NO. OF STAFF: 435
- ★ ROOM SERVICE: around the clock
- ★ ORIENTATION: rooms overlook Melbourne Cricket Ground, Yarra Park and Fitzroy Gardens
- ★ FURTHER DEVELOPMENTS: extra recreation facilities including tennis and squash courts
- ★ CREDIT CARDS: Carte Blanche, American Express, Master Charge, Eurocard, Diners Club, Hilton Hotels, Bankamericard and Air Canada
- ★ OWNING COMPANY: The T. & G. Mutual Life Assurance Society Ltd
- ★ GENERAL MANAGER: Frank D. Christie
- ★ DISTANCE TO BEACH: 5 km
- ★ DISTANCE TO SHOPS: 800 m
- ★ DISTANCE FROM AIRPORT: 24 km

There is always an exception to everything and the Melbourne Hilton is surely an exception to what I have said elsewhere about Australian hotels – it's one of the best and also one which can compete internationally with any big city hotel. Though I don't like the architecture much, the whole hotel, as befits Melbourne, is very gentlemanly and very quiet, despite its size. Rooms are particularly attractive – simple and beautifully furnished in a good international style which does not offend, the lighting is perfect – a rare thing – and items like beds, linen and equipment are of the best. There is one public-room chandelier I don't much care for but the rest is extremely tasteful, spacious, cool and welcoming. Service is well above average for a chain hotel and so is the food which I thought was very appetizing.

THE HOTEL WINDSOR, Spring Street, Melbourne, Victoria 3000

- ★ TELEPHONE: (03) 630261
- ★ CABLES: Telwindsor Melbourne
- ★ TELEX: AA30437
- ★ IN OPERATION: 98 years
- ★ RESERVATIONS: LRI/Lawson, UK and Europe/Utell International, The Americas and Asia/Loews Representation International, U.S.A.,

Canada, Mexico, London and Tokyo/Stinnes Touristic Representations, Frankfurt/Oberol Hotels Reservation Offices

★ ROOMS: 171
★ SUITES: 20
★ RESTAURANTS: White Hart Grill, Grand Dining Room, Windsor Luncheon Club and Windsor Lounge
★ BARS: 3 – Cricketers Bar, Winston Cocktail Lounge and Windsor Corner Bar
★ SHOPS: 1 – hairdressing salon
★ DISCOTHEQUE: no – live music in Grand Dining Room & Lounge
★ CONFERENCE ROOMS: 3 (70 to 370)
★ BANQUETING ROOMS: 3 (50 to 210)
★ STANDARD BEDROOM SIZE: 28 m^2
★ PRIVATE BALCONIES: no
★ SWIMMING POOL: no

★ RECREATIONAL ACTIVITIES: all facilities are available within a short distance of the hotel
★ GARDENS: Fitzroy Gardens opposite
★ NO. OF STAFF: 200
★ ROOM SERVICE: around the clock
★ ORIENTATION: faces Parliament Building
★ CREDIT CARDS: American Express, Bankcard, Visa, Diners Club, Master Charge
★ OWNING COMPANY: Government of Victoria
★ OPERATING COMPANY: Oberoi Hotels (Australia) Pty Ltd
★ GENERAL MANAGER: Mr Robert M. Arnold
★ DISTANCE TO BEACH: 5 km
★ DISTANCE TO SHOPS: ½ km
★ DISTANCE FROM AIRPORT: 20 km

Most people in the hotel world know that when, a few years ago, the Windsor was taken over by an Indian company, Australia's most toffee-nosed city, Melbourne, nearly stopped the world to get off. I mean to say . . . Indians running the Windsor! Well, now they know, and when they enter the portals of this illustrious hostelry, they leave their prejudices behind. The Windsor is a gem, an expensive one at that since it cost millions to give it back its Victorian splendour. From the stained glass to the stairway banisters and from the magnificent dining room to the period carpets, the Windsor and its restoration have been a labour of love for this well meaning and talented Indian company. It's paying off too since people realize that they don't build hotels like this any more and it is a joy to see tick over so perfectly. The rooms are vast of course (Victorians loved space and grandeur) but now the plumbing and the electricals work like a dream. Food is, shall we say, distinguished. One feels that Cesar Ritz would have loved the place.

Sydney

THE REGENT SYDNEY, 199 George Street, Sydney, N.S.W. 2000

★ TELEPHONE: 238 0000
★ CABLES: no
★ TELEX: AA73023
★ IN OPERATION: 18 months
★ RESERVATIONS: Regent International Hotels in Frankfurt, Hong Kong, London, Los Angeles, New York, Singapore, Tokyo
★ ROOMS: 578
★ SUITES: 42
★ RESTAURANTS: 3
★ BARS: 3
★ DISCOTHEQUE: there is a live music policy at the hotel which includes different types of music being played throughout much of the day and evening
★ SHOPS: 5 – pharmacy, hair & beauty

salon, souvenirs, clothes, jewellery
★ CONFERENCE ROOMS: 5 (540 to 900)
★ BANQUETING ROOMS: 5 (30 to 1200)
★ STANDARD BEDROOM SIZE: 28 m^2
★ PRIVATE BALCONIES: no
★ SWIMMING POOL: yes – fresh water, 20 × 9 m
★ RECREATIONAL ACTIVITIES: associate membership at nearby golf clubs, squash clubs, gymnasiums and tennis courts
★ GARDENS: no
★ NO. OF STAFF: 853
★ ROOM SERVICE: around the clock
★ ORIENTATION: faces all directions
★ CREDIT CARDS: all major cards
★ OWNING COMPANY: Ausintel Investments Australia

* ★ **OPERATING COMPANY:** Regent International Hotels
* ★ **GENERAL MANAGER:** Mr W. Ted Wright
* ★ **DISTANCE TO BEACH:** 8 km
* ★ **DISTANCE TO SHOPS:** hotel is in centre of city
* ★ **DISTANCE FROM AIRPORT:** 15 km

It is very difficult to surprise anyone any more in the hotel business and one gets the feeling that all great hotel builders are desperately looking for a plus. I could have suggested the word 'quality' but accountants would not have liked it. Yet this is exactly what this company, with sixteen hotels around the world, has managed to do – to inject a feeling of qualitative pluses in everything they do. Sydney's new Regent is a good case – the newest, biggest hotel down under and I for one reckon Sydney deserved it. Despite soaring costs everywhere, there is nothing cheap here – rooms are bigger than usual, much quieter and splendidly furnished in twenty-first century style which is not at all off-putting – just plain up to date. But it is when one looks at the small details, the coathangers, the telephones, the room doorbells and the magnificent bathroom fittings that the whole thing begins to make sense. New hotels don't come much better than this. I liked the atrium-sized lobby – always an eye opener. I liked even better the fact that every room has a writing desk – many hotel companies have forgotten that. This is indeed the mostest in this part of the world. Full marks.

SEBEL TOWN HOUSE, 23 Elizabeth Bay Road, Elizabeth Bay, N.S.W. 2011

* ★ **TELEPHONE:** (02) 358-3244
* ★ **CABLES:** Sebelhotel
* ★ **TELEX:** 20067
* ★ **IN OPERATION:** since 1963
* ★ **RESERVATIONS:** The Leading Hotels of the World
* ★ **ROOMS:** 165 doubles
* ★ **SUITES:** 23
* ★ **RESTAURANTS:** 1
* ★ **BARS:** 1
* ★ **DISCOTHEQUE:** no
* ★ **SHOPS:** 2 – gift shop and beauty and hairdressing salon
* ★ **CONFERENCE ROOMS:** 4 (20 to 250)
* ★ **BANQUETING ROOMS:** 6 (20 to 500)
* ★ **STANDARD BEDROOM SIZE:** 47 m^2
* ★ **PRIVATE BALCONIES:** yes
* ★ **SWIMMING POOL:** yes – fresh water, heated, 10 × 4 m
* ★ **RECREATIONAL ACTIVITIES:** sauna
* ★ **GARDENS:** roof garden/sundeck
* ★ **NO. OF STAFF:** 230
* ★ **ROOM SERVICE:** around the clock
* ★ **ORIENTATION:** views of Sydney Harbour
* ★ **CREDIT CARDS:** Diners Club, American Express, Master Charge and Visa
* ★ **OWNING COMPANY:** Sebel Town House, Mirvac Pty Ltd
* ★ **GENERAL MANAGER:** Michael J. Hall
* ★ **DISTANCE TO BEACH:** 1km
* ★ **DISTANCE TO SHOPS:** 300 m
* ★ **DISTANCE FROM AIRPORT:** 7 km

One American lady tycoon wrote in recently and said that she had just returned from two weeks in the Pacific. 'Apart from Japan and Hong Kong,' she wrote, 'Sebel Town House was the best city hotel I encountered in the whole trip . . .' How nice to have one's own opinions vindicated in such a positive manner (sometimes, it's the other way around . . .). I too like this hotel very much indeed and, at the risk of making enemies, I would suggest it is the best hotel in Australia.

It is not just one of those ever-present concrete blocks. It has personality (that of the genial owner), character, good taste and that hard-to-define feeling of wellbeing which is so rare. One is at home, comfortable, well cared for and known by name. Bedrooms are quite large, nicely furnished and with superb views of that incredible city. Service is smiling and efficient – I remember the valet who almost apologized for having replaced a missing button on a shirt. There is a top floor swimming pool, again with fantastic views.

In the restaurant, your table groans with the best things Australia can offer – especially the seafood, the steaks and of course the wines. Definitely a highly civilized hotel in the heart of an exciting city.

SHERATON-WENTWORTH HOTEL, 61–101 Phillip Street, Sydney, N.S.W. 2000

- ★ TELEPHONE: 230-0700
- ★ CABLES: Wenthotel Sydney
- ★ TELEX: AA 21227
- ★ IN OPERATION: since December 1966
- ★ RESERVATIONS: Sheraton Reservations, worldwide
- ★ ROOMS: 398 doubles 17 singles
- ★ SUITES: 33
- ★ RESTAURANTS: 4 – Garden Court International Restaurant, Impressions Grill Room, The Last Train Coffee Shop and the Old Sydney Buttery
- ★ BARS: 5
- ★ DISCOTHEQUE: live music with dancing for dinner in the Garden Court Restaurant
- ★ SHOPS: 16
- ★ CONFERENCE ROOMS: 13 (10 to 1000)
- ★ BANQUETING ROOMS: 13 (10 to 600)
- ★ STANDARD BEDROOM SIZE: 25 m^2
- ★ PRIVATE BALCONIES: no
- ★ SWIMMING POOL: no
- ★ GARDENS: no
- ★ NO. OF STAFF: 620
- ★ ROOM SERVICE: around the clock
- ★ ORIENTATION: the main facade faces Phillip Street and the city
- ★ CREDIT CARDS: American Express and Wentworth Hotel
- ★ OWNING COMPANY: operated by Sheraton Corp
- ★ GENERAL MANAGER: Peter Thompson
- ★ DISTANCE TO BEACH: 5 km
- ★ DISTANCE TO SHOPS: 100 m
- ★ DISTANCE FROM AIRPORT: 8 km

A 'pommie' (from POHM, prisoner of His Majesty, written on early convicts' clothes, i.e. British) came back from a week at the Wentworth recently with this anecdote: 'They not only took all my telephone messages when I was out but they listed them in order and when I got back, the telephone operator used to ring me and ask "Shall I ring them back in turn, sir?" . . . Not a bad hotel at all – for Australia . . .'. The last convict ship cast anchor here over one hundred years ago – plenty time enough for a tradition of service to lose its flavour of compulsion. It is now untrue to assume that Australians don't know the hotel business. Here, at the Wentworth is ample demonstration of this. Its service is excellent and the food in its several restaurants is far above Australia's admittedly still depressed average. The hotel never seems to sleep and yet, when you are in your room, you hear little noise. Those rooms are average in size but well, if perhaps a little impersonally, furnished. Management is obviously very much on its toes and you will like the Wentworth because it does not pretend to be other than a thoroughly good city hotel.

AUSTRIA

Dürnstein

HOTEL SCHLOSS DURNSTEIN, A-3601 Dürnstein, Donau

- ★ TELEPHONE: 02711 212
- ★ CABLES: Dürnstein
- ★ TELEX: 071 147
- ★ IN OPERATION: since 1970
- ★ RESERVATIONS: Relais et Chateaux
- ★ ROOMS: 31 doubles 4 singles
- ★ SUITES: 2
- ★ RESTAURANTS: 1
- ★ BARS: 1
- ★ DISCOTHEQUE: no
- ★ SHOPS: hairdresser
- ★ CONFERENCE ROOMS: 1 (30)
- ★ BANQUETING ROOMS: 3 (30 to 100)
- ★ STANDARD BEDROOM SIZE: 19–65 m^2
- ★ PRIVATE BALCONIES: yes – some rooms
- ★ SWIMMING POOL: yes – fresh water, heated, 72 m^2
- ★ RECREATIONAL ACTIVITIES: sauna
- ★ GARDENS: no
- ★ NO. OF STAFF: 33
- ★ ROOM SERVICE: around the clock
- ★ ORIENTATION: facing Danube River
- ★ CREDIT CARDS: American Express, Diners Club, Eurocard, Visa and Master Charge
- ★ OWNING COMPANY: privately owned
- ★ GENERAL MANAGER: Hans Thiery
- ★ DISTANCE TO SHOPS: 100 m
- ★ DISTANCE FROM AIRPORT: 105 km

Occasionally, one hotel can sum up a country better than all the guidebooks ever written. The view from Dürnstein, seen while sitting on that divine terrace overlooking the Danube at its most beautiful, looking at the riverboats gliding by, could melt an Ayahtollah. Inside, amid the lovely period furnishings were some of those gorgeous enamel stoves which one would love to take home if only the owner was not looking. As for the pastries on the post-lunch trolley, they might get a little stale if one took them home but they would still be better than any one could buy. Bedrooms are often vast and very beautiful – mine had a magnificent carved ceiling of great beauty. Bathrooms are adequate and sometimes very grand. This used to be the country home of the Starhemberg family – as glamorous a name as you could find in Austrian history. Furnishings are splendid, parquet floors shining with the patina of time and the staff are absolutely charming and most helpful. The food is more than one can cope with, as is usually the case in this country, so go easy with each course.

St. Christoph

ARLBERG-HOSPIZ, A-6580 St. Christoph

★ TELEPHONE: 05442 26110
★ CABLES: no
★ TELEX: 058 17515
★ IN OPERATION: 598 years
★ RESERVATIONS: direct
★ ROOMS: 101
★ SUITES: 46
★ RESTAURANTS: 5
★ BARS: 2
★ DISCOTHEQUE: yes
★ SHOPS: yes – souvenirs, newspapers etc
★ CONFERENCE ROOMS: 3 (20 to 200)
★ BANQUETING ROOMS: 1 (125)
★ STANDARD BEDROOM SIZE: 20 m²
★ PRIVATE BALCONIES: some rooms

★ SWIMMING POOL: yes – fresh water
★ RECREATIONAL ACTIVITIES: sauna, steambath, whirlpool, solarium, Kneip
★ GARDENS: yes
★ NO. OF STAFF: 96
★ ROOM SERVICE: 07.00–03.00
★ ORIENTATION: rooms face south and north
★ CREDIT CARDS: credit cards only accepted for the restaurant and bar
★ OWNING COMPANY: Family owned – Adolf and Gerda Werner
★ GENERAL MANAGER: Adolf Werner
★ DISTANCE FROM AIRPORT: 200 km

The Tirol, that enchanting Alpine province of Austria, has a lot of hotels – most of which are good only for a quick wash-and-brush-up between one ski run and another. Not so the Arlberg-Hospiz which has existed as an inn – though not in its present form – for over 500 years. Let's just say that it has had time to mature. The new building is quite charming – unostentatious, well designed and extremely comfortable. Rooms are a good size and so are public rooms and all are handsomely lined with lovely old timbers (some not so old perhaps) which are lovingly tended. Food is abundant and varied and the staff are nice and pleased to see you. If I had to place a finger on one feature of this hotel, I would say cheerfulness – there is a lot of sing-songing, slapping-your-lederhosen and much joshing and tinkling of wine glasses. You won't be bored and you will be well looked after.

Salzburg

HOTEL OSTERREICHISCHER HOF, Schwarzstrasse 5–7, 5024 Salzburg

★ TELEPHONE: 72541
★ CABLES: Austriahotel
★ TELEX: 633 590
★ RESERVATIONS: Steigenberger Reservation Service
★ ROOMS: 120

★ SUITES: 2
★ RESTAURANTS: 5
★ BARS: 1
★ DISCOTHEQUE: no
★ SHOPS: none
★ CONFERENCE ROOMS: 4 (10 to 350)

★ BANQUETING ROOMS: 4 (10 to 350)
★ STANDARD BEDROOM SIZE: 24 m²
★ PRIVATE BALCONIES: yes
★ SWIMMING POOL: no
★ GARDENS: no
★ NO. OF STAFF: 230
★ ROOM SERVICE: 07.00–22.00
★ ORIENTATION: rooms face river

★ CREDIT CARDS: American Express, Diners Club and Eurocard
★ OWNING COMPANY: Blanckenstein-Segur-Cabanac OHG
★ GENERAL MANAGER: Herbert Prinz
★ DISTANCE TO SHOPS: walking distance
★ DISTANCE FROM AIRPORT: 5 km

The music around this hotel may be Mozart but the food is certainly Wagnerian – I have never seen such fantastic and beautiful portions of everything; I feel sure that if I ate as much as I was given there would be a Hoteleditordämmerung. Obviously, the great musicians who stayed at the Osterreichischer Hof over the years (Bruno Walter, Toscanini, Backhaus, Oistrakh et al) must have been careful. This, Salzburg's best hotel, is not a grand hotel in the strict sense of the word but it is very good indeed, very comfortable and admirably run and its position across the river Salzbach gives you a chance to see Wolfgang Amadeus' city properly and leave its streets to the trippers. Rooms are good and comfortable, sometimes a little old-fashioned but always spotlessly clean and fresh and the service is of a high standard considering that this hotel must have one of the highest occupancy rates in Austria.

HOTEL SCHLOSS FUSCHL, 5322 Hof Bei, Salzburg

★ TELEPHONE: 06229/253
★ CABLES: Fuschlschloss
★ TELEX: 633454
★ IN OPERATION: 39 years
★ RESERVATIONS: The Leading Hotels of the World
★ ROOMS: 49 doubles 15 singles
★ SUITES: 8
★ RESTAURANTS: 3
★ BARS: 1
★ DISCOTHEQUE: no
★ SHOPS: none
★ CONFERENCE ROOMS: 1 (up to 60)
★ BANQUETING ROOMS: 2 (up to 120)
★ STANDARD BEDROOM SIZE: 24 m²
★ PRIVATE BALCONIES: yes – most rooms

★ SWIMMING POOL: yes – fresh water, 4 × 8 m
★ RECREATIONAL ACTIVITIES: sauna, massage, 9-hole golf course, boating, surfing, tennis, bowling and rifle range
★ GARDENS: yes
★ NO. OF STAFF: 150
★ ROOM SERVICE: 07.00–01.00
★ ORIENTATION: facing east over lake
★ CREDIT CARDS: American Express, Diners Club and Eurocard
★ OWNING COMPANY: private
★ GENERAL MANAGER: Uwe Zeilerbauer
★ DISTANCE TO BEACH: 100 m (private)
★ DISTANCE TO SHOPS: 15 km
★ DISTANCE FROM AIRPORT: 35 km

Standing at the head of the famous lake (The White Horse Inn isn't far away) and surrounded by a truly magnificent park, this is one of the most celebrated castle hotels in the Austrian heartland – a place of such charm, such beauty and such refinement that there is no possible way it could be better. Built during the fifteenth/sixteenth century, Fuschl is a period pearl with vaulted rooms and tortuous passages leading to great vistas of painted ceilings and panelled walls and suddenly emerging into an absolutely divine lakeside terrace where poetic fantasy comes naturally, both on your plate and in your mind. The interior dining room has a caisson ceiling of great beauty and the wintergarden room is one of the most romantic I know. Down below, in the marbled entrails of this fantastic house, the pale green swimming pool is fit for Rhine maidens. Rooms naturally vary in size but not in decor – all quite perfectly furnished, with period pieces beautifully arranged. Service is quiet and dignified and when you sit in one of the Savonarola chairs in the bar sipping some delicious plum brandy, you might be forgiven for thinking that this is the only way to live.

Vienna

HOTEL IM PALAIS SCHWARZENBERG, Schwarzenbergplatz 9, A-1030 Vienna

- ★ TELEPHONE: (0222) 78-45-15
- ★ CABLES: Pensionpalais
- ★ TELEX: 13 61 24
- ★ IN OPERATION: since 1957
- ★ RESERVATIONS: call tollfree Preferred Hotels or any major airline
- ★ ROOMS: 33 doubles 2 singles
- ★ SUITES: 4
- ★ RESTAURANTS: 1
- ★ BARS: 1
- ★ DISCOTHEQUE: no
- ★ SHOPS: none
- ★ CONFERENCE ROOMS: 8 (up to 300)
- ★ BANQUETING ROOMS: 8 (up to 1000)
- ★ STANDARD BEDROOM SIZE: 25 m^2
- ★ PRIVATE BALCONIES: no
- ★ SWIMMING POOL: no

- ★ RECREATIONAL ACTIVITIES: tennis and nearby an 18-hole golf course, sauna, horse riding, swimming and sailing
- ★ GARDENS: yes – 75 acres of private park
- ★ NO. OF STAFF: 102
- ★ ORIENTATION: rooms face private gardens – south/west
- ★ ROOM SERVICE: around the clock
- ★ CREDIT CARDS: Diners Club, Eurocard, Master Charge and Visa
- ★ OWNING COMPANY: Prince Karl Johannes von Schwarzenberg
- ★ GENERAL MANAGER: Pierre Roth
- ★ DISTANCE TO SHOPS: 5 minutes' walking distance
- ★ DISTANCE FROM AIRPORT: 20 km

As I wrote in the last edition, if you have a weakness for grand palaces, this is the place to stay. It is lodged in a wing of the great Schwarzenberg family's ancestral home, right in the middle of Vienna and with its own 75-acre park. The entrance is so discreet that you have to look hard to find the word 'hotel'.

Once inside, it's a different world. Magnificent public rooms ablaze with history: beautiful panelling, paintings and tapestries and furniture that rightly belongs in a museum. Beds are especially stately – one could hold a new Congress of Vienna in most of them. For myself, alas, I always manage to get a crick in the neck in this hotel – the Schwarzenberg's ceilings, all painted caissons, are absolutely magnificent.

The staff are nice, helpful and very, very discreet and some of them look as if they had been there when Franz Josef was on the throne of the Dual Monarchy. The food has improved a little since my last visit but I for one would not travel to Austria for it. It does not much matter – Vienna, with its many gastronomic spots, is all around.

HOTEL IMPERIAL, Karntnerring 16, 1015 Vienna

- ★ TELEPHONE: (0222) 65 17 65
- ★ CABLES: Imperialhotel Wien
- ★ TELEX: 01/12630
- ★ IN OPERATION: since 1873
- ★ RESERVATIONS: direct or The Leading Hotels of the World
- ★ ROOMS: 100 doubles 45 singles
- ★ SUITES: 17
- ★ RESTAURANTS: 2 – Main Dining Room and Viennese Cafe-Restaurant
- ★ BARS: 1
- ★ DISCOTHEQUE: no – but piano music in the restaurants
- ★ SHOPS: none
- ★ CONFERENCE ROOMS: 2 (up to 80)
- ★ BANQUETING ROOMS: 4 (up to 160)

- ★ STANDARD BEDROOM SIZE: 25 m^2
- ★ PRIVATE BALCONIES: no
- ★ SWIMMING POOL: no
- ★ GARDENS: no
- ★ NO. OF STAFF: 222
- ★ ROOM SERVICE: 06.00–23.30
- ★ ORIENTATION: main facade facing the famous Ringstrasse
- ★ CREDIT CARDS: American Express, Diners Club and Eurocard
- ★ OWNING COMPANY: Vereinigte Österreichische Hotel A.G.
- ★ GENERAL MANAGER: Otto N. K. Heinke
- ★ DISTANCE TO SHOPS: walking distance
- ★ DISTANCE FROM AIRPORT: 15 km

Everything about the Imperial is imperial, from the portrait of Franz Josef (larger than life) staring at you from behind his muttonchop whiskers, to the vivacious Austrian baroque of one of the grandest palace hotels in the old world and one which is very dear to all who believe that the first world war killed more than people. Just staying there is like being invited at court. Fantastic marble halls succeed each other like a series of optical illusions, chandeliers glitter and the staff are so marvellously suave and urbane that they could instantly join the diplomatic corps. Rooms and suites are colossal, filled either with gorgeous rococo furniture or the last word in modern. Bathrooms are palatial and admirably equipped and room service, always with a red rose on the tray, is instant. The Imperial has a way of making you feel better, more civilized, more aware of what matters in behaviour and good manners and it also works like a charm thanks to one of the best managements in Europe. The food is superabundant, alas, and this is no hotel for the panic-stricken weight-watcher.

BAHAMAS
Eleuthera
WINDERMERE ISLAND HOTEL AND CLUB, P.O. Box 25, Rock Sound, Eleuthera

★ TELEPHONE: (809) 332-2566
★ CABLES: Windermere Eleuthera Bahamas
★ TELEX: no
★ IN OPERATION: 15 years
★ RESERVATIONS: Windermere Island Club, Greenwich, U.S.A./Robert Reid Associates Ltd, London
★ ROOMS: 21
★ SUITES: 10 and 10 2-bedroomed apartments
★ RESTAURANTS: 1
★ BARS: 1 and a bar at the beach
★ DISCOTHEQUE: no – but live music twice a week by Calypso singer or native band
★ SHOPS: tennis house has a shop for club items
★ CONFERENCE ROOMS: 1 (35 m^2: up to 50)
★ BANQUETING ROOMS: 2 (30 to 60)
★ STANDARD BEDROOM SIZE: 25 m^2
★ PRIVATE BALCONIES: all rooms have balcony or terrace

★ SWIMMING POOL: yes – fresh water, 10 × 5 m
★ RECREATIONAL ACTIVITIES: 6 tennis courts, bicycles, sunfish, windsurfing, waterskiing, snorkelling, canoeing, bone-fishing. Shelling and bird watching. Golf about 45 minutes away
★ GARDENS: yes
★ NO. OF STAFF: 60
★ ROOM SERVICE: 08.00–09.30
★ ORIENTATION: rooms overlook 2½ mile beach and Atlantic Ocean and face east
★ CREDIT CARDS: none
★ OWNING COMPANY: Windermere Beach Apartments Ltd
★ GENERAL MANAGER: Mr Allen G. Sawer
★ DISTANCE TO BEACH: 30 m
★ DISTANCE TO SHOPS: nearest towns 15–30 km
★ DISTANCE FROM AIRPORT: 30 km (Rock Sound); 40 km (Governor's Harbour)

The trouble with so-called tropical beach resorts is that no sooner have you discovered one than it is no longer worthwhile because travel agents have been there before you and filled it with people you would not wish to meet back home. The charming Bahamas, with some of the clearest seas in the world surrounding them, are, alas, a bit like that. In my opinion if you want the Bahamas and exclusivity, you either take your own yacht or go to Windermere Island, one of the few, very few places that has kept its end up. Let's hope it never becomes really 'popular'. Its beaches are among the finest anywhere, its facilities are great and somehow it never appears overdone and that is obviously because great taste and much fastidiousness have gone into its making. Good-looking simplicity would be my verdict and that, in these days, is difficult enough to find. Service is discreet and smiling and the food nicely technicolour. What counts however is that here is a small hotel (and club of course) which likes remaining small. This guide, which is known to be very snobbish when it comes to quality, has to acknowledge the fact that some of the nicest people it knows (and does not know) choose Windermere Island regularly. A good reason to go and try it for yourself.

BELGIUM

Bruges

HOTEL DUC DE BOURGOGNE, Huidenvettersplaats 12, 8000 Bruges

- ★ TELEPHONE: (050) 33 20 38
- ★ CABLES: Bourgogne-Bruges
- ★ IN OPERATION: 18 years
- ★ RESERVATIONS: direct
- ★ ROOMS: 8 doubles 1 single
- ★ SUITES: 1
- ★ RESTAURANTS: 1
- ★ BARS: none
- ★ DISCOTHEQUE: no
- ★ SHOPS: none
- ★ CONFERENCE ROOMS: none
- ★ BANQUETING ROOMS: none – but can cater for small groups of up to 45 persons
- ★ STANDARD BEDROOM SIZE: varied
- ★ PRIVATE BALCONIES: yes – some rooms
- ★ SWIMMING POOL: no
- ★ GARDENS: no
- ★ NO. OF STAFF: 20
- ★ ROOM SERVICE: 07.30–23.00 – breakfast in room
- ★ ORIENTATION: rooms overlook the canal and Tanners Square
- ★ CREDIT CARDS: American Express, Diners Club, Master Charge and Visa
- ★ OWNING COMPANY: private
- ★ GENERAL MANAGER: Willy Van de Vyver
- ★ DISTANCE TO BEACH: 13 km
- ★ DISTANCE TO SHOPS: 3 minutes
- ★ DISTANCE FROM AIRPORT: 123 km

With a mere nine rooms this is one of the smallest hotels in the guide – but small is beautiful. Here, in this ravishing old house by the side of the canal in Bruges is miniaturised perfection, a hotel so lovingly furnished and so marvellously kept that it opens your eyes to the finer possibilities of decoration. There are only two reasons to come here – apart from seeing Bruges of course. One is sleeping – in the truly ducal bedrooms, all magnificently furnished in priceless period pieces, lovely great beds and softer-than-soft carpets. The other reason is eating, for the Duc de Bourgogne is one of the most celebrated restaurants in Belgium, a country where they take their sustenance very seriously indeed. You eat in a fantastic tapestried and beamed room, agleam with *objets d'art* and yet the most artistic thing of all is the food on your plate. Quite apart from being Belgian-colossal, it is also extremely choice and lovingly presented as are the wines that go with it. After that it really is a struggle to go out and see this, perhaps the most beautiful city in Flanders.

Brussels

HOTEL AMIGO, Rue de L'Amigo 1/3, B. 1000 Brussels

- ★ TELEPHONE: 02.511.59.10
- ★ CABLES: Amigotel
- ★ TELEX: 21618
- ★ IN OPERATION: since 1958
- ★ RESERVATIONS: American Wolfe International, New York/Utell International, London
- ★ ROOMS: 146 doubles 27 singles
- ★ SUITES: 10
- ★ RESTAURANTS: 1
- ★ BARS: 1
- ★ DISCOTHEQUE: no
- ★ SHOPS: 1 – boutique and news stand, etc, and porter's desk
- ★ CONFERENCE ROOMS: 5 (18 to 100)
- ★ BANQUETING ROOMS: 4 (24 to 200)
- ★ STANDARD BEDROOM SIZE: 23 m^2
- ★ PRIVATE BALCONIES: only the presidential suite
- ★ SWIMMING POOL: no
- ★ GARDENS: no
- ★ NO. OF STAFF: 130
- ★ ROOM SERVICE: around the clock
- ★ ORIENTATION: main facade east
- ★ CREDIT CARDS: American Express, Diners Club, Eurocard and Visa
- ★ OWNING COMPANY: Société Hôtelière St. Michel
- ★ GENERAL MANAGER: P. Bouchard
- ★ DISTANCE TO SHOPS: walking distance
- ★ DISTANCE FROM AIRPORT: 20 km

Brussels, this capital of good living and the new Europe, always leaves me in something of a quandary when it comes to hotels. So many have mushroomed to accommodate Eurocrats and their minions that it is hard to avoid the concrete monolithic leviathans which one can find anywhere these days. This is the principal reason that makes me go for the Amigo, just behind the gothic town hall on the Grand Place. It stands on its own, a fine period building with, inside, quality and individuality. Some of the rooms may not be large enough or palatial enough for some but I infinitely prefer them to the alternative elsewhere. They are well and comfortably furnished in a pleasing way, beautifully kept and serviced. Here one feels like an individual guest – not a transcontinental silicon chip. Besides all this, unless you are one of the above-mentioned Eurocrats, you are where you should be – right in the heart of this very ancient capital. Or, if you are a Eurocrat, you would do well to shift your living allowance to this hotel.

Herbeumont

HOSTELLERIE DU PRIEURÉ DE CONQUES, Route de Florenville 176, B-6803 Herbeumont

★ TELEPHONE: 061-41 14 17
★ CABLES: no
★ TELEX: no
★ IN OPERATION: since March 1964
★ RESERVATIONS: direct or Relais et Chateaux
★ ROOMS: 11
★ RESTAURANTS: 1
★ BARS: 1
★ DISCOTHEQUE: no – but live music during lunch and dinner times
★ SHOPS: none
★ CONFERENCE ROOMS: 1 (15)
★ BANQUETING ROOMS: none
★ STANDARD BEDROOM SIZE: 18 m^2
★ PRIVATE BALCONIES: no

★ SWIMMING POOL: no
★ RECREATIONAL ACTIVITIES: fishing and walking
★ GARDENS: yes
★ NO. OF STAFF: 12
★ ROOM SERVICE: only for breakfast
★ ORIENTATION: all rooms face south
★ CREDIT CARDS: American Express, Diners Club and Eurocard
★ OWNING COMPANY: Hostellerie du Prieuré de Conques S.A.
★ GENERAL MANAGERS: Mr and Mrs F. de Naeyer
★ DISTANCE TO SHOPS: 15 km (Florenville)
★ DISTANCE FROM AIRPORT: 75 km (Luxembourg)

In a small and interesting country which, unfortunately, is not known for the quality of its *hotels de campagne*, here is an exception: a charming eighteenth-century priory deep down in the wooded hills of the Ardennes and so very quiet that a solitary bee at work sounds like an unsilenced motorcycle. The Prieuré is tiny, white-painted and most attractive with handsome lawns and beautiful trees. It is by no means a grand hotel – just a peaceful country place. Rooms are not overlarge but furnished with taste and sensible equipment and the modern bathrooms work very well. There are never more than about twenty people around: interesting people usually – pleasant places attract the best often enough. Take a walk into some of the loveliest countryside in Northern Europe, or just eat – *à la Belge* – which means a lot and very good.

Noirefontaine

AUBERGE DU MOULIN HIDEUX, B. 6831 Noirefontaine

★ TELEPHONE: (061) 467015
★ CABLES: no
★ TELEX: 41989
★ IN OPERATION: 30 years

★ RESERVATIONS: David B Mitchell & Co Inc, New York/Relais et Chateaux, Paris
★ ROOMS: 10
★ SUITES: 3

- ★ RESTAURANTS: 1
- ★ BARS: 1
- ★ DISCOTHEQUE: no
- ★ SHOPS: 1
- ★ CONFERENCE ROOMS: none
- ★ BANQUETING ROOMS: none
- ★ STANDARD BEDROOM SIZE: 30 m²
- ★ PRIVATE BALCONIES: 2 rooms have balconies
- ★ SWIMMING POOL: no
- ★ RECREATIONAL ACTIVITIES: tennis, walking in the forest nearby, fishing in river close to hotel
- ★ GARDENS: yes – with two small lakes
- ★ NO. OF STAFF: 20
- ★ ROOM SERVICE: 08.30–23.00
- ★ ORIENTATION: all rooms look onto the garden
- ★ CREDIT CARDS: Visa, Mastercard, Access, Eurocard
- ★ OWNING COMPANY: Mr & Mrs Lahire
- ★ GENERAL MANAGER: Charles Lahire
- ★ DISTANCE TO SHOPS: 20 km
- ★ DISTANCE FROM AIRPORT: 160 km (Brussels)

The historical reason for this place being named 'The Hideous Millhouse' is very amusing indeed but it would take half a page to explain it all, so you will have to go there yourself. All we can tell you is that you will find nothing at all hideous about it – very much the contrary. On the banks of a half-forgotten stream in the lovely, wooded Ardennes is this beautiful old building which has mellowed with time and care. The spot is rural in the extreme – no noise, no bustle but only good taste and an appreciation of what constitutes a really fine country hotel. Rooms are splendidly and lovingly furnished with country antiques and kept quite spotless. Service is quiet and discreet and since there cannot be many guests the place is yours – long rambles in the woods, quiet afternoons spent dreaming by the two lakes – what more could one want? Certainly not good food since it is all here. We told some friends not to miss the Peter fish with lobster and truffles – they telephoned us just to say how good it was!

BERMUDA

CAMBRIDGE BEACHES, Cambridge Road, Somerset 9-08

★ TELEPHONE: 809.294.0331
★ CABLES: Beaches, Bermuda
★ TELEX: 3250 Beach B.A.
★ IN OPERATION: 59 years
★ RESERVATIONS: Reservation Systems Inc
★ COTTAGES: 66
★ SUITES: 15
★ RESTAURANTS: 1
★ BARS: 2
★ DISCOTHEQUE: no – but live music
★ SHOPS: none
★ CONFERENCE ROOMS: 1 (up to 25)
★ BANQUETING ROOMS: none
★ STANDARD BEDROOM SIZE: 40–65 m^2
★ PRIVATE BALCONIES: yes
★ SWIMMING POOL: yes – salt water, 50 × 70 ft

★ RECREATIONAL ACTIVITIES: 3 tennis courts, sail boats, power boats, snorkelling and golf nearby
★ GARDENS: yes (25 acres)
★ NO. OF STAFF: 90
★ ROOM SERVICE: breakfast only
★ ORIENTATION: all rooms face the sea
★ CREDIT CARDS: no
★ OWNING COMPANY: Frascati Hotels Ltd
★ GENERAL MANAGER: Michael J. Winfield
★ DISTANCE TO BEACH: 10 beaches on property
★ DISTANCE TO SHOPS: nearby
★ DISTANCE FROM AIRPORT: 28 km

When people say they are going to Bermuda, I always suggest they should eschew those stupendous palaces dedicated to the pleasures of a certain type of New York weekender and try, instead, something like Cambridge Beaches. This is as near the original Bermuda as you can get – an elegant eighteenth-century mansion in the less frenetic part of the island. Pink and white – the prevailing scheme of decoration – it has a lot of charm, and its cottages have large, airy bedrooms, sitting rooms, terraces and gardens all around.

No fewer than ten beaches, mostly private, await your pleasure. You are on your own in a cosy and charming locality. The staff are friendly, the food tends to be American orientated and the drinks are tall and frosty. Although not personally bowled over by Bermuda I find Cambridge Beaches highly congenial.

LANTANA COLONY CLUB, Somerset Bridge, Sandys 9–20, Bermuda

★ TELEPHONE: 809-294-0141
★ CABLES: Lantana Bermuda
★ TELEX: no
★ IN OPERATION: since 1958
★ RESERVATIONS: David B. Mitchell & Co Inc, New York/Joyce B. Clarke Associates, Montreal
★ ROOMS: 54
★ SUITES: Master Suites, Bermuda De Luxe and Lanai Suites and private cottage suites
★ RESTAURANTS: 2 – main dining room and attached Solarium and La Plage
★ DISCOTHEQUE: no – but dancing to a trio every Tuesday, Thursday and Saturday
★ SHOPS: 1
★ CONFERENCE ROOMS: none
★ BANQUETING ROOMS: none
★ STANDARD BEDROOM SIZE: 25–30 m^2

★ PRIVATE BALCONIES: all suites and cottages
★ SWIMMING POOL: yes – fresh water, 6 × 13 m
★ RECREATIONAL ACTIVITIES: tennis, with golf and horse riding nearby. Also water skiing, reef and deep sea fishing, putting, croquet and sailing
★ GARDENS: yes
★ NO. OF STAFF: 81
★ ROOM SERVICE: 08.00–10.00 (breakfast only)
★ ORIENTATION: fronting upon The Great Sound
★ CREDIT CARDS: none
★ OWNING COMPANY: Lantana Colony Club Ltd
★ GENERAL MANAGER: Paul A. Leseur

For a few years the Lantana Hotel had an off period (it happens to hotels as well as people) but now it is once again one of the most pleasant places in Bermuda. It drapes its pink-washed houses all around some charming, springlike gardens and the whole place has a feeling of cheerful intimacy which is most agreeable. You can have a room in the main house or, much better, one of the cottage suites which are quite splendid with their king- and queen-sized beds, sitting rooms and terraces. Though this is obviously a holiday hotel, the catering is particularly good with culinary efforts that denote a clear understanding of what the art is about. The main restaurant is most attractive as is the wine list and there is a solarium-garden dining room which gives you the best of the view and the weather. Food is fine and there have been many improvements in this attractive hotel.

CANADA

Vancouver

THE VANCOUVER MANDARIN, 645 Howe Street, Vancouver, BC V6C 2Y9

★ TELEPHONE: (604) 678 1122
Tollfree in US & Canada
1-800-663-0787
★ CABLES: Vancouver Mandarin, Vancouver
★ TELEX: 0451179
★ RESERVATIONS: The Leading Hotels of the World
★ ROOMS: 197
★ SUITES: 16
★ RESTAURANTS: 4
★ BARS: 3
★ DISCOTHEQUE: no – but live music
★ SHOPS: none
★ CONFERENCE ROOMS: 4 (12 to 40)
★ BANQUETING ROOMS: 3 (12 to 30, 35)
★ STANDARD BEDROOM SIZE: 32–42 m^2

★ PRIVATE BALCONIES: none
★ SWIMMING POOL: yes
★ GARDENS: no
★ NO. OF STAFF: 186
★ ROOM SERVICE: around the clock
★ ORIENTATION: east-west. Upper east floors have harbour view; west rooms have park view
★ CREDIT CARDS: all major cards: American Express, Diners Club, Carte Blanche, Mastercard, Visa
★ OWNING COMPANY: Mandarin International Hotels Ltd
★ GENERAL MANAGER: Ian Barbour
★ DISTANCE TO SHOPS: across the street there is a large indoor shopping mall
★ DISTANCE FROM AIRPORT: 25 minutes

The arrival of a new Mandarin hotel anywhere makes news. In Canada – a country not noted for really good hotels – and especially in a spectacular city like Vancouver, it's better than that: the beginning of a new age. As befits the parent company (probably the best hotel company in the world) there is nothing cheap or in the least vulgar about this Mandarin. This is no convention hotel, crackling with telephone bells and rollcalls, but a really fine pad for those who like to live well. One of the little things I like is the provision of door chimes in the rooms so that nobody intrudes unless you let them in. Good too are the light dimmers. What counts in the end is the quality of the decor – it is gently subdued and in excellent taste – and the fine service – anyone who has gone through the Mandarin mill instinctively knows what is expected of him. Rooms are big and beautifully equipped and bathrooms don't have the prison atmosphere one so often finds. The food is fine all round. Of course the Vancouver Mandarin is young and has time on its side. I am sure it will make it among the great.

CARIBBEAN

Barbados

COBBLERS COVE, St. Peter, Barbados, West Indies

- ★ TELEPHONE: 22291
- ★ CABLES: Cobblers
- ★ TELEX: WB 2314
- ★ IN OPERATION: 16 years
- ★ RESERVATIONS: Windotel, London/Robert Reid Associates, New York and Toronto
- ★ ROOMS: 38 (complete suites with kitchenettes)
- ★ RESTAURANTS: 1
- ★ BARS: 1
- ★ DISCOTHEQUE: no – but live music three or four times a week according to season
- ★ SHOPS: none
- ★ CONFERENCE ROOMS: none
- ★ BANQUETING ROOMS: none
- ★ STANDARD BEDROOM SIZE: 52 m², including bedroom, bathroom, living room and kitchen
- ★ PRIVATE BALCONIES: yes
- ★ SWIMMING POOL: yes – fresh water
- ★ RECREATIONAL ACTIVITIES: waterskiing, windsurfing, snorkelling, yacht charter, scuba diving and glass-bottom boat. Gold and tennis nearby
- ★ GARDENS: yes
- ★ NO. OF STAFF: 60
- ★ ROOM SERVICE: 07.30–23.00

★ ORIENTATION: some rooms face west overlooking the sea and others overlook the gardens
★ CREDIT CARDS: American Express and Visa
★ OWNING COMPANY: Hayton Ltd
★ GENERAL MANAGER: Richard Williams
★ DISTANCE TO BEACH: walking distance
★ DISTANCE TO SHOPS: 16 km
★ DISTANCE FROM AIRPORT: 22 km

One might say that this hotel is what Barbados is all about – small, intimate, friendly and comfortably laid out in the tropical manner. On the whole it is very nice to know that all the people who would not like Cobblers Cove don't go there and if you like loud pop music, plastic decor and the like, I would respectfully suggest that you should keep away.

Cobblers is like a home – in fact the central mansion used to be one. The rest is made up of handsome two-storey structures and on each floor there is a large, well-furnished bedroom (complete with dressing room next to the bathroom), a semi-outdoor living room also fully furnished and even a little kitchenette should you feel like tossing your own salad. The terrace is handsome indeed, partly shaded by lovely trees and with a swimming pool, of course, and, down a few steps, is an incomparable beach. Cobblers is never crowded, never strident, never overdone. Everything is just so – in the British manner of course – simply very relaxing and good-tempered. The staff are among the best and most helpful I have ever encountered anywhere and one feels that the intelligent management's master's eye is everywhere. Food is good and wholesome, the wine list will last your holiday and the drinks are what tropical drinks should be: long and cool.

You can be alone at Cobblers if that's what you want and this is a blessed relief after so much razzmatazz. It's a private place.

CORAL REEF CLUB, St. James, Barbados, West Indies

★ TELEPHONE: 22372
★ CABLES: Coral Barbados
★ TELEX: 2407 WB
★ IN OPERATION: 30 years
★ RESERVATIONS: Robert Reid Associates, London/Ralph Locke, New York
★ ROOMS: 68 doubles 10 singles
★ SUITES: none
★ RESTAURANTS: 2
★ BARS: 2
★ DISCOTHEQUE: live music every night
★ SHOPS: 3 – 'The Casual Shop', ladies' hairdressing and water sports shop
★ CONFERENCE ROOMS: 1 (50)
★ BANQUETING ROOMS: none
★ STANDARD BEDROOM SIZE: 16 m²
★ PRIVATE BALCONIES: yes
★ SWIMMING POOL: yes – fresh water, 45,000 gallons, irregular shape
★ RECREATIONAL ACTIVITIES: tennis, scuba diving, sailing, waterskiing and snorkelling
★ GARDENS: yes
★ NO. OF STAFF: 200
★ ROOM SERVICE: around the clock
★ ORIENTATION: rooms face sea
★ CREDIT CARDS: Visa
★ OWNING COMPANY: Trade Winds Hotels Ltd
★ GENERAL MANAGER: Budge O'Hara
★ DISTANCE TO BEACH: walking distance
★ DISTANCE TO SHOPS: 1 km
★ DISTANCE FROM AIRPORT: 30 km

My problem about Coral Reef is trying to find new adjectives to describe it. The best of the great traditional hotels of Barbados? No doubt about that. The most in demand? Just try and get in during the high season. Coral Reef has been one of the finest resort hotels in the world for so long that it knows all the tricks – the cheerful and very tasteful decor, the flowers everywhere, the little touches of luxury, the food which is as good to eat as it is to look at – not always the case in the Caribbean.

Here, amidst twelve acres of gardens, carefully manicured every morning, is a meandering gaggle of divinely conceived cottages, all private, all immaculate, with large airy rooms and splendid private terraces. You are on your own and yet service is there, at the touch of a button. It goes without saying that Coral Reef has a superb beach and a very attractive swimming pool with outdoor furniture designed for the purpose – not something they bought in the sales. The wine list is one of those I would take with me as bedside reading. Coral Reef is intensely civilized in the European manner, well tempered, beautiful to look at and run by a man who knows instinctively that only the best will do. If you are at Coral Reef during the high season you should certainly consider yourself lucky. There are not many places like it.

British Virgin Islands

LITTLE DIX BAY, P.O. Box 70, Virgin Gorda

★ TELEPHONE: (809) 495-5555
★ CABLES: Dixbay V6BVI
★ TELEX: 318916+
★ IN OPERATION: 20 years
★ RESERVATIONS: Rockresorts Reservations
★ ROOMS: 84
★ SUITES: none
★ RESTAURANTS: 2 – Pavilion Terrace and Sugar Mill Terrace
★ BARS: 2
★ DISCOTHEQUE: live music for dancing three nights each week on pavilion terrace
★ SHOPS: 1
★ CONFERENCE ROOMS: none
★ BANQUETING ROOMS: none
★ STANDARD BEDROOM SIZE: 29 m²

★ PRIVATE BALCONIES: yes
★ SWIMMING POOL: no
★ RECREATIONAL ACTIVITIES: tennis, horse riding, snorkelling, scuba diving, sailing, swimming and water skiing
★ GARDENS: yes
★ NO. OF STAFF: 220
★ ROOM SERVICE: for breakfast only
★ ORIENTATION: facing north-east and directly on the beach
★ CREDIT CARDS: American Express and Diners Club
★ OWNING COMPANY: Rockresorts Inc
★ GENERAL MANAGER: Joel Jennings
★ DISTANCE TO BEACH: 20 m
★ DISTANCE TO SHOPS: 400 m
★ DISTANCE FROM AIRPORT: 800 m

At the risk of being repetitive, since the last edition I have absolutely no reason to change my mind about this hotel. Little Dix Bay works on the principle that it takes a rich man to know what a rich man wants when he chooses a holiday. The millionaire in this case is the ubiquitous Laurence Rockefeller and with Little Dix Bay he has succeeded again – here, in 300 acres of one of the most gorgeous tropic isles – Virgin Gorda – are simplicity, quiet and privacy. A series of cone-shaped thatched cottages on stilts, open to the breeze or not, depending on how you feel, blend with the landscape. The simple cane furniture is somehow the happiest choice for the farouche architecture. In the middle of the beach there is the central pavilion with open-air dining rooms and bars. Food is American-style.

A stone's throw away is the beach to end all beaches, unromantically called The Baths. Nothing on earth is as expensive as the simple life when the rich are leading it. Now, Little Dix also has its own yacht harbour. One sailing friend who blew in recently sent me a card, saying: 'After all you said, I expected champagne on tap when I moored . . .' For all I know they are probably working on it.

PETER ISLAND HOTEL, Box 211, Road Town, Tortola, British Virgin Islands

★ TELEPHONE: (809) 494-2561-3
★ CABLES: Petertel
★ TELEX: 7923 VB
★ IN OPERATION: 14 years
★ RESERVATIONS: direct or travel agents
★ ROOMS: 52
★ SUITES: 2 – 1 3- and 1 4-bedroomed villa
★ RESTAURANTS: 2 – one main restaurant and a beach restaurant

★ BARS: 2
★ DISCOTHEQUE: no – but live music
★ SHOPS: 1
★ CONFERENCE ROOMS: 1 (50)
★ BANQUETING ROOMS: none – only main dining room
★ STANDARD BEDROOM SIZE: 50 m²
★ GARDENS: yes
★ PRIVATE BALCONIES: 26 on upstairs

rooms, and terraces on 26 downstairs rooms
★ SWIMMING POOL: yes – salt water, 17 m long
★ RECREATIONAL ACTIVITIES: tennis, horse riding, snorkelling and sunfish, also scuba, deep sea fishing, sailing and power boat excursions at a charge
★ NO. OF STAFF: 107
★ ROOM SERVICE: 08.00–10.00 breakfast and 20.00–21.30 dinner

★ ORIENTATION: north-east
★ CREDIT CARDS: all major credit cards
★ OWNING COMPANY: Peter Island Estates Ltd
★ GENERAL MANAGER: David E. Benson
★ DISTANCE TO BEACH: resort on own island with 3 beaches
★ DISTANCE TO SHOPS: 9 km
★ DISTANCE FROM AIRPORT: 18 km

As everyone knows, the Caribbean – and its hotels – have had their ups and downs in recent years, especially downs. Peter Island is a typical example: I loved it from the very start and then, by and by, complaints began to reach me: food had become 'quelconque', service surly, maintenance doubtful. I was just about to commit another hotel murder when suddenly, other reports came in: 'marvellous', 'new lease of life', 'very expert new management'. Well, I am so glad because Peter Island basically deserves to succeed. It always was an unusual hotel, simple and yet very comfortable with very functional cottage-style bedrooms, modern and very clean. What matters is Peter Island – you have it to yourself, clear seas, superb beaches, total privacy and lots of skin-diving, scuba, fishing and sailing if you want an active time. Now that Peter Island is back on the hotel straight-and-narrow, I have decided to stay the executioner's knife. Besides, I have fond memories of this part of the world: as part of someone's joke, I was once marooned for the day on the desert island next door – only Raquel Welch was missing. It is also comforting to know that there are still British Virgins.

Dominican Republic

CASA DE CAMPO HOTEL, VILLAS AND COUNTRY CLUB,
P.O. Box 140, La Romana

★ TELEPHONE: (809) 556-3345
★ CABLES: no
★ TELEX: ITT 346 0398 RCA 326 4360
★ IN OPERATION: 8 years
★ RESERVATIONS: G & W Hotels, New York/Ski Sport Sonne Schwarz, Germany
★ ROOMS: 177
★ SUITES: 6
★ RESTAURANTS: 8
★ BARS: 10
★ DISCOTHEQUE: yes and live music for dancing or listening to in some of the restaurants
★ CONFERENCE ROOMS: 7
★ BANQUETING ROOMS: 6
★ STANDARD BEDROOM SIZE: 30 m²

★ PRIVATE BALCONIES: all rooms
★ SWIMMING POOL: 5 – all fresh water
★ RECREATIONAL ACTIVITIES: golf, tennis, polo, riding club, sailing
★ GARDENS: yes
★ NO. OF STAFF: 800
★ ROOM SERVICE: 07.00–22.00
★ ORIENTATION: rooms face gardens, golf course or ocean
★ CREDIT CARDS: all major credit cards
★ OWNING COMPANY: G & W Hotels
★ GENERAL MANAGER: Anthony Bayarri
★ DISTANCE TO BEACH: on the property – 6 minutes by complimentary shuttle bus
★ DISTANCE TO SHOPS: 12 minutes by complimentary shuttle bus
★ DISTANCE FROM AIRPORT: 95 km

Readers have been telling us for years to go to Casa de Campo and now that we have done so, we wonder how we could have missed it for so long – the ultimate, eye-dazzling resort of resorts in the Caribbean, but not the Caribbean you would expect since this one has a Spanish accent. Our trouble is that we don't know where to begin. With 7000 acres of glorious, unspoilt countryside? With the eight restaurants and the ten bars? With all the things you can do there from riding to golfing? With the resort's own jet airport? Frankly, the thing that struck us most in all this fantasy of luxurious living was the decor (much of it by Oscar de la Renta), the finished quality, the imagination, the superb colours – everything in such good taste that you fall in love with it at first sight. Then there are the beaches, unsullied and so vast that despite the size of the hotel you can quite easily be on your own. Rooms come in all shapes, sizes and varieties. You can have a suite, a casita, a villa or any combination you care to name – everything superbly furnished and serviced. The food is great but please don't ask us what we ate – we were only there three days and only had time for Continental and Dominican and no opportunity for French, Chinese or American. Of course you won't be alone at Casa de Campo because it's people who make a place like this and here there are only beautiful people. Rich too.

Guadeloupe

HOTEL MERIDIEN GUADELOUPE, BP 37, 97118 St. Francois, Guadeloupe, French West Indies

- ★ TELEPHONE: 84-4100
- ★ CABLES: Homer, Pointe-a-Pitre
- ★ TELEX: 019 774
- ★ IN OPERATION: 12 years
- ★ RESERVATIONS: all Air France offices and Meridien hotels, worldwide
- ★ ROOMS: 273
- ★ SUITES: 8
- ★ RESTAURANTS: 3 – Le Saint Charles, Le Balaou, Le Cazazoma (beach)
- ★ BARS: 2
- ★ DISCOTHEQUE: yes
- ★ SHOPS: 8 – hairdresser, local handicrafts, perfumery, dress shop
- ★ CONFERENCE ROOMS: 3 (50 to 250 m²)
- ★ BANQUETING ROOMS: 3 (25 to 325 m²)
- ★ STANDARD BEDROOM SIZE: 21 m²
- ★ PRIVATE BALCONIES: yes – all rooms
- ★ SWIMMING POOL: yes
- ★ RECREATIONAL ACTIVITIES: tennis, pedaloes, volleyball, sunfish, sailing boats, water skiing, windsurfing, golf course. Casino within walking distance
- ★ GARDENS: yes
- ★ NO. OF STAFF: 250
- ★ ROOM SERVICE: around the clock
- ★ ORIENTATION: north-west and south-west
- ★ CREDIT CARDS: American Express, Diners Club, Carte Blanche, Master Charge, Eurocard, Access, Visa, Inter-Bank, Carte En Route
- ★ OWNING COMPANY: Société des Hotels Meridiens
- ★ GENERAL MANAGER: Michel Noblet
- ★ DISTANCE TO SHOPS: 29 km
- ★ DISTANCE FROM AIRPORT: 32 km

For any traveller, moving from an Anglophone Caribbean island to a Francophone one is like going from the Moon to Saturn – a different world. Guadeloupe is more West Indian than most and yet it's French with a vengeance and cosmopolitan too. Even Prunier de Paris have a branch-restaurant there and nearby is this splendid, shining Meridien near the little fishing town of St. Francois which, by now, is the St. Tropez of Guadeloupe. I would call the Meridien a hotel a-gogo – there is so much to do, so much activity that one certainly does not have time to get bored. There is a superb and extremely well-equipped beach with bar and a rather nice rustic restaurant where the food is anything but rustic. I only stayed here five days but I counted eleven different kinds of cuisine available. Buffets are technicolour and, thank goodness, they taste French and the sit-down meals are among the best I have had in a resort hotel. Rooms are large, well furnished if rather international and the public rooms, facing all those tropical gardens are excellently planned. Service is good and smiling and the management is obviously well up to the mark. If you want the Caribbean and Life with a capital 'L', the Meridien Guadeloupe is a very good choice.

Haiti

RELAIS DE L'EMPEREUR, Petit Goave, Haiti

★ TELEPHONE: Petit Goave 507 Port au Prince 29551
★ CABLES: no
★ TELEX: (ITT) 2030474
★ IN OPERATION: 4 years
★ RESERVATIONS: David B. Mitchell & Co/Relais et Chateaux/Robert Reid Associates/Princess Reservation Service
★ ROOMS: none
★ SUITES: 10
★ RESTAURANTS: 1
★ BARS: 1
★ DISCOTHEQUE: no, but live music
★ SHOPS: none
★ CONFERENCE ROOMS: none
★ BANQUETING ROOMS: none
★ STANDARD BEDROOM SIZE: 111 m² (suites)
★ PRIVATE BALCONIES: all suites have balconies
★ SWIMMING POOL: Olympic sized pool at Cocoyer Beach

★ RECREATIONAL ACTIVITIES: all hedonistic pleasures catered for, tennis court and croquet lawn at Cocoyer Plantation
★ GARDENS: yes
★ NO. OF STAFF: 40
★ ROOM SERVICE: around the clock
★ ORIENTATION: suites overlook bay or Southern hills
★ CREDIT CARDS: all major credit cards
★ OWNING COMPANY: private – Olivier Coquelin
★ GENERAL MANAGER: Paul François Richli
★ DISTANCE TO BEACH: hotel's own private beach, Plantation Cocoyer, is 30 minutes by boat
★ DISTANCE TO SHOPS: Port au Prince: 63 km
★ DISTANCE FROM AIRPORT: 63 km (Port au Prince)

We may be wrong but to our knowledge only one man would have been crazy enough to give birth to the Relais de L'Empereur in Haiti – Olivier Coquelin, of whom an American writer once said, 'If anyone could convince a Trappist monk that decadence is virtue, it is he'. Quite. Coquelin – French/New Yorker plus a bit of here and there – has imagination, a real showman's flair and, happily, extremely good taste. He took this crazy house in the middle of a Haitian village and transformed it into a place of fantastic, extravagant beauty, with four-poster beds all over, unique mirrors in some indiscreet places, beautiful terraces and food to make the gods come down to earth. The fact that it did not have a beach did not bother Monsieur Coquelin – thirty minutes away by boat (you can't get there any other way) is the amazingly beautiful Cocoyer Beach where the greeny-blue water is so clear you can see your toes on the sandy bottom. Relais de L'Empereur is what every great resort hotel should be but is not – slightly mad, beautiful, amusing and totally unlike anywhere else. It is showbiz – with style.

Jamaica

THE HALF MOON CLUB,

- ★ TELEPHONE: (809) 953-2211
- ★ CABLES: Halfmoon
- ★ TELEX: 291 5326
- ★ IN OPERATION: 31 years
- ★ RESERVATIONS: Robert Reid Associates Inc, New York/Jamaica Reservation Service, Florida/C.A.I.R.S. Hotel Representatives, Toronto/Windotel Ltd, London
- ★ ROOMS: 69 rooms 62 apartments
- ★ SUITES: 60
- ★ RESTAURANTS: 2 – Sea Grape Terrace and The Club House Grill
- ★ BARS: 2
- ★ DISCOTHEQUE: yes – also live dinner music and live dance music with nightly shows
- ★ SHOPS: 13 – beauty salon and barber shop, gifts and souvenirs, pharmacy, men's shop, 2 dress shops, crystal, china, jewellery, watches and linen shops
- ★ CONFERENCE ROOMS: 3 (15 to 150)
- ★ BANQUETING ROOMS: 3 (15 to 350)
- ★ STANDARD BEDROOM SIZE: 30 m²
- ★ PRIVATE BALCONIES: yes

- ★ SWIMMING POOL: yes – 2 major pools and 17 cottage pools – all fresh water
- ★ RECREATIONAL ACTIVITIES: 13 tennis courts (4 floodlit), 4 floodlit squash courts, 18-hole golf course, windsurfing, sailing, snorkelling, deep sea fishing, sauna, massage salon, riding, shuffleboard and table tennis
- ★ GARDENS: yes – 400 acres
- ★ NO. OF STAFF: 320
- ★ ROOM SERVICE: 08.00–23.00
- ★ ORIENTATION: all rooms face directly onto the beach and sea
- ★ FURTHER DEVELOPMENTS: plans are being drawn up for the construction of golf villas beside the golf course
- ★ CREDIT CARDS: American Express, Diners Club, Master Charge, Bankamericard, Visa and Barclaycard
- ★ OWNING COMPANY: Half Moon Bay Ltd
- ★ MANAGING DIRECTOR: Heinz E. W. Simonitsch
- ★ DISTANCE TO BEACH: walking distance
- ★ DISTANCE TO SHOPS: 1 km
- ★ DISTANCE FROM AIRPORT: 9 km

Here is a hotel that has been listed in this book since the very beginning ten years ago and, unless the management is struck by lightning (heaven forbid . . .), it's likely to stay where it is – among the finest resort hotels anywhere in the world. Half Moon manages to be everything to everyone – from the honeymooner to the tycoon just taking five. Superbly run by one of the great personalities of the hotel world, it is so successful that the word recession has never been in its vocabulary. Here, you can have anything you like, from Malossol caviar to Bâtard Montrachet and from one of the finest beaches in Jamaica to its greatest golf course: just go across the road to see it, play of course and then dine in the magnificent club house. You will never stop talking about it. At Half Moon you can have a room, a suite and any one of a gaggle of absolutely divine 'cottages' (Marie Antoinette would have liked them . . .) each with its private garden, private swimming pool, living room and gracious decor. The service is personal and the food is just whatever you fancy. As for the beach – a mile of it – it's the Caribbean at its best. Half Moon? You can't miss. There is only one like it.

JAMAICA INN, P.O. Box 1, Ocho Rios, Jamaica, West Indies

- ★ TELEPHONE: 974-2514
- ★ CABLES: Jamaicainn
- ★ TELEX: no
- ★ IN OPERATION: 35 years
- ★ RESERVATIONS: Ray Morrow Associates/Windotel Ltd, London
- ★ ROOMS: 50
- ★ SUITES: 2
- ★ RESTAURANTS: 1
- ★ BARS: 2

- ★ DISCOTHEQUE: no – but small orchestra nightly
- ★ SHOPS: none
- ★ CONFERENCE ROOMS: none
- ★ BANQUETING ROOMS: none
- ★ STANDARD BEDROOM SIZE: 23 m²
- ★ PRIVATE BALCONIES: yes
- ★ SWIMMING POOL: yes – fresh water, 25,000 gallons
- ★ RECREATIONAL ACTIVITIES: tennis nearby

and golf and horse riding 3 miles
away
★ GARDENS: yes
★ NO. OF STAFF: 105
★ ROOM SERVICE: 07.30–24.00
★ ORIENTATION: rooms face the sea
★ CREDIT CARDS: American Express

★ OWNING COMPANY: C. P. Morrow and
M. P. Archibald
★ GENERAL MANAGER: owner management
★ DISTANCE TO BEACH: walking distance
★ DISTANCE TO SHOPS: 1 km
★ DISTANCE FROM AIRPORT: 90 km
(Montego Bay)

Now managed by one of its owners, this is still one of the top hotels of the Caribbean – perhaps not for the young but for all those who have lived and know it all. The first thing you notice is the absence of the showbiz element: Jamaica Inn is just a superbly conceived hotel facing its splendid beach which, everywhere, is only a step away from your outdoor living room, framed with white balustrades and with everything you want at hand. One dines on one of the most famous terraces in the West Indies (it used to be on almost every Jamaican poster) and, there is no doubt about it, this is the good life. People come here year after year and some are lucky (and rich) enough to book the famed White Suite which stands in isolated splendour at the end of the promontory and yes, if you have to ask how much it is, you can't afford it. Jamaica Inn is a legend all right and although it now has stiff competition, I fervently hope that it will know how to keep in step.

PLANTATION INN, P.O. Box 2, Ocho Rios, Jamaica

★ TELEPHONE: 974-2501-3
★ CABLES: Plantation
★ TELEX: 2134 WATJAM
★ IN OPERATION: 29 years
★ RESERVATIONS: Carib Resorts, Inc,
Miami/Windotel, London/Muriel Fleger
International, Toronto
★ ROOMS: 65
★ SUITES: 14
★ RESTAURANTS: 1
★ BARS: 2
★ DISCOTHEQUE: resident band
★ SHOPS: 1 (boutique)
★ CONFERENCE ROOMS: 1 (80 m^2)
★ BANQUETING ROOMS: 1 (30)
★ STANDARD BEDROOM SIZE: 30 m^2
★ PRIVATE BALCONIES: all rooms

★ SWIMMING POOL: 1 – fresh water
★ RECREATIONAL ACTIVITIES: tennis,
watersports
★ GARDENS: yes
★ NO. OF STAFF: 140
★ ROOM SERVICE: 07.30–24.00
★ ORIENTATION: all rooms face the ocean
★ CREDIT CARDS: American Express,
Master Charge, Visa, Eurocard and
Diners Club
★ OWNING COMPANY: Watsons (O.C.B.)
Ltd
★ GENERAL MANAGER: Rudi Schoenbein
★ DISTANCE TO BEACH: on the beach
★ DISTANCE TO SHOPS: 3 km
★ DISTANCE FROM AIRPORT: 100 km

In the last edition of this book I wrote that I often followed good general managers. If they moved from one hotel to another, I moved too and this has never been more true than in the case of Plantation Inn – once much neglected and down-at-heel and now one of the best and friendliest hotels in the Caribbean. It is now in its third winter season under new ownership and new management and for the past two years I have received many letters of praise. One German lady wrote: 'I found this hotel excellent, unstuffy and most comfortable . . .'
It was always a good-looking pad of course, graceful, neo-colonial architecture plus charm and space. The two beaches are among the best and there is a pretty swimming pool just below the dining terrace where, at night, only candlelight competes with Jamaica's velvety, starry night. Rooms have enough size to be uncrowded and are furnished with an easy, informal style which is a pleasure to the eye, and there are good terraces. The staff are superb – cheerful and glad to help. They serve English afternoon tea, too. Plantation Inn isn't just making it – it's got there.

ROUND HILL HOTEL, P.O. Box 64, Montego Bay, Jamaica, West Indies

★ TELEPHONE: 809-952-5150-5
★ CABLES: Roundhill
★ TELEX: no
★ IN OPERATION: 28 years
★ RESERVATIONS: Robert F. Warner, Inc, New York/Morris Associates, London/Muriel Fleger, Toronto
★ ROOMS: 36 doubles 5 singles
★ SUITES: 70
★ RESTAURANTS: 3
★ BARS: 2
★ DISCOTHEQUE: no – but dancing nightly with featured entertainers and calypso band
★ SHOPS: 2
★ CONFERENCE ROOMS: 1 (60 to 150)
★ BANQUETING ROOMS: 2 (45 to 200)
★ STANDARD BEDROOM SIZE: 27 m^2

★ PRIVATE BALCONIES: yes
★ SWIMMING POOL: yes – 13
★ RECREATIONAL ACTIVITIES: snorkelling, water skiing, sailing and deep sea fishing and tennis. Golf and horse riding close by
★ GARDENS: yes
★ NO. OF STAFF: 245
★ ROOM SERVICE: 08.00–23.00
★ ORIENTATION: rooms face sea and garden
★ CREDIT CARDS: none
★ OWNING COMPANY: Round Hill Development Ltd
★ MANAGING DIRECTOR: Michael J. Kemp
★ DISTANCE TO BEACH: on the beach
★ DISTANCE TO SHOPS: 15 km
★ DISTANCE FROM AIRPORT: 17 km

Round Hill is not a hotel – more a way of life. Here on this rounded cape just west of Montego Bay is one of the most original resorts in the business – lots of lush, tropical land, one small but super beach, flowers everywhere and, dotted about, a whole series of absolutely heavenly Jamaican-style cottages, some with their own pools. There are great verandahs, airy rooms with high ceilings and splendid Caribbean resort furniture and very good bathrooms. The rooms in the main buildings are good and acceptable – but not really to be compared with the cottages. At Round Hill, a very private but very convivial place, life gets going at night when you dine on the lovely terrace or even the beach – with Jamaican fireflies dancing above and the moon out. In such a widespread place, service is remarkably good and cheerful and the food ranks high in the Caribbean. Round Hill has had mixed management fortunes in past years but now seems set fair for some time to come.

√√ TRIDENT VILLAS AND HOTEL, P.O. Box 119, Port Antonio, Jamaica

★ TELEPHONE: 993 2602/993 2705
★ CABLES: Trivil
★ TELEX: no
★ IN OPERATION: 16 years
★ RESERVATIONS: Mr Bruce Baxter, First Resort Corp, 200 Madison Avenue, New York, N.Y. 10016, U.S.A. (Tel: 212 689 3048). Windotel Ltd.
★ ROOMS: 14 cottages, 8 studio apartments
★ SUITES: 2 (Prime Minister Suite, Imperial Suite)
★ RESTAURANTS: 1
★ BARS: 1 cocktail bar
★ DISCOTHEQUE: Calypso trio and pianist
★ SHOPS: 1 – boutique and art gallery with local fashions, needlework, arts and crafts, gifts
★ CONFERENCE ROOMS: 1
★ BANQUETING ROOMS: 1

★ STANDARD BEDROOM SIZE: 33 m^2
★ PRIVATE BALCONIES: yes – some rooms
★ SWIMMING POOL: yes – fresh water
★ RECREATIONAL ACTIVITIES: tennis, swimming, snorkelling, riding, water skiing
★ GARDENS: yes
★ NO. OF STAFF: 50
★ ROOM SERVICE: around the clock
★ ORIENTATION: some with balcony or patio facing the sea
★ CREDIT CARDS: Visa, American Express
★ OWNING COMPANY: Mr Earl Levy
★ GENERAL MANAGER: Noel David Hutchison
★ DISTANCE TO BEACH: own private beach
★ DISTANCE TO SHOPS: 3 km
★ DISTANCE FROM AIRPORT: international airport: 70 km; local airport: 12 km

If they judge by the number of hotels we list in Jamaica, readers can guess that we have a very special liking for the place. We do and always have done. Though there are other lovely islands, Jamaica is for us the only real country in the Caribbean. We love Port Antonio, too, the slightly raffish corner discovered by Errol Flynn all those years ago, but until the present owner got to Trident Villas we would not have stayed there. Things have changed. Trident is charming, comfortable, good-looking and a resort hotel that does not pretend to be the Grand hotel this or that. All its rooms have been redesigned, with good verandahs, lovely ceiling fans, there just for the decor, and attractive cane furniture everywhere plus pleasant colour schemes. The beach at Trident is small but good and the whole peninsula on which the hotel stands is pleasant – only a short distance from Port Antonio, a small town of great character and a few minutes from the famous rafting on the Rio Grande river. At evening time, Trident is elegant enough to make you feel good.

Nevis

ZETLAND PLANTATION, Gingerland, Nevis, West Indies

★ TELEPHONE: (809) 465 5454
★ CABLES: no
★ TELEX: 4855 JANSTRAV KC
★ IN OPERATION: 14 years
★ RESERVATIONS: direct
★ ROOMS: 3
★ SUITES: 17
★ RESTAURANTS: 1
★ BARS: 1
★ DISCOTHEQUE: yes
★ SHOPS: yes – clothes, jewellery and local crafts
★ CONFERENCE ROOMS: 1 – outdoor pavilion (50 people)
★ BANQUETING ROOMS: dining area (50 people)
★ STANDARD BEDROOM SIZE: 25 m^2

★ PRIVATE BALCONIES: yes – most rooms
★ SWIMMING POOL: yes – fresh water
★ RECREATIONAL ACTIVITIES: tennis; riding and water sports can be arranged
★ GARDENS: yes
★ NO. OF STAFF: 21
★ ROOM SERVICE: 08.00–21.00
★ ORIENTATION: facing the sea
★ CREDIT CARDS: Visa, Master Charge, American Express
★ OWNING COMPANY: Resort Villas International
★ GENERAL MANAGER: Barbara Frazer
★ DISTANCE TO BEACH: 8 km
★ DISTANCE TO SHOPS: 6 km
★ DISTANCE FROM AIRPORT: 18 km

Nevis is what every Caribbean island should be like but is not any more – unpolluted and virginal, without mass tourism but with a quiet charm that gets you the moment you arrive. Most hotels on the island are good insofar as they do not look like hotels but Zetland is by far the best. High up on the slopes of the one and only mountain there is the central Manor House where one eats and drinks and meets people. All around are the quite charming villas, light and airy and gay and each with a superb bedroom, living room and bathroom. They are highly private and stand in their own grounds but most are no more than a few minutes' walk from the central building. Furnishings are bright, cheerful and comfortable and there is a great feeling of space – not least of all in the 300 acres of the plantation itself. About eight kilometres away by Minimoke is the splendid Pinney's Beach, one of the finest in the Caribbean, but of course the hotel has its own swimming pool. I would without hesitation recommend Zetland for those who want the West Indies natural and old style.

St. Kitts

THE GOLDEN LEMON, Dieppe Bay, St. Kitts, West Indies

★ TELEPHONE: (809) 465-7260
★ CABLES: Golemon
★ IN OPERATION: 20 years

★ RESERVATIONS: Scott Calder International, New York
★ ROOMS: 17

★ SUITES: 3
★ RESTAURANTS: 1
★ BARS: 1
★ DISCOTHEQUE: local band occasionally
★ SHOPS: 2 – duty free shop with perfumes, jewellery, clothes and craft shop
★ CONFERENCE ROOMS: none
★ BANQUETING ROOMS: none
★ STANDARD BEDROOM SIZE: 20 m^2
★ PRIVATE BALCONIES: most rooms
★ SWIMMING POOL: yes – fresh water
★ RECREATIONAL ACTIVITIES: snorkelling, tennis, golf, riding, mountain climbing

and day trips to other islands can be arranged
★ GARDENS: hotel surrounded by walled gardens
★ NO. OF STAFF: 30
★ ROOM SERVICE: 07.00–24.00
★ ORIENTATION: most rooms face the sea
★ CREDIT CARDS: none
★ OWNING COMPANY: Arthur Leaman
★ GENERAL MANAGER: Kathleen Fallon
★ DISTANCE TO BEACH: 150 m
★ DISTANCE TO SHOPS: 22 km
★ DISTANCE FROM AIRPORT: 22 km

On an island that is certainly not known for the quality of its hotels, here is a real find: one of the two or three nicest small hotels in the Caribbean – very chic, very appealing and absolutely gorgeous when it comes to decor. And so it should be since it is the brainchild of a man who used to be decorating editor of *House and Garden*.

Arthur Leaman rescued this 'Great House' from total oblivion and turned it into a place of infinite charm: small, friendly and totally private in its own walled garden and facing an unusual black sand beach. The word here is simple period elegance, with every room done up differently with genuine island furniture, fresh colours, canopied beds and ceiling fans – of course. As your eye roves around, it comes to rest happily on yet one more piece of great artistry. There is a wealth of carefully chosen tropical flora, frequented by finches and hummingbirds and a discreet and charming swimming pool lined with beautiful *chaise-longues*. The food, served in the elegant, period dining room under candlelight, shows that professional designers sometimes eat too – it is perfection itself, light, different and imaginative and served in great style. If you want the Caribbean away from the obvious, The Golden Lemon it must be.

St. Martin

LA SAMANNA, BP 159 Marigot, 97150 St. Martin, French West Indies

★ TELEPHONE: 875122
★ CABLES: Shobal/St. Martin
★ TELEX: 919892 GL
★ IN OPERATION: 10 years
★ RESERVATIONS: direct or David B. Mitchell, New York
★ ROOMS: 11
★ SUITES: 46
★ RESTAURANTS: 1 – Nouvelle Cuisine
★ BARS: 2
★ DISCOTHEQUE: yes
★ SHOPS: 1 – boutique
★ CONFERENCE ROOMS: none
★ BANQUETING ROOMS: none
★ STANDARD BEDROOM SIZE: 17 m^2
★ PRIVATE BALCONIES: yes
★ SWIMMING POOL: yes – fresh water 10 × 20 m

★ RECREATIONAL ACTIVITIES: tennis, snorkelling, windsurfing, scuba, water skiing and sailing
★ GARDENS: yes
★ NO. OF STAFF: 100
★ ROOM SERVICE: continental breakfast only
★ ORIENTATION: east/west – all rooms face the sea
★ CREDIT CARDS: American Express, Master Charge and Visa
★ OWNING COMPANY: Soc. Hôtelière de la Baie Longue
★ GENERAL MANAGER: James Frankel
★ DISTANCE TO BEACH: on the beach
★ DISTANCE TO SHOPS: 15 minutes
★ DISTANCE FROM AIRPORT: 5 km

Tiny St. Martin is two-thirds Dutch and one-third French and therein lies one of the funniest stories of colonial days which, alas, would take half this book to tell. The joke had always been that one slept on the Dutch side because hotels were cleaner and one ate on the French side because the food was better. Now that La Samanna is there, it's the only place really worth going to St. Martin for – one of the most unusual and most attractive small resort hotels anywhere and once again in these latitudes, it took American owners to make this particular dream come true. There is a long low white building and lots of cottages spread along an endless white beach. You can lose your neighbours just by staying on your own divine terrace or by walking a bit further on the beach. It is a deliciously informal and easy-going resort hotel which still manages the right touches when needed. The decor is fresh and quite charming and the food better than that – La Samanna is the only place in the Caribbean that offers *la nouvelle cuisine* with West Indian overtones. If you are looking for a really unusual place, I don't think you'd be disappointed.

St. Vincent

COTTON HOUSE, Mustique Island, St. Vincent, Grenadines

- ★ TELEPHONE: 84621/84622
- ★ CABLES: Mustico St. Vincent
- ★ TELEX: 7562 COTTONH VQ
- ★ IN OPERATION: since 1970
- ★ RESERVATIONS: Utell International, worldwide
- ★ ROOMS: 19
- ★ SUITES: none
- ★ RESTAURANTS: 2 – continental and Caribbean fare
- ★ BARS: 2 – poolside and main lounge
- ★ DISCOTHEQUE: no, but occasional visit by gifted local musicians
- ★ SHOPS: 1 – local handicrafts, toiletries and island fashions
- ★ CONFERENCE ROOMS: none
- ★ BANQUETING ROOMS: none
- ★ STANDARD BEDROOM SIZE: 25 m^2
- ★ PRIVATE BALCONIES: yes
- ★ SWIMMING POOL: yes – fresh water

- ★ RECREATIONAL ACTIVITIES: tennis, sailing, snorkelling, riding and 12 miles of coral sand beaches; motor scooters/Minimokes available
- ★ GARDENS: no – but private beaches
- ★ NO. OF STAFF: 30
- ★ ROOM SERVICE: 07.00–22.00
- ★ ORIENTATION: ocean view
- ★ CREDIT CARDS: American Express, Visa
- ★ OWNING COMPANY: Guy de la Houssaye
- ★ GENERAL MANAGER: Robert B. Hoflund
- ★ DISTANCE TO BEACH: 150 m to our Caribbean/Atlantic beaches. Free transport to all others
- ★ DISTANCE TO SHOPS: located on hotel grounds
- ★ DISTANCE FROM AIRPORT: 1 km (transfers are free by hotel) private 'out island' runway

If you read the social columns anywhere from London to Dallas, you can't very well get away from the privately-owned island of Mustique in those heavenly microdots, the Grenadines. Some of the people who are somebody have been there or own a pad there – and I say this because Mustique is small and very, but very selective and now that it belongs to an eminent Frenchman from nearby Martinique, its services work too. As for the Cotton House, it's really a non-hotel – more of a place where one meets one's friends. There is no noise, no glitter, no cheap sensations, just this gorgeous green Caribbean islet belted with some of the most beautiful beaches in the business. The main house is an old, converted sugarmill, very clubby and quite charming. The rest are the cottages, very fresh and cheerful and all done up in excellent taste. Cotton House may appear rustic. So did Marie Antoinette at times.

U.S. Virgin Islands

CANEEL BAY INC, P.O. Box 720, St. John

- ★ TELEPHONE: 809 776 6111
- ★ CABLES: Caneelbay, St. Thomas VI
- ★ TELEX: 3470019 (via ITT)
- ★ IN OPERATION: 32 years

- ★ RESERVATIONS: Rockresorts Inc, 800-223-7637
- ★ ROOMS: 168
- ★ SUITES: none

★ RESTAURANTS: 3
★ BARS: 3
★ DISCOTHEQUE: no – but live music
★ SHOPS: 2 – clothing, souvenirs and sundries
★ CONFERENCE ROOMS: none
★ BANQUETING ROOMS: none
★ STANDARD BEDROOM SIZE: 60 m^2
★ PRIVATE BALCONIES: yes – most rooms
★ SWIMMING POOL: no
★ RECREATIONAL ACTIVITIES: tennis, sailing, scuba and snorkelling, hiking, windsurfing, bicycling and riding

★ GARDENS: yes
★ NO. OF STAFF: 400
★ ROOM SERVICE: 08.00–10.00 and 19.00–21.00
★ ORIENTATION: all rooms face beach
★ CREDIT CARDS: American Express, Visa and Master Charge
★ OPERATING COMPANY: Rockresorts Inc
★ GENERAL MANAGER: Michael F. Glennie
★ DISTANCE TO BEACH: on the beach
★ DISTANCE TO SHOPS: 16 km
★ DISTANCE FROM AIRPORT: 14 km

Quite apart from the fact that I am sure he is a very nice man, the legendary Mr Laurence Rockefeller is one of my favourite hotel entrepreneurs. There can seldom be a man who spoils as little and creates as much as he does and Caneel Bay, among his other creations, is no exception. It is an entire and absolutely gorgeous Caribbean peninsula – seemingly untouched but cleverly beautiful and there is more space here than anywhere else I know, roughly one acre per guest. One could also measure the rooms by the acre – they are enormous – lovely stone, real timber floors, vistas of windows and nothing but gentle beauty all around. Beds are convention-sized and so are the shining bathrooms. Yet there is nothing showy or vulgar. There are no fewer than seven private beaches, all absolutely superclean, lots of watersports and also some curiosities. I found in the gardens a plant that only grows in the Pacific. On being asked, the manager said, 'Mr Rockefeller is a very keen botanist, you know.' The food is American – and guaranteed safe for any tum. If you are all right for petrodollars or Dubai gold bars, I can't think of a better place to spend them.

DENMARK
Copenhagen
HOTEL KONG FREDERIK, Vester Voldgade 23-27, DK-1552 Copenhagen V

★ TELEPHONE: (01) 125902
★ CABLES: Frederikhotel
★ TELEX: 19702
★ IN OPERATION: since 1962; renovated 1978
★ RESERVATIONS: Utell International, worldwide
★ ROOMS: 127
★ SUITES: 5
★ RESTAURANTS: 2 – Queen's Grill and Queen's Garden (summer only)
★ BARS: 1
★ DISCOTHEQUE: no
★ SHOPS: none
★ CONFERENCE ROOMS: King's Gallery (up to 100)
★ BANQUETING ROOMS: King's Gallery (up to 100)

★ STANDARD BEDROOM SIZE: 25 m^2
★ PRIVATE BALCONIES: some rooms
★ SWIMMING POOL: no
★ GARDENS: yes
★ NO. OF STAFF: 170
★ ROOM SERVICE: around the clock
★ ORIENTATION: faces west
★ CREDIT CARDS: all major ones
★ OWNING COMPANY: K/S Radhusplasens Hoteller
★ GENERAL MANAGER: Per Mortensen
★ DISTANCE TO BEACH: 5 km
★ DISTANCE TO SHOPS: hotel located in shopping district
★ DISTANCE FROM AIRPORT: 10 km

Having recently returned to Copenhagen – something I forgot to do for so long – I am delighted to be able to add one more address in the lovely Danish capital. Which of the two you choose is your affair but the Kong Frederik struck me as one of the brightest, most cheerful city hotels I have seen in Europe. It's worth going there just for that delightful Queen's Garden courtyard restaurant – they keep your feet warm with a heated floor and aquavit takes care of the rest. The whole hotel is charmingly furnished with good, well-chosen pieces and every room is different as befits such an old building. As usual in Denmark, I found the place so clean that one could eat breakfast off the floor – happily for one's posture one does not have to. The food everywhere is Danish – fabulous and that's enough said. What must be said is that the quality of service is well above the average: nothing is too much trouble in this well-organized multi-lingual hotel. A very good choice.

PLAZA – A SHERATON HOTEL, 4 Bernstorffsgade, DK-1577 Copenhagen V

* ★ TELEPHONE: (01) 14 92 62
* ★ CABLES: Theplaza
* ★ TELEX: 15330
* ★ IN OPERATION: 12 years
* ★ RESERVATIONS: direct
* ★ ROOMS: 42 doubles 42 singles
* ★ SUITES: 14
* ★ RESTAURANTS: 2 – The Baron of Beef and The Silver Club
* ★ BARS: 1
* ★ DISCOTHEQUE: no
* ★ SHOPS: none
* ★ CONFERENCE ROOMS: 1 (50)
* ★ BANQUETING ROOMS: 1 (50)
* ★ STANDARD BEDROOM SIZE: 17 m² plus bathroom
* ★ PRIVATE BALCONIES: no
* ★ SWIMMING POOL: no
* ★ GARDENS: no
* ★ NO. OF STAFF: 100
* ★ ROOM SERVICE: 07.00–22.30
* ★ ORIENTATION: overlooking Tivoli gardens
* ★ CREDIT CARDS: American Express, Diners Club, Master Charge, Eurocard, Visa and Access
* ★ OWNING COMPANY: Plaza Co Ltd; managed by the Sheraton Corporation
* ★ GENERAL MANAGER: Mr Kai Mikkelsen (Director)
* ★ DISTANCE TO BEACH: 15 km
* ★ DISTANCE TO SHOPS: 500 m
* ★ DISTANCE FROM AIRPORT: 15 km

Copenhagen – that most cheerful and welcoming of capital cities – has had a chequered history where the hotel business is concerned. The quantity is there but often quality is missing – that's why, without hesitation, I have picked the refurbished Plaza as one of the two best hotels in this capital. It started as a kind of station hotel but has very quickly developed into a small but extremely elegant place – I particularly like the rooms and the suites which are quiet, tastefully furnished and beautifully equipped. Decor is sensible – mostly done in the suede-brown range which is most attractive. This hotel has one of the most original bars I have ever seen – in the library – sumptuously decorated with good leather and nice pictures, books and an exceedingly friendly and comfortable feel. The two dining rooms must be visited, not just for the Danish food which is superlative but because they could be object-lessons on how to furnish a restaurant.

Fredensborg

HOTEL STORE KRO, Slotsgade 6, 3480 Fredensborg

* ★ TELEPHONE: 02-280047
* ★ CABLES: Store Kro
* ★ TELEX: no
* ★ IN OPERATION: since 1723
* ★ RESERVATIONS: direct
* ★ ROOMS: 49
* ★ SUITES: 3
* ★ RESTAURANTS: 1
* ★ BARS: 1
* ★ DISCOTHEQUE: no
* ★ SHOPS: none
* ★ CONFERENCE ROOMS: 6 (smallest 20 m², largest 180 m²)
* ★ BANQUETING ROOMS: 3 (smallest 12 m², largest 180 m²)
* ★ STANDARD BEDROOM SIZE: 18 m²

★ PRIVATE BALCONIES: some rooms
★ SWIMMING POOL: no
★ RECREATIONAL ACTIVITIES: area suitable for walks
★ GARDENS: yes
★ NO. OF STAFF: 32
★ ROOM SERVICE: around the clock
★ ORIENTATION: some rooms overlook gardens

★ CREDIT CARDS: all major cards
★ OWNING COMPANY: Dansk Magisterforening
★ GENERAL MANAGER: Sven Kristiansen
★ DISTANCE TO BEACH: 12 km
★ DISTANCE TO SHOPS: 150 m
★ DISTANCE FROM AIRPORT: 65 km

Some years ago in Denmark, having discovered the delights of some of the small country hotels, I swore I would go back and look for some more. I did and I have and this is now the second appearance of Store Kro in this book. I am quite sure it won't be the last because readers will love it. It is basically an old manor house, originally built in 1723 by King Frederik IV (he was probably fed up with putting up so many guests in his own Fredensborg Castle nearby . . .) and since then much renovated and added to, but it has kept the royal touch: splendid public rooms ornamented by priceless furniture, mostly Danish antiques, and a fresh, uncluttered feel that one must appreciate. Everything is in its place. Bedrooms are all individual so you can choose your own and service is gentle, smiling and efficient. There are splendid gardens all around in this particularly royal part of Denmark just a few miles from Copenhagen. Yet undoubtedly, what I will remember best about Store Kro is the food – I got almost as much fun photographing the cold table as I did partaking of it! Scandinavia's (and France's . . .) delicacies are all here: fresh, natural and of the highest quality and they are all so beautifully arranged that it seems a shame to upset the order. Dinners are great, too.

Millinge, Fyn

STEENSGAARD HERREGARDS PENSION, D-5642 Millinge, Fyn

★ TELEPHONE: 09-61.94.90
★ CABLES: no
★ TELEX: no
★ IN OPERATION: since 1956
★ RESERVATIONS: direct
★ ROOMS: 13 doubles 2 singles
★ SUITES: none
★ RESTAURANTS: 1
★ BARS: 1
★ DISCOTHEQUE: no
★ SHOPS: none
★ CONFERENCE ROOMS: 1 (15 to 20)
★ BANQUETING ROOMS: sitting rooms can be adapted to banqueting rooms accommodating up to 100
★ STANDARD BEDROOM SIZE: 20–46 m^2
★ PRIVATE BALCONIES: no – public terraces

★ SWIMMING POOL: no
★ RECREATIONAL ACTIVITIES: tennis, horse riding and pleasant walks through forests and fields
★ GARDENS: yes – park
★ NO. OF STAFF: 12
★ ROOM SERVICE: 08.00–23.00
★ ORIENTATION: terraces face south
★ CREDIT CARDS: none
★ OWNING COMPANY: Peter Hansen
★ GENERAL MANAGERS: Kirsten Lund & Bent Lillemark
★ DISTANCE TO BEACH: 2 km
★ DISTANCE TO SHOPS: 7 km
★ DISTANCE FROM AIRPORT: 42 km (Beldringe)

A country's hospitality should be judged by hotels away from the big cities, by the small, the remote and the ordinary. Not knowing much about Denmark, a sight like Steensgaard makes one feel the standards must be high. I came across it by accident and will surely return; it is a charming little manor house, a fourteenth-century all-timbered building blending carelessly into a great park where generations of cultivated Danes must have had a hand in creating it. Splendid panelled walls, marvellous parquet flooring and extremely pretty furniture combine to ravish the eye. Public rooms are elegantly private – it could be your drawing room if you were lucky enough to own such a place. Being a small place, everybody at Steensgaard knows you, what you like and how you like it within a short time of your arrival.

Nyborg

HOTEL HESSELET, 5800 Nyborg

★ TELEPHONE: 09 31 30 29
★ CABLES: Hesselet
★ TELEX: no
★ IN OPERATION: since 1967
★ RESERVATIONS: direct
★ ROOMS: 43
★ SUITES: 3
★ RESTAURANTS: 1
★ BARS: none
★ DISCOTHEQUE: no – but live music can be arranged if desired
★ SHOPS: none
★ CONFERENCE ROOMS: 1 (120)
★ BANQUETING ROOMS: 3 (20, 60 and 70)
★ STANDARD BEDROOM SIZE: 32 m^2
★ PRIVATE BALCONIES: 14 rooms have private terraces
★ SWIMMING POOL: yes – fresh water, 10 × 5 m

★ RECREATIONAL ACTIVITIES: massage, 2 saunas, tennis, horse riding, billiards, table tennis and international 18-hole golf course
★ GARDENS: yes
★ NO. OF STAFF: 45
★ ROOM SERVICE: 07.00–23.00
★ ORIENTATION: the main façades face west
★ CREDIT CARDS: Eurocard, American Express and Diners Club
★ OWNING COMPANY: Kai Wolhardt and Karl Haustrup
★ GENERAL MANAGER: Mrs Lissi Haustrup
★ DISTANCE TO BEACH: directly on the beach
★ DISTANCE TO SHOPS: 2 km
★ DISTANCE FROM AIRPORT: 45 km

This rather unusual hotel, our readers agree, is both different and interesting. It is Scandinavian/Japanese and hyper-modern but not jarringly so – with flowers everywhere and an Eastern attention to small details. Here is an oddity indeed. Rooms are large by European standards and they all have an agreeable sitting area so that you are not forever perched on the edge of the bed. The beds are worth a mention – they are among the most comfortable I have ever rested weary bones on. There is also a marvellous indoor swimming pool where the surroundings are rustic-green. Only an hour away from Copenhagen, this astonishing blend of East and West has certainly captured the attention of some of our most discriminating readers.

DJIBOUTI

DJIBOUTI SHERATON HOTEL, B.P. 1924, Djibouti, République de Djibouti

★ TELEPHONE: 35-04-05
★ CABLES: no
★ TELEX: 5912 DJ SHER
★ IN OPERATION: since December 1981
★ RESERVATIONS: Sheraton Hotels or Sheraton Reservation Offices
★ ROOMS: 198
★ SUITES: 2
★ RESTAURANTS: 2 and a poolside snack bar
★ BARS: 2 – 1 poolside bar and Khamsin Bar
★ DISCOTHEQUE: yes
★ SHOPS: 2 – boutique and news stand plus a travel agent counter

★ CONFERENCE ROOMS: 1 (up to 150)
★ BANQUETING ROOMS: 1 (up to 150)
★ STANDARD BEDROOM SIZE: 18 m^2
★ PRIVATE BALCONIES: no
★ SWIMMING POOL: yes – fresh water, oval shaped, 20 × 15 m
★ RECREATIONAL ACTIVITIES: 1 tennis court, fishing, deep sea fishing, scuba diving – best coral reef and tropical fish viewing half hour from hotel and casino; the hotel is planning to build a beach club on a nearby island
★ GARDENS: yes
★ NO. OF STAFF: 220

★ ROOM SERVICE: around the clock
★ ORIENTATION: all rooms face the sea
★ CREDIT CARDS: yes
★ OWNING COMPANY: Société hotelière d'état

★ GENERAL MANAGER: Nicholas Gonzalez
★ DISTANCE TO BEACH: hotel by the sea, nearest beach 50 m
★ DISTANCE TO SHOPS: 1 km
★ DISTANCE FROM AIRPORT: 6 km

Another one of those places where only mad dogs and Englishmen used to go – except that in this case, it was Frenchmen, until the locals gained a sort of French-protected independence. Djibouti – a setting fit for Peter Lorre – is right there on the Horn of Africa and now, since the Djibouti Sheraton has opened its 200 rooms you can even drink the water (though the bar is better stocked, especially with French wines). In this part of the world there has never been anything like it. In any other geographical context, one might perhaps look and pass on. Here you look and stay. It's a friendly hotel too, with nice Gallic touches and quite a lot of life. Decor is international but one can live with it and as for the food, the answer is that whoever it was who said that British imperialists left good policemen behind and the French left good food must have been thinking of Djibouti. Not far away you can go to the beach, try scuba diving in the Red Sea and shoot off to islands which are hardly marked on the map. Djibouti for your next stopover? That's travelling with a vengeance.

EGYPT

Aswan

HOTEL ASWAN OBEROI, Elephantine Island, Aswan

★ TELEPHONE: 23455
★ CABLES: Obhotel Aswan
★ TELEX: 92120 OBROI UN
★ IN OPERATION: since 1975
★ RESERVATIONS: Loews Representation International, U.S.A., Canada, Mexico, London and Tokyo/Stinnes Touristic Representation, Frankfurt/Oberoi Hotels Reservation Offices
★ ROOMS: 160
★ SUITES: 38, 16 villas
★ RESTAURANTS: Orangerie, Coffee Shop, The Nashwah (night club) and Floating Restaurant (on request)
★ BARS: Elephantine Bar
★ DISCOTHEQUE: yes – and live music
★ SHOPS: 25 – including a bank
★ CONFERENCE ROOMS: 1 (150)
★ BANQUETING ROOMS: 1 (150)
★ STANDARD BEDROOM SIZE: 18 m²

★ PRIVATE BALCONIES: yes
★ SWIMMING POOL: yes – fresh water, 30 × 20 m
★ RECREATIONAL ACTIVITIES: tennis, sailing, health spa & beauty parlour
★ GARDENS: yes
★ NO. OF STAFF: 415
★ ROOM SERVICE: around the clock
★ FURTHER DEVELOPMENTS: 150 additional rooms
★ CREDIT CARDS: American Express, Diners Club, Bankamericard, Master Charge, Eurocard and Visa
★ OPERATING COMPANY: Oberoi Hotels International
★ GENERAL MANAGER: Mr Ibrahim Dessouki
★ DISTANCE TO SHOPS: walking distance of 10 km
★ DISTANCE FROM AIRPORT: 18 km

One lady I met in the lobby of the Aswan Oberoi was bubbling over with enjoyment. 'I just love Egypt,' she enthused. 'It's really quite civilized, isn't it?' Probably the pharaohs would have agreed with her although I must admit that Aswan was never quite like this in the hotel field in the pre-Oberoi days and I remember it buzzing with helicopter-sized mosquitoes. While this hotel cannot be on a par with anything that ancient Egypt has to offer, it is nevertheless a very welcome oasis of peace, coolness and efficiency in a country that, however interesting, is a bit hard on the traveller. Here everything works smoothly and with commendable efficiency. It's a hotel built for passing tourists of course – the size of the rooms show it – and nobody stays long enough to complain. But the rest certainly makes a change – the telephone works, the moneychanger does not skin you alive and the bellboy's 'yes, mister' comes with a great wide grin. One can drink anything without fear of the Nefertitis and the food, if not distinguished, is perfectly acceptable. Apart from the architecture (happily it won't last as long as Karnak) a good effort it certainly is and one can now brush one's teeth and get a suit pressed in Aswan.

Cairo

CAIRO SHERATON HOTEL & CASINO, P.O. Box 11, Galae Square, Giza, Cairo

- ★ TELEPHONE: 983000
- ★ CABLES: Sheraco Cairo, A.R.E.
- ★ TELEX: (927) 92041 & (927) 382 Shera UN
- ★ IN OPERATION: since March 1970
- ★ RESERVATIONS: Sheraton Reservation Offices, worldwide
- ★ ROOMS: 396 doubles 10 singles
- ★ SUITES: 50
- ★ RESTAURANTS: 4
- ★ BARS: 3
- ★ DISCOTHEQUE: live music
- ★ SHOPS: 6
- ★ CONFERENCE ROOMS: 1 (400)
- ★ BANQUETING ROOMS: 1 (350)
- ★ STANDARD BEDROOM SIZE: 25 m^2

- ★ PRIVATE BALCONIES: yes
- ★ SWIMMING POOL: yes – fresh water, 11.5 × 10 m
- ★ GARDENS: no
- ★ NO. OF STAFF: 820
- ★ ROOM SERVICE: around the clock
- ★ ORIENTATION: facing Nile and Galae Square
- ★ CREDIT CARDS: Bankamericard, Master Charge, American Express and Diners Club
- ★ OWNING COMPANY: Egyptian Government
- ★ GENERAL MANAGER: Ahmed Basmi
- ★ DISTANCE TO SHOPS: 8 km
- ★ DISTANCE FROM AIRPORT: 26 km

Only a few years ago there was not a single hotel in Cairo where one would have dared to send anyone, not even one's tax collector. Now, the Egyptian capital has four of international standing – two American chains, one French and one Indian and competition is intense. The Cairo Sheraton certainly deserves mention – 25 storeys right on the bank of the Nile facing the old city with the Pyramids in the distance, where everything works from the message service to the air-conditioning. The Sheraton silhouette – not unpleasant – simply rather slab-like, must be accepted. What is remarkable in a way is how this chain hotel has been furnished – very elegantly indeed in a kind of periodless Curzon Street Baroque that soon grows on one. Service is fast and attentive and more than willing and the food, in all the varieties offered in the four restaurants, is well up to what one might expect.

HOTEL MENA HOUSE OBEROI, Pyramids Road, Giza, Cairo

- ★ TELEPHONE: 855444 and 857999
- ★ CABLES: Obhotel
- ★ TELEX: 92316 and 93096 OBHTL UN
- ★ IN OPERATION: since 1973
- ★ RESERVATIONS: Loews Representation International, New York, London/Oberoi Hotels, India/Stinnes Touristic Representation, Frankfurt/Al Ghanim Travel, Kuwait/Onder Hotel Representatives, Hong Kong/Utell International, Dnata, Dubai, United Arab Emirates/any Oberoi Hotel or reservation service
- ★ ROOMS: 520
- ★ SUITES: 15

- ★ RESTAURANTS: 6 – Khan El Khalili, Al Rybayyat, Moghul Room, Oasis, Abu Nawas and Mena Cafe
- ★ BARS: 2 – Mameluke Bar and Lobby Bar
- ★ DISCOTHEQUE: yes – the Saddle
- ★ SHOPS: 8
- ★ CONFERENCE ROOMS: 1 (200)
- ★ BANQUETING ROOMS: 1 (200)
- ★ STANDARD BEDROOM SIZE: 21 m^2
- ★ PRIVATE BALCONIES: yes
- ★ SWIMMING POOL: yes – fresh water, 40 × 30 m
- ★ RECREATIONAL ACTIVITIES: 18-hole golf course, tennis, riding
- ★ GARDENS: yes

★ **NO. OF STAFF:** 1100

★ **ROOM SERVICE:** around the clock

★ **ORIENTATION:** hotel located at the foot of the Pyramids of Giza

★ **CREDIT CARDS:** Diners Club, American Express, Bankamericard and Visa

★ **OWNING COMPANY:** Oberoi Hotels (India) Pvt Ltd

★ **GENERAL MANAGER:** Mr Kaval Nain

★ **DISTANCE TO SHOPS:** 10 km

★ **DISTANCE FROM AIRPORT:** 30 km

It is hard to believe that it is only eleven years since this clever and hard working India-based company took over what was a fusty old palace and turned it into a hotel which now enjoys worldwide fame. And deserves it too. Everybody who has been to Mena House loves it.

Once, it was a khedivial weekend place, then the habitual watering place of colonial Brits and then the meeting place of Roosevelt and Churchill and, later, of Anwar Sadat and Menachem Begin. In those days it had a curious, forlorn, Turkish-type decadence and now it is back in all its glory. Away from the hurly-burly of Cairo (very hurly indeed), Mena House is so near the Pyramids that when I rose in the morning and walked onto my terrace I could almost touch Cheops' great pile – probably the most prestigious location in Egypt. The hotel's fabric has been renewed but not re-made. The old wooden balconies are still there, so are those splendid 'musharabyiah' screens which are so much a part of Arabic art, and everywhere Mena House shines with good taste. Even the Coffee Shop, called Khan el-Khalili after Cairo's great bazaar, is a

masterpiece. Elsewhere, amidst gardens and around the pool, are the new wings – cool, spacious and elegant.

Above all, this hotel has character and personality. People smile, help and are totally unstinting in the service they give and it is obvious that the excellent management has done its homework. The food runs from good to superb and the Indian restaurant is particularly to be recommended. As in all great hotels, it's being there that counts. Full marks for a great success.

NILE HILTON HOTEL, Tahrir Square, Cairo

★ TELEPHONE: 750666/740777
★ CABLES: Hiltels Cairo
★ TELEX: 92222/92354 Hiltls UN
★ IN OPERATION: since February 1959
★ RESERVATIONS: Hilton International
★ ROOMS: 462 (all rooms are singles and doubles)
★ SUITES: 69
★ RESTAURANTS: 6 – El Nile Rotisserie, Pizzeria, Belvedere Supper Club, Taverne du Champ de Mars, Ibis Coffee Shop and Tropicana
★ BARS: 3
★ DISCOTHEQUE: yes
★ SHOPS: men's wear, ladies' wear, patisserie, silver jewellery and antiques, bazaars, florist, camera shop, bookshop, car rental, beauty/hairdressing parlour, barber shop, airlines, travel agent, banks, papyrus
★ CONFERENCE ROOMS: 6 (30 to 800)

★ BANQUETING ROOMS: 6 (30 to 500)
★ STANDARD BEDROOM SIZE: 24 m^2
★ PRIVATE BALCONIES: yes – all rooms
★ SWIMMING POOL: yes – fresh water, 22 m
★ RECREATIONAL ACTIVITIES: 2 clay tennis courts, health club with gymnasium, sauna, steam bath and massage; golf, squash and horse riding nearby; water sports and boat rentals by arrangement
★ GARDENS: yes
★ NO. OF STAFF: 950
★ ROOM SERVICE: around the clock
★ ORIENTATION: rooms face Nile and city
★ CREDIT CARDS: Carte Blanche, American Express, Master Charge, Eurocard, Diners Club, Bankamericard and Hilton Hotels
★ GENERAL MANAGER: Roman Rickenbacher
★ DISTANCE TO SHOPS: walking distance
★ DISTANCE FROM AIRPORT: 24 km

Part of the trinity of great Hiltons in this part of the world (the other two being Athens and Istanbul), the Nile Hilton still deserves every praise. By now, it has to contend with its corporate brother just down the banks of the Nile and this is going to make its success all the more remarkable. The hotel is more than twenty years old which, in Hilton terms, makes it almost an antique and in this space of time it has acquired a patina and a tradition of its own. It has elegance, good looks and just enough bustle and glitter to remind you of where you are. Service is quite superb – instant, smiling and ever present. The swimming pool is one of the best in Cairo and just across the Nile is the Gezira Sporting Club where you can be energetic. The Hilton navy, Isis and Osiris, is moored down below waiting to sail you upstream to the wonders of the land of the Pharaohs. But not, I hope, before you have had time to sample the food in the Rotisserie – one of the two or three best hotel restaurants in Cairo.

Nothing is missing here. The Nile Hilton is a great hotel.

RAMSES HILTON, Corniche El Nil, Cairo

★ TELEPHONE: 777444
★ CABLES: Hiram Cairo
★ TELEX: 94260/2
★ IN OPERATION: since May 1981
★ RESERVATIONS: direct or Hilton Reservation Service

★ ROOMS: 880
★ SUITES: 80
★ RESTAURANTS: 6 – La Brasserie Coffee Shop, Citadel Grill, La Patisserie, Pool Snack Bar, Two Season Supper Club, Falafel Oriental Restaurant

★ BARS: 3 – Citadel Bar, Garden Bar, Club 36
★ DISCOTHEQUE: yes, and live music
★ SHOPS: 16
★ CONFERENCE ROOMS: 10 (from 50 to 500)
★ BANQUETING ROOMS: 6 (from 25 to 500)
★ STANDARD BEDROOM SIZE: 26 m^2
★ PRIVATE BALCONIES: all rooms
★ SWIMMING POOL: yes – fresh water
★ RECREATIONAL ACTIVITIES: swimming and health club; golf, tennis and riding can be arranged nearby

★ GARDENS: yes
★ NO. OF STAFF: 1,200
★ ROOM SERVICE: around the clock
★ ORIENTATION: south-east, overlooking Nile
★ CREDIT CARDS: all major credit cards
★ OWNING COMPANY: operated by Hilton International
★ GENERAL MANAGER: Ahmed El Nahas
★ DISTANCE TO SHOPS: walking distance
★ DISTANCE FROM AIRPORT: 24 km

As a professional hotel watcher, I have inevitably looked closely at Hilton operations over the years and I must admit that on some occasions in the now distant past, I shook my head in despair. Now, more often than not, I doff my hat to the world's universal host because they have been big enough to learn from their own past mistakes and these days, when a new Hilton opens, one looks carefully.

A case in point is Cairo's second Hilton – a statement of pride – 35 storeys rising above this frenetic and absolutely fascinating city, and with even a glass elevator which reveals a new Nile at every touch of the button. So far, so eye-filling. The outside architecture does not thrill me and I must admit that the colossal statue of the old man (Ramses II, I mean . . .) in the lobby fills one with awe. Then you begin to realize the idea behind it all: the vast lobby reminds you of Karnak and Luxor with huge, massive pillars of porphyry rising everywhere like those of a temple. But there is more to it than that. You begin to notice the finish of every item – the edge of the bar, the hinges of a door, the fit of the carpets, the opulent but not disagreeable room decor and you finally have to admit that here are people who know how to build a hotel – they have the experience, the knowhow, the values and if the good taste is also there, the results are unmatchable in the new hotel line. That must be acknowledged. Inevitably, the Ramses has everything: five restaurants (the food is extremely good), three bars, swimming pool, shops galore. One expects that. What is not always quite so automatic is the quality of the management which in this case is of the highest.

Hurghada

HURGHADA SHERATON HOTEL, Hurghada, Red Sea

★ TELEPHONE: 785
★ CABLES: no
★ TELEX: 92750 UN SHERGA
★ IN OPERATION: 4 years
★ RESERVATIONS: Sheraton Hotel or Reservations Offices, Brussels, Cairo, Frankfurt, London, Milan, Paris, Stockholm
★ ROOMS: 165
★ SUITES: none
★ RESTAURANTS: 1
★ BARS: 1
★ DISCOTHEQUE: no
★ SHOPS: 1 – newsagent/giftshop
★ CONFERENCE ROOMS: 4 (10 to 35)
★ BANQUETING ROOMS: 4 (10 to 35)
★ STANDARD BEDROOM SIZE: 25 m^2

★ PRIVATE BALCONIES: all rooms
★ SWIMMING POOL: 1 – salt water, 30 × 20 m
★ RECREATIONAL ACTIVITIES: full range of watersports
★ GARDENS: no
★ NO. OF STAFF: 75
★ ROOM SERVICE: 07.00–24.00
★ ORIENTATION: all rooms have sea or mountain view
★ CREDIT CARDS: all major credit cards
★ OWNING COMPANY: Egyptian General Company for Tourism and Hotels
★ GENERAL MANAGER: A. Bakri
★ DISTANCE TO BEACH: on the beach
★ DISTANCE TO SHOPS: 1 km
★ DISTANCE FROM AIRPORT: 5 km

Who on earth goes to the Red Sea coast of Egypt? I do and so will you, I suggest, before very long because this grand and austere desert coast with its fringe along one of the greatest coral reefs in the world is a place of the future. Out there are dozens of beach-girt islands such as you have never seen before. One can fly to Hurghada in 45 minutes from Cairo – which I think is a pity. Do as I did – drive, and you'll feel that you are aiming at the end of the world. You are in fact aiming at the Hurghada Sheraton – one of the most courageous hotel enterprises I have seen recently. All right, I could have done without the drum-like architecture (you know what architects are like . . .). But for what it is, where it is, at the edge of this marine paradise, the Hurghada Sheraton deserves every compliment. It is clean, well planned, quite handsome inside, around its interior garden, and the rooms – very, very good indeed – are totally silent. Service is gay and cheerful and the food better than one has any right to expect in this kind of location. And when you have had enough of the pale blue sea, drive on back across the desert and meet the Nile at Luxor. You won't forget the trip.

EIRE
Cong

ASHFORD CASTLE, Cong, Co Mayo

- ★ TELEPHONE: (094) 22644
- ★ CABLES: no
- ★ TELEX: 24749
- ★ IN OPERATION: since 1973
- ★ RESERVATIONS: Aer Lingus, Great Britain, Germany, France and U.S.A./Loews Representation International, worldwide/Irish Tourist Board, Central Reservations, London

- ★ ROOMS: 72 twin/doubles
- ★ SUITES: 6
- ★ RESTAURANTS: 1
- ★ BARS: 2 – Cocktail Bar and Dungeon Bar
- ★ DISCOTHEQUE: live music
- ★ SHOPS: 1
- ★ CONFERENCE ROOMS: 1 (150)
- ★ BANQUETING ROOMS: 1 (100)
- ★ STANDARD BEDROOM SIZE: 30 m^2

★ PRIVATE BALCONIES: no
★ SWIMMING POOL: no
★ RECREATIONAL ACTIVITIES: 9-hole golf course and 2 tennis courts, with horse riding nearby
★ GARDENS: yes – 300 acres
★ NO. OF STAFF: 70
★ ROOM SERVICE: 08.00–10.00, afterwards on request
★ ORIENTATION: rooms face Lough Corrib and gardens
★ FURTHER DEVELOPMENTS: a new conference centre within the next two years
★ CREDIT CARDS: all credit cards
★ OWNING COMPANY: John A. Mulcahy Co Ltd
★ GENERAL MANAGER: Rory J. C. Murphy
★ DISTANCE TO BEACH: 40 km
★ DISTANCE TO SHOPS: 40 km
★ DISTANCE FROM AIRPORT: 128 km

If it was not there, Ashford Castle would have to be invented – the kind of Irish stately home where the 'Troubles' never happened. Although it is not all that old, Ashford seems to have been there forever and then some more, a great stone-built pile backed by green fields and woods and facing a beautiful lake. Among other things it has 300 acres of gardens, 4000 acres of nature reserve and 27,000 acres of shoot. Public rooms are grand, wood-panelled and exceedingly well furnished with much of the eighteenth century's best mahogany. Bedrooms are large and airy, high-ceilinged and very well equipped with good beds and solid, unpretentious Irish country-style furniture, lots of room for your clothes and your luggage and, what is so rare these days, good lighting. In as far as you can see Ireland from a hotel you can see it from this one.

Dublin

GRESHAM HOTEL, O'Connell Street, Dublin 1

★ TELEPHONE: 746881
★ CABLES: no
★ TELEX: 25308
★ IN OPERATION: founded 1817
★ RESERVATIONS: Ryan's Tours Inc, New York/Ryan Tourist Group, London/Utell International, worldwide/Loews Representation International, New York/Expotel Ltd, London/Selective Hotel Reservations, New York
★ ROOMS: 174
★ SUITES: 6
★ RESTAURANTS: 1
★ BARS: 1 and another scheduled to open in autumn 1984
★ DISCOTHEQUE: yes
★ SHOPS: 1 – selling a variety of products
★ CONFERENCE ROOMS: 7 (4 to 400)
★ BANQUETING ROOMS: 7 (up to 400)
★ STANDARD BEDROOM SIZE: 10 m^2
★ PRIVATE BALCONIES: no – but there are 4 terrace suites
★ SWIMMING POOL: no
★ RECREATIONAL ACTIVITIES: the hotel is close to the sea, tennis courts, golf courses, riding stables, cricket pitches, rugby and soccer fields
★ GARDENS: no
★ NO. OF STAFF: 145
★ ROOM SERVICE: 07.00–23.00 for meals; around the clock for drinks & snacks
★ ORIENTATION: suites overlook Dublin city and mountains; rooms face all directions
★ CREDIT CARDS: American Express, Visa, Access, Diners Club, Carte Blanche
★ OWNING COMPANY: The Ryan Hotel Group
★ GENERAL MANAGER: Dennis Fryer
★ DISTANCE TO BEACH: 10 km
★ DISTANCE TO SHOPS: Hotel in centre of Dublin
★ DISTANCE FROM AIRPORT: 15 km

Twice in the ten-year lifespan of this guide we have changed our minds about Dublin hotels. Sorry about that, but there have been many changes on the scene and most of them downward. Now we think we are sure that the Gresham is the best – at least it is done up in genuine, sensible good taste which is more than one can say for its competitors. The location of course is terrific – it could not be better placed. Its rooms, whether period or modern, are good, efficient and beautifully serviced and with no hint of hotelese exaggeration. Public rooms are quite elegant, with clever little touches here and there – this vase, or that mirror or that picture. As a building, the Gresham was not built yesterday, of course – it dates back to 1817 and although the plumbing has happily been changed, the proportions of the place have not. Service is on the whole Irish and smiling. The food, we thought, was a little obvious but with so many marvellous eateries nearby one does not mind.

Newmarket-on-Fergus

DROMOLAND CASTLE, Newmarket-on-Fergus, Co Clare

★ TELEPHONE: 061-71144
★ CABLES: Dromoland Castle, Co Clare
★ TELEX: 26854
★ IN OPERATION: 22 years
★ RESERVATIONS: McDonough Hotels, U.S.A./Relais de Campagne Group, France
★ ROOMS: 67
★ SUITES: none
★ RESTAURANTS: 1
★ BARS: 2
★ DISCOTHEQUE: live entertainment in the bar each evening
★ SHOPS: 1
★ CONFERENCE ROOMS: 1 (up to 200)
★ BANQUETING ROOMS: 2 (70 to 120)
★ STANDARD BEDROOM SIZE: 28 m^2
★ PRIVATE BALCONIES: no – but terrace with seating equipment

★ SWIMMING POOL: no
★ RECREATIONAL ACTIVITIES: tennis, 9-hole golf course, croquet, fishing (both river and lake) with horse riding nearby
★ GARDENS: yes
★ NO. OF STAFF: 90
★ ROOM SERVICE: around the clock
★ ORIENTATION: rooms overlook woods and parkland
★ CREDIT CARDS: American Express, Barclaycard, Visa and Diners Club
★ OWNING COMPANY: Mr B. P. McDonough (Marmac Corporation)
★ GENERAL MANAGER: Miss Patricia Barry
★ DISTANCE TO SHOPS: 11 km
★ DISTANCE FROM AIRPORT: 13 km (Shannon)

Some people, when they get to Dromoland Castle, don't quite believe it or the rest of Ireland either. Cecil B. de Mille must have been there yesterday afternoon to run it up out of pasteboard and glue. But look closer and it becomes real, even to its root in the distant past when Brian Boru was king of all Ireland. It took an American (naturally) to make Dromoland come true. How he made the plumbing work through walls five feet thick is a major miracle of the art of sanitary engineering. Dromoland is vast – corridors without beginning or end, acres of carpets, walls hung with enough pictures to fill the Louvre, public rooms that look like the nave of Westminster Abbey and, outside, that pervasive green Irishness which is without comparison. Rooms vary greatly in character but they are always well cared for. Service does not vary and the food is Irish from the estate. Here you can play golf or croquet, ride, fish or just sit and dream that you have arrived in a time-zone not yet blown apart by two world wars.

Waterville

WATERVILLE LAKE HOTEL, Waterville, Co Kerry

★ TELEPHONE: Waterville 7 and 066-23100
★ CABLES: no
★ TELEX: 28246
★ IN OPERATION: since 1972
★ RESERVATIONS: Irish Tourist Board/Aer Lingus/Brendan Tours, U.S.A./L.R.I., New York
★ ROOMS: 94 doubles

★ SUITES: 8
★ RESTAURANTS: 1
★ BARS: 2 – Cocktail and Skelligs Bar
★ DISCOTHEQUE: live music
★ SHOPS: 1 – clothing, souvenirs, post cards etc
★ CONFERENCE ROOMS: 1 (100) – suites can be converted to meeting rooms for 25

★ BANQUETING ROOMS: none – but one room can be converted for banqueting purposes, seating 40 persons
★ STANDARD BEDROOM SIZE: 28 m²
★ PRIVATE BALCONIES: yes – 40 rooms
★ SWIMMING POOL: 1 – indoor, heated; also a jacuzzi, sauna and sunbed
★ RECREATIONAL ACTIVITIES: 2 tennis courts, golf and horse riding nearby
★ GARDENS: yes
★ NO. OF STAFF: 100
★ ROOM SERVICE: 08.00–10.00 for breakfast, afterwards on request

★ ORIENTATION: most rooms face lake and mountains
★ CREDIT CARDS: all credit cards
★ OWNING COMPANY: John A. Mulcahy Co Ltd
★ GENERAL MANAGER: Peter Prendiville
★ DISTANCE TO BEACH: 500 m
★ DISTANCE TO SHOPS: 80 km
★ DISTANCE FROM AIRPORT: 60 km (Cork); 192 km (Shannon)

One American friend sent to Waterville some time back returned agog with enthusiasm for the salmon fishing. 'You know,' he said, 'the fish positively queued up . . .' Those of us who tend to prefer salmon à l'oseille on a plate also feel that way about this hotel. Just right for blowing away the cobwebs of city life. A modern hotel built with respect for the landscape, it drapes itself on the shore of the incomparable Lough Currane, looking to blue waters and green mountains. There is a par 74 golf course and all the riding you could want. What impresses, however, is that here is a perfect example of what a modern country hotel should be like. It is extremely spacious, elegant, free of unnecessary trappings, intelligently furnished and nowhere is one shut off from the Ireland around you. Rooms are large, so are the beds, and bathrooms function perfectly. Service being one of Ireland's best points, here it is even better – people are quite charming. The food, as long as it is local, is superb.

FINLAND
Helsinki
HOTEL HESPERIA, Mannerheimintie 50, 00260 Helsinki 26

★ TELEPHONE: 90-441 311
★ CABLES: Hesperiahotel Helsinki
★ TELEX: 12-2117
★ IN OPERATION: since May 1972
★ RESERVATIONS: Supranational, Omaha, London, Frankfurt, Paris and Milan
★ ROOMS: 262 doubles 20 singles
★ SUITES: 4
★ RESTAURANTS: 3 – Steakhouse, main restaurant and Night Club
★ BARS: 3 – Lobby, Night Club and Sauna Bar
★ DISCOTHEQUE: live music in the Night Club by international top bands and famous singers
★ SHOPS: 5
★ CONFERENCE ROOMS: 9 (6 to 350)
★ BANQUETING ROOMS: 9 (6 to 400)
★ STANDARD BEDROOM SIZE: 22 m²
★ PRIVATE BALCONIES: no
★ SWIMMING POOL: yes – fresh water,

indoor, 8 × 14 m with small cold plunge bath
★ RECREATIONAL ACTIVITIES: saunas and solarium
★ GARDENS: no
★ NO. OF STAFF: 280
★ ORIENTATION: overlooks Hesperia Park and Toolo Bay
★ FURTHER DEVELOPMENTS: Another 100 rooms being built
★ CREDIT CARDS: American Express, Diners Club, Eurocard, Master Charge and Visa
★ OWNING COMPANY: Helsingin Osuuskauppa
★ GENERAL MANAGER: Mr Frank Moberg
★ DISTANCE TO SHOPS: 1 km
★ DISTANCE FROM AIRPORT: 20 km (Helsinki-Vantaa); air terminal 50 m from hotel and a heli-pad on roof of hotel

Marshal Mannerheim, the great saviour of Finland, would not have cared for the slightly odd-looking submarine Night Club but for the rest of the Hesperia I thought that it fitted very well as a big city hotel. Rooms are scrupulously clean and extremely well maintained in every respect – you feel that someone has been looking around before you checked in. The lobby, very large and straight out of the pages of a design magazine, has real leather, real Italian marble and real timber, which is not always so in modern hotels. The first floor dining room is one of the most comfortable I have ever dined in – I am large and chairs are too often small – and the food is excellent if you stick to the fishy Finnish specialities and, though you won't be able to pronounce their names, the taste will come as a pleasant surprise.

FRANCE

Avignon

HOSTELLERIE LE PRIEURÉ, 7 Place du Chapitre, B.P. 12, 30400 Villeneuve les Avignon

- ★ TELEPHONE: (90) 251820
- ★ CABLES: Prieuré-Avignon
- ★ TELEX: 431042
- ★ IN OPERATION: since 1943
- ★ RESERVATIONS: Relais et Chateaux, Paris
- ★ ROOMS: 20 doubles 6 singles
- ★ SUITES: 9
- ★ RESTAURANTS: 1 – lunch and dinner also served in the garden during the summer
- ★ BARS: 1
- ★ DISCOTHEQUE: no
- ★ SHOPS: none
- ★ CONFERENCE ROOMS: 2 (each of 40)
- ★ BANQUETING ROOMS: 3 (20 to 130)
- ★ STANDARD BEDROOM SIZE: 30 m²
- ★ PRIVATE BALCONIES: 18 rooms

- ★ SWIMMING POOL: yes – fresh water, 18 × 8 m
- ★ RECREATIONAL ACTIVITIES: 2 tennis courts
- ★ GARDENS: yes
- ★ NO. OF STAFF: 48
- ★ ROOM SERVICE: 07.00–22.00
- ★ ORIENTATION: rooms face all sides
- ★ CREDIT CARDS: Diners Club, American Express, Eurocard, Access, Master Charge and Interbank
- ★ OWNING COMPANY: Jacques R. Mille
- ★ GENERAL MANAGER: Jacques R. Mille
- ★ DISTANCE TO SHOPS: walking distance
- ★ DISTANCE FROM AIRPORT: 100 km (Marseilles)

The cardinal who, in the fourteenth century, built himself this residence in a lovely village just the other side of the Rhône from Avignon, left it in his will to '12 canons, 12 priests and two deacons'. Without disrespect, I am glad they left because the Prieuré then became a hotel so special, so pretty and so mellow that I always stay there longer than I should. Whether you have a room in the old house, with its serpentine staircases or one in the new wing, you can be certain of comfort. Furniture is mostly of the period, good but very, very expensive: it looks as if it belongs there. The family that runs this hotel knows a great deal about hospitality and it shows in a host of small details. Yet, in the end, two things count most here: the absolutely ravishing, tree-shaded courtyard and the food they serve there – classic French provincial and deserving of the approval of Brillat-Savarin himself.

Barbizon

HÔTELLERIE DU BAS-BRÉAU, 77630 Barbizon

- ★ TELEPHONE: (6) 966 40 05
- ★ CABLES: no
- ★ TELEX: 690 953
- ★ IN OPERATION: 45 years
- ★ RESERVATIONS: Relais et Chateaux, Paris/Jacques de Larsay, New York
- ★ ROOMS: 12
- ★ RESTAURANTS: 1
- ★ BARS: 1
- ★ DISCOTHEQUE: no
- ★ SHOPS: none
- ★ CONFERENCE ROOMS: 2 (10 to 25)
- ★ BANQUETING ROOMS: 1 (25)
- ★ STANDARD BEDROOM SIZE: 20 m^2
- ★ PRIVATE BALCONIES: yes
- ★ SWIMMING POOL: no

- ★ RECREATIONAL ACTIVITIES: horse riding within walking distance; golf and saunas 6 km away; indoor tennis court
- ★ GARDENS: yes
- ★ NO. OF STAFF: 49
- ★ ROOM SERVICE: around the clock
- ★ ORIENTATION: all rooms face gardens, terrace and private courtyard
- ★ CREDIT CARDS: American Express, Eurocard, Master Charge, Intercard and Access
- ★ OWNING COMPANY: privately owned
- ★ GENERAL MANAGER: J.-P. Fava
- ★ DISTANCE TO SHOPS: walking distance
- ★ DISTANCE FROM AIRPORT: 35 km (Orly); 75 km (Charles de Gaulle)

Provincials are traditionally the butt of many Parisian jokes but here, in the tranquil green of the great forest of Fontainebleau, tucked away in a village once made famous by the Barbizon painters is a hostelry which I would put among the best in Europe. R. L. Stevenson once lived here for quite a while and I envy him. The gardens are nice and informal and though the rooms vary in size and type, they are all furnished with pleasant country antiques – just right for this place.

One word of warning: when you go to Bas-Bréau, bring your appetite with you. The Fava family, who have owned this hotel for three generations, are known even among their competitors for a fare which can only be described as Rabelaisian. Though notice is taken of 'la nouvelle cuisine' (or what's left of it), this is French gastronomy at its unchanging best. It is served in an elegant restaurant patronized by celebrities from all over the world. As for the wines – you don't even have to look at the impressive list. Just ask Jean-Pierre Fava.

Les Baux de Provence

OUSTAU DE BAUMANIÈRE, 13520 Maussane Les Alpilles, Les Baux de Provence

- ★ TELEPHONE: (90) 97 33 07
- ★ CABLES: no
- ★ TELEX: 420203
- ★ IN OPERATION: 39 years

- ★ RESERVATIONS: direct
- ★ ROOMS: 15
- ★ SUITES: 11
- ★ RESTAURANTS: 1

★ BARS: 1
★ DISCOTHEQUE: no
★ SHOPS: 1
★ CONFERENCE ROOMS: 1 (100)
★ BANQUETING ROOMS: 1 (100)
★ STANDARD BEDROOM SIZE: 30 m^2
★ PRIVATE BALCONIES: yes
★ SWIMMING POOL: yes – fresh water, 25 × 15 m
★ RECREATIONAL ACTIVITIES: 1 tennis court and riding

★ GARDENS: yes
★ NO. OF STAFF: 75
★ ROOM SERVICE: 07.00–24.00
★ ORIENTATION: rooms face south
★ CREDIT CARDS: American Express, Visa and Diners Club
★ OWNING COMPANY: R. Thuilier
★ GENERAL MANAGER: R. Thuilier
★ DISTANCE TO BEACH: 50 km
★ DISTANCE TO SHOPS: 18 km
★ DISTANCE FROM AIRPORT: 45 km

By now every gourmet-critic in the world has made the pilgrimage to Monsieur Thuilier's establishment and there is no point in competing. I like good food without making a religion of it but would just say that if you think you know French cuisine, you don't, until you have been to Baumanière. For the purpose of this guide, the interest lies more in the atmosphere and the possibility of staying a night or two in this mellow and gentle manor house in this historic and unusual village which is something one can do if one tries. And try is the word since there are only a few rooms and much in demand at that. As a hotel Baumanière is unostentatious, comfortable and extremely well run – almost like a private house. Rooms are very handsome – solid French country furniture, four-poster beds and great chimney-pieces where everything shines with centuries of beeswax and elbow grease. Some very pretty gardens and a pleasant swimming pool provide the correct cadre to digest a famous lunch and the whole of old-fashioned Provence is around you.

Beaulieu-sur-Mer

HOTEL LA RÉSERVE DE BEAULIEU, 06310 Beaulieu sur Mer

★ TELEPHONE: (93) 01 00 01
★ CABLES: Reserve Beaulieu sur Mer
★ TELEX: Reserve 470301 F
★ RESERVATIONS: direct
★ ROOMS: 50
★ SUITES: 3
★ RESTAURANTS: 2 – including one in summer only with direct access by sea
★ BARS: 2
★ DISCOTHEQUE: no
★ SHOPS: none
★ CONFERENCE ROOMS: 2 (30 and 50)
★ BANQUETING ROOMS: 2 (30 and 50)
★ STANDARD BEDROOM SIZE: 20 m^2
★ PRIVATE BALCONIES: yes – on second floor

★ SWIMMING POOL: yes – salt water, heated in winter
★ GARDENS: yes
★ NO. OF STAFF: 96
★ ROOM SERVICE: 07.30–22.00
★ ORIENTATION: most rooms face the sea
★ CREDIT CARDS: no
★ OWNING COMPANY: S.A. Réserve de Beaulieu
★ GENERAL MANAGER: Henri Maria
★ DISTANCE TO BEACH: facing the sea
★ DISTANCE TO SHOPS: 80 m
★ DISTANCE FROM AIRPORT: 12 km (Nice)

The price of quality being what it is, they do not build hotels like this any more, so if you wish to see how things were done in great Riviera resorts in days gone by, try La Réserve. Not that there is anything old-fashioned about it for this comparatively small hotel has kept up its vintage very well. It is merely that it manages to blend resort living – beautiful coast views, terraces, swimming pool and such like with, inside, a well-tempered elegance which can hardly be bettered. Most hotels for instance choose darkish upholstery – it lasts longer – but not at La Réserve where chairs, sofas, curtains run the pastel gamut from pale cream to light blues and greens. Rooms are discreet and comfortable and public rooms like the long Grill and its lovely ceiling are so *distingué* that one feels privileged to be there. Service is exceedingly suave and the food, I feel, deserves far better accolade than its single Michelin star.

Cap d'Antibes

HOTEL DU CAP-EDEN ROC, Cap d'Antibes, Boulevard Kennedy, F-06604

★ TELEPHONE: (93) 61 39 01
★ CABLES: Capotel Antibes
★ TELEX: 470763 T
★ IN OPERATION: since 1881
★ RESERVATIONS: The Leading Hotels of the World
★ ROOMS: 91
★ SUITES: 8
★ RESTAURANTS: 2
★ BARS: 2
★ DISCOTHEQUE: no
★ SHOPS: none
★ CONFERENCE ROOMS: 2 (25 and 150)
★ BANQUETING ROOMS: 2 (50 and 200)
★ STANDARD BEDROOM SIZE: 25 m^2
★ PRIVATE BALCONIES: yes
★ SWIMMING POOL: yes – salt water, heated

★ RECREATIONAL ACTIVITIES: 4 tennis courts, yachting, deep sea fishing and water skiing
★ GARDENS: yes – 15-acre park
★ NO. OF STAFF: 165
★ ROOM SERVICE: around the clock
★ ORIENTATION: main facade faces Mediterranean
★ CREDIT CARDS: no
★ OWNING COMPANY: Eufra, Zurich
★ GENERAL MANAGER: Jean-Claude Irondelle
★ DISTANCE TO BEACH: walking distance
★ DISTANCE TO SHOPS: 4 km
★ DISTANCE FROM AIRPORT: 20 km

When does a hotel become a legend? I suppose it is when it resembles the Cap d'Antibes and, in these days when Riveria real estate is priceless, it has the gall to stand aloof in a 15-acre park and hang the consequences. Its guests are nutty enough to have insisted that a dog's cemetery be included, and they often book, six months ahead, one of the beach cabanas whence you can telephone for your ice-cold Krug. There is a kind of delightful folly about the Cap which never palls. It goes back probably to the Scott Fitzgerald–Tallulah Bankhead–Noel Coward era when those who had what it takes and the money to go with it, could really live it up in style. Behind its balustrades its chandeliers and its glow, the Cap is quite marvellous – with rooms of all sizes, beautifully kept in an informal way, very discreet, and where the suites really are suites. The staff are among the most experienced in the world – nothing fazes them and the management belongs in the stratosphere of hotelkeeping. Down the gardens is the celebrated Eden Roc with its beautiful bodies and its beautiful food. If you ask for fish, they bring you the whole technicolour platter to choose from. This is a hotel that offers complete privacy and the best of everything. You are either equal to the Cap d'Antibes or you are not.

Cannes

HOTEL MAJESTIC, P.B., 163, 060403 Cannes

★ TELEPHONE: (93) 68 91 00
★ CABLES: Majesticotel
★ TELEX: 470787
★ IN OPERATION: since 1926
★ RESERVATIONS: Steigenberger Reservation Service/Worldwide Travel Agents/Air France Reservation System
★ ROOMS: 175 doubles 75 singles
★ SUITES: 12
★ RESTAURANTS: 2 – large restaurant and grill room
★ BARS: 1

★ DISCOTHEQUE: no – but night club 'Jackpot' at the Palm Beach Casino
★ SHOPS: 8
★ CONFERENCE ROOMS: 3 (30 to 120)
★ BANQUETING ROOMS: 2 (30 to 250)
★ STANDARD BEDROOM SIZE: 35 m^2
★ PRIVATE BALCONIES: yes – in 70 rooms
★ SWIMMING POOL: yes – salt water
★ GARDENS: yes – around the swimming pool
★ NO. OF STAFF: 250
★ ROOM SERVICE: around the clock

★ ORIENTATION: main facade faces the south and the sea, the wings face east and west and the back faces north
★ FURTHER DEVELOPMENTS: it is intended to build a further 20 rooms in a wing along the front of the hotel
★ CREDIT CARDS: Visa, Diners Club, Master Charge and American Express
★ OWNING COMPANY: Chaine Lucien Barrière
★ GENERAL MANAGER: Jaques Bardet
★ DISTANCE TO BEACH: walking distance
★ DISTANCE TO SHOPS: 50 m
★ DISTANCE FROM AIRPORT: 30 km

In the past I have given the Majestic such rave notices that one reader at least accused me of having shares in the company that runs it. Alas, I wish I had. For me the Majestic is the rarest of species – a truly grand hotel in a resort setting. It is smooth, serene, elegant, supremely confident and so well operated that even the *bagagiste* knows you by name. As for the barman, just walk in there after a couple of years and he knows what your favourite drink is.

Rooms are timeless, spotless and ranging from large to vast and the furniture is what Cesar Ritz might have ordered. From its colonnaded lobby to its vast, chandeliered 'Belle Epoque' restaurant, the Majestic shines with a splendour that is hard to equal. Service is impeccable. In so many hotels these days, one is faced with a multitude of grubby little cards and notices telling you of services that you assume are there anyway. In your Majestic room there is only the Ericsson telephone. Ask and ye shall be answered – day or night, Sundays or holidays.

The small front garden, with its swimming pool, is unique in Cannes where space costs money, and the food in the grillroom is enough to make you forget all other pleasures – or almost all. Sa Majesté le Majestic is what it says – regal.

Chinon

CHÂTEAU DE MARÇAY, 37500 Chinon

★ TELEPHONE: (47) 930347
★ CABLES: no
★ TELEX: 751475
★ IN OPERATION: 13 years
★ RESERVATIONS: Relais et Chateaux
★ ROOMS: 26 doubles
★ SUITES: 4
★ RESTAURANTS: 1
★ BARS: 1
★ DISCOTHEQUE: no
★ SHOPS: none
★ CONFERENCE ROOMS: 2 (10 and 40)
★ BANQUETING ROOMS: 1 (20 to 150)
★ STANDARD BEDROOM SIZE: 30 m^2
★ PRIVATE BALCONIES: no
★ SWIMMING POOL: yes – fresh water
★ GARDENS: yes
★ NO. OF STAFF: 30
★ ROOM SERVICE: around the clock
★ FURTHER DEVELOPMENTS: 10 more rooms and another dining room
★ CREDIT CARDS: Visa
★ OWNING COMPANY: M. Mollard
★ GENERAL MANAGER: Mr Philippe Mollard
★ DISTANCE TO SHOPS: 6 km
★ DISTANCE FROM AIRPORT: Tours (Parcay Meslay) 40 km

It is one of the great attractions of the Loire Valley that one does not have to go far to find a good hotel. This one, a short drive from royal Chinon, is a fine example of what can be done by an individual owner with good ideas and a sense of hospitality. Originally fifteenth century, it still has that white stone of Touraine and those dreamy black-topped towers. There is a swimming pool, a very pretty park extremely well tended and a great feeling of peace and quiet – almost '*un vieux parc solitaire et glacé*'. Decor is charmingly muted, with good country antiques, nice carpets, pretty curtains. Rooms inevitably come in all sizes and some of those in the towers are particularly fine, with high, beamed ceilings and modern bathrooms where one has no right to expect them. Service is quiet and reliable – they do know you as an individual – and the food is above average. A good place from which to take in the Loire Valley.

Deauville

NORMANDY HOTEL, Rue Jean Mermoz, 14800 Deauville

- ★ TELEPHONE: (31) 88-09-21
- ★ CABLES: Normanhotel
- ★ TELEX: 170617 F
- ★ IN OPERATION: since 1912
- ★ RESERVATIONS: direct
- ★ ROOMS: 310
- ★ SUITES: 20
- ★ RESTAURANTS: 1
- ★ BARS: 1
- ★ DISCOTHEQUE: no
- ★ SHOPS: none
- ★ CONFERENCE ROOMS: 13 (12 to 150)
- ★ BANQUETING ROOMS: 4 (30 to 250)
- ★ STANDARD BEDROOM SIZE: 25 m^2
- ★ PRIVATE BALCONIES: yes – some rooms
- ★ SWIMMING POOL: yes – heated, Olympic size
- ★ RECREATIONAL ACTIVITIES: 26 tennis courts and golf 4 km from hotel, horse riding, games room
- ★ GARDENS: no
- ★ NO. OF STAFF: 180
- ★ ROOM SERVICE: around the clock
- ★ ORIENTATION: main facade faces west, others east and north
- ★ CREDIT CARDS: American Express and Diners Club
- ★ OWNING COMPANY: Chaine Lucien Barrière
- ★ GENERAL MANAGER: Michel Crauffon
- ★ DISTANCE TO BEACH: 100 m
- ★ DISTANCE TO SHOPS: adjacent
- ★ DISTANCE FROM AIRPORT: 8 km

Bracing Deauville has long been Paris-by-the-sea and used to be the traditional address for a 'dirty weekend' – a sort of French Brighton. Inflation and a change of moral climate have killed this habit but Deauville remains cheerful and gay and the

Normandy is by far its best hotel. It looks like a large Normandy farmhouse – the style is Edwardian Stockbrokers Tudor. Inside, the hotel is one of the most chic in France, very, but very elegant, superbly furnished in the grand manner. It was built just before the first world war when space was not as expensive as it is now and it shows. The Normandy is an unending vista of colossal public rooms which are the perfect mirror for your companion's evening dress. Most bedrooms are colossal too and some have the largest wardrobes I have ever seen – big enough for all those fur coats and mother-in-law too. Service is the best and the food, especially the seafood, is quite excellent. Across the road is the famed Casino and some of the most famous shops in France – just in case you should be lucky.

Eze-sur-Mer

HOTEL CAP ESTEL, 06360 Eze-sur-Mer

★ TELEPHONE: (93) 01 50 44
★ CABLES: Capstel Eze
★ TELEX: 470305 Capstel Eze
★ IN OPERATION: 30 years
★ RESERVATIONS: direct
★ ROOMS: 42
★ SUITES: 7

★ RESTAURANTS: 2 – including one open air by the pool
★ BARS: 2
★ DISCOTHEQUE: no
★ SHOPS: none
★ CONFERENCE ROOMS: 1 (30)

★ BANQUETING ROOMS: 1 (40 to 50) facilities for 80 persons in the garden during summer months
★ STANDARD BEDROOM SIZE: 25 m²
★ PRIVATE BALCONIES: yes
★ SWIMMING POOL: yes – salt water, one indoor (10 × 5 m) and one outdoor (25 × 8 m) both heated
★ RECREATIONAL ACTIVITIES: sauna, table tennis, water skiing and golf practice
★ GARDENS: yes

★ NO. OF STAFF: 55
★ ROOM SERVICE: around the clock
★ ORIENTATION: all rooms face the sea
★ CREDIT CARDS: Eurocard, Access and Master Charge
★ OWNING COMPANY: Cap Estel, S.A.
★ GENERAL MANAGER: Robert Squarciafichi (Chairman)
★ DISTANCE TO BEACH: on the beach
★ DISTANCE TO SHOPS: 3 km
★ DISTANCE FROM AIRPORT: 18 km

I have yet to meet anyone, but *anyone* who does not love the Cap Estel. Among so many slums of tomorrow – the hotels that are rising on the Côte d'Azur – this hotel really does stand out. No Riviera hotel has a larger, more private garden (it stands on its own little cape all by itself). No hotel of its size has both an indoor and an outdoor swimming pool. None that I know has that graceful Edwardian Baroque architecture. A princess built it in plusher years at a time when, rightly or wrongly, princesses were not pilloried by students' committees and as a hotel it has always been run by Robert Squarciafichi, one of France's best and most individual hoteliers.

This graceful mansion has everything you could possibly wish: large, airy, high-ceilinged bedrooms, quietly and comfortably furnished, good bathrooms, gorgeous balconies, green trees everywhere and blue waters. It has a tiny but very private beach and terraces and quiet spots all around. There is a lively, convivial bar and the public rooms are elegant, late Offenbach. Like a private house belonging to the very rich it makes life worthwhile – the food here is Mediterranean-fresh, good-looking and the very sight of it is guaranteed to titillate your tastebuds.

Luynes

DOMAINE DE BEAUVOIS, 37230 Luynes

★ TELEPHONE: (47) 55 50 11
★ CABLES: no
★ TELEX: Dombauv 750204 F
★ IN OPERATION: 15 years
★ RESERVATIONS: Relais et Chateaux, Paris
★ ROOMS: 36 doubles 3 singles 1 villa
★ SUITES: 7
★ RESTAURANTS: 3
★ BARS: 1
★ DISCOTHEQUE: no
★ SHOPS: none
★ CONFERENCE ROOMS: 3 (18 to 60)
★ BANQUETING ROOMS: 1 (150 to 180)
★ STANDARD BEDROOM SIZE: 25/30 m²
★ PRIVATE BALCONIES: no – old castle
★ SWIMMING POOL: yes – fresh water, heated, 22 × 10 m

★ RECREATIONAL ACTIVITIES: tennis, fishing and horse riding; 18-hole golf course 25 km away
★ GARDENS: yes – 380 acres of wooded park
★ NO. OF STAFF: 45/50
★ ROOM SERVICE: 07.00–24.00 (beverage only)
★ ORIENTATION: south-east
★ CREDIT CARDS: Visa
★ OWNING COMPANY: S.A.G.E.I.
★ GENERAL MANAGER: Patrick C. Ponsard
★ DISTANCE TO SHOPS: 13 km
★ DISTANCE FROM AIRPORT: 16 km Tours (Parcay Meslay)

Beauvois is the end-product of what happens when a cultured millionaire (in this case the irrepressible Monsieur Traversac) takes over an old chateau. The place is reborn. Originally fifteenth century (only the central tower now remains), the château belonged to a succession of *grands seigneurs* who built this bit and that bit and so on. Now in the centre of 350 splendid acres of woods and grassland and facing a swimming pool that has to be seen to be believed, Beauvois is one of the nicest country hotels in France, close to all that is worth seeing in the Loire Valley – that avenue of kings. Rooms are very grand (especially those in the tower) but not overpowering and they are intelligently and comfortably furnished and appointed, and the plumbing, which must have cost a fortune, works very well. It is all very quiet, very peaceful and elegant. Though we did not care all that much for the decor of the restaurant, we feel that gourmet-critics (which means every Frenchman) have not yet done full justice to this hotel – the food is very good indeed.

Nice

HOTEL NEGRESCO, 37 Promenade des Anglais, 06000 Nice

★ TELEPHONE: (93) 88-39-51
★ CABLES: Negrescotel
★ TELEX: 460 040
★ IN OPERATION: since 1912
★ RESERVATIONS: The Leading Hotels of the World, New York/Steigenberger Reservation Service, Frankfurt
★ ROOMS: 100 doubles 60 singles
★ SUITES: 15
★ RESTAURANTS: 2 – La Rotonde and Chantecler
★ BARS: 1 – Le Relais
★ DISCOTHEQUE: no – but piano music in the bar
★ SHOPS: shopping arcade – gifts, perfume, ladies' and men's wear, jewellery, toys etc
★ CONFERENCE ROOMS: 9 (60 to 700)

★ BANQUETING ROOMS: 6(40 to 1100)
★ STANDARD BEDROOM SIZE: 35 m^2
★ PRIVATE BALCONIES: yes
★ SWIMMING POOL: no – private beach opposite hotel
★ GARDENS: flowered terraces
★ NO. OF STAFF: 200
★ ROOM SERVICE: 07.00–24.00
★ ORIENTATION: facing the sea
★ CREDIT CARDS: American Express, Carte Bleue, Eurocard, Master Charge, Access and Visa
★ OWNING COMPANY: Mrs J. Augier Mesnage (privately owned)
★ GENERAL MANAGER: Mr Michel Palmer
★ DISTANCE TO BEACH: walking distance
★ DISTANCE TO SHOPS: walking distance
★ DISTANCE FROM AIRPORT: 3 km

The Negresco is now classed as a French National Monument – and that is the structure only. Inside, it is one of the most beautifully furnished hotels in the world; a symphony of Art Nouveau or Le Modern Style, whichever you prefer, blends marvellous period pieces with great textiles and carpets to make the world safe for Edward VII. Bedrooms are all different, all palatial and more than comfortable and we can hardly bear to leave the often stupendous bathrooms. Public rooms form a whole series of visual delights of which one never tires. Service is on a par – among the best anywhere – they brush your clothes and shine your shoes as a matter of habit. Management is, of course, of the greatest and the owner celebrated the world over. What is new is the Negresco's attiude to cuisine under Jacques Maximin in the Chantecler restaurant which deserves great praise.

Noves

AUBERGE DE NOVES, 13550 Noves

★ TELEPHONE: (90) 941921
★ CABLES: no
★ TELEX: 431312 F Auberno
★ IN OPERATION: 27 years
★ RESERVATIONS: direct or Relais et Chateaux, Paris
★ ROOMS: 20
★ SUITES: 2
★ RESTAURANTS: 1
★ BARS: 1

★ DISCOTHEQUE: no
★ SHOPS: 1 – boutique
★ CONFERENCE ROOMS: 1 (30)
★ BANQUETING ROOMS: 1 (30 to 40)
★ STANDARD BEDROOM SIZE: 30 m^2
★ PRIVATE BALCONIES: yes
★ SWIMMING POOL: yes – fresh water, heated, 15 × 7 m
★ GARDENS: yes
★ NO. OF STAFF: 35/40

★ ROOM SERVICE: 07.00–22.00
★ ORIENTATION: main facade faces west
★ FURTHER DEVELOPMENTS: more suites and tennis courts
★ CREDIT CARDS: Visa, Master Charge and American Express

★ OWNING COMPANY: Auberge de Noves S.A.
★ GENERAL MANAGER: Lalleman family
★ DISTANCE TO SHOPS: 15 km
★ DISTANCE FROM AIRPORT: 65 km (Marseille)

I have always had a soft spot for this hotel, one of the nicest country pads in France and only a few minutes from Avignon. It is an oldish country house, surrounded by miraculously beautiful gardens and much of Provence at your feet. It is relaxed, run by a family and one feels immediately at home. Rooms are larger than average in France, prettily rustic and very comfortable. The great prize, however, is dinner on the tree-shaded terrace – immaculate tables, a menu that is a work of art and food that is well worth the journey. France, happily, has quite a number of such places and in my opinion the Auberge de Noves is in the front rank.

Paris

HOTEL DE CRILLON, 10 Place de la Concorde, 75008 Paris

★ TELEPHONE: 265 2424
★ CABLES: Crilonotel
★ TELEX: 290 241
★ IN OPERATION: since 1909
★ RESERVATIONS: direct telex 290 204/The Leading Hotels of the World, worldwide
★ ROOMS: 120 doubles 32 singles
★ SUITES: 48
★ RESTAURANTS: 2
★ BARS: 1 + 1 cocktail lounge
★ DISCOTHEQUE: no
★ SHOPS: 1 – and showcases
★ CONFERENCE ROOMS: 5 (up to 130)
★ BANQUETING ROOMS: 5 (up to 130)
★ STANDARD BEDROOM SIZE: 26 m^2

★ PRIVATE BALCONIES: yes
★ SWIMMING POOL: no
★ GARDENS: no – but two inside courtyards
★ NO. OF STAFF: 230
★ ROOM SERVICE: around the clock
★ ORIENTATION: south overlooking Place de la Concorde
★ CREDIT CARDS: American Express, Diners Club, Eurocard, Access, Master Charge, Carte Bleue and Carte Blanche
★ OWNING COMPANY: The Hotel de Crillon
★ GENERAL MANAGER: Mr Philippe Roche
★ DISTANCE TO SHOPS: 3 minutes
★ DISTANCE FROM AIRPORT: 35 km (Charles de Gaulle); 25 km (Orly)

The Crillon – the hotel with the noblest, grandest facade in Paris right there on the Place de la Concorde – was built as a sumptuous private residence in the eighteenth century (no wonder they had the French Revolution over there) and remains magnificent and stately, with superb marbles, great columns, Gobelins tapestries and priceless carpets. Sipping Pol Roger in your suite at dusk, looking out at Paris, must be one of the greatest indulgences. Rooms, but especially suites, are vast and decorated in superb period style but the great bar is now ultra-modern though the restaurant remains happily ageless which means that you are not put off from looking and tasting the very refined food on your plate. Bathrooms have been refurnished – mostly with his-and-hers, and work excellently. The Crillon is a hotel of enormous presence and dignity and if you stay there, most people know who you are – an American diplomat, an English duke, a German tycoon or Monsieur le Préfet from somewhere.

HÔTEL PLAZA-ATHÉNÉE, 25 Avenue Montaigne, 75008 Paris

★ TELEPHONE: 723-7833
★ CABLES: Plazatene Paris
★ TELEX: 650092 Plaza
★ IN OPERATION: since 1913

★ RESERVATIONS: The Leading Hotels of the World/Trusthouse Forte Hotels Ltd, worldwide
★ ROOMS: 218

* **SUITES:** 44
* **RESTAURANTS:** 2 – Regence and Relais
* **BARS:** 2
* **DISCOTHEQUE:** yes
* **SHOPS:** none
* **CONFERENCE ROOMS:** 6 (30 to 150)
* **BANQUETING ROOMS:** 6 (30 to 250)
* **STANDARD BEDROOM SIZE:** 29 m^2
* **PRIVATE BALCONIES:** none
* **SWIMMING POOL:** no
* **RECREATIONAL ACTIVITIES:** none
* **GARDENS:** no
* **NO. OF STAFF:** 420

* **ROOM SERVICE:** around the clock
* **ORIENTATION:** some rooms face Avenue Montaigne, some the Garden Court, others smaller courts
* **CREDIT CARDS:** American Express, Diners Club, Eurocard, THF, Carte Blanche and Visa
* **OWNING COMPANY:** Trusthouse Forte Hotels Ltd
* **GENERAL MANAGER:** Franco Cozzo
* **DISTANCE TO SHOPS:** walking distance
* **DISTANCE FROM AIRPORT:** 35 km

Having had to send its nearby stable-mate to the guillotine (a personal reaction only), I am delighted to say that I cannot find any reason at all for making the Plaza Athénée share the same fate. On the contrary. This grand old Paris hotel is still absolutely tops. It is superbly run, very elegant indeed and has an air of quiet sophistication which is very hard to achieve. Rooms are vast, suites president-sized and the service is heavenly – so quick and prompt and quality-oriented that you can find no fault at all. There are other good hotels in Paris – in fact quite a few that are not in this book – but this one is surely a favourite with all international travellers who know how to live when they come down to earth. I would say it is worth staying there just to have your *petit déjeuner* overlooking the Paris roofs and as for the food in general, have no fear: lunch in the restaurants is a very pleasant gastronomic experience put forward with immense style.

HOTEL RITZ, 15 Place Vendôme, 75041 Paris, Cedex 01

* **TELEPHONE:** 260 38 30
* **CABLES:** Ritzotel Paris
* **TELEX:** 220262/670112
* **TELEFAX:** 260.23.71
* **IN OPERATION:** since 1898
* **RESERVATIONS:** The Leading Hotels of the World
* **ROOMS:** 156
* **SUITES:** 53 – some with direct telex
* **RESTAURANTS:** 2 – The Vendôme Restaurant and L'Espadon Grill
* **BARS:** 3 – Espadon, Hemingway and Vendôme
* **DISCOTHEQUE:** no
* **SHOPS:** elegant shopping gallery
* **CONFERENCE ROOMS:** 1 (18 to 20)
* **BANQUETING ROOMS:** 3 (80 to 100)
* **STANDARD BEDROOM SIZE:** 34 m^2
* **PRIVATE BALCONIES:** yes
* **SWIMMING POOL:** no

* **GARDENS:** yes – in the summer months lunch and dinner can be enjoyed in the Vendôme and Espadon gardens
* **NO. OF STAFF:** 400
* **VALET AND ROOM SERVICE:** around the clock
* **ORIENTATION:** main facade on Place Vendôme – most rooms overlook private gardens
* **FURTHER DEVELOPMENTS:** creation of health club, swimming pool, boutiques, a new restaurant with dancing facilities (no discotheque)
* **CREDIT CARDS:** Diners Club, American Express, Carte Blanche, Master Charge, Eurocard, Interbank and Access
* **OWNING COMPANY:** The Ritz Hotel Ltd
* **MANAGING DIRECTOR:** Mr Frank Klein
* **DISTANCE TO SHOPS:** walking distance
* **DISTANCE FROM AIRPORT:** 30 km

Most people have noticed how stable the government of France is these days. Yet in 1981 it nearly fell when Parisians woke up to find that someone, and a foreigner at that, had bought the Ritz. *'Mais, c'est une crime!'* The government, which carries out most of its work in the Ritz Bar anyway (the Rue Cambon one of course) deliberated but stayed on. So did the Ritz of course – *'Le Ritz restera toujours le Ritz'*. If anything, now that there is solid money behind it, the hotel might even improve which, admittedly, would be extremely difficult since this is the finest old city hotel in the world. Some time ago, the new management decided that it was about time some of those lovely *fin de siècle* doorhandles should be renewed. Alas, nobody made them quite like that any more. So they went and got a craftsman to make them again – by hand.

There are so many stories about this monument to the great Cesar Ritz that they have filled books – and in this space one cannot compete, except by mentioning personal experiences. It is the only hotel known to me where if you ring room service at two a.m. and ask timidly for scrambled eggs, the order arrives noiselessly on a trolley, with a single rose in a vase and enough gleaming silver for a four-course dinner. The Ritz is discreet, perfect, immaculate. From the great ornate salons to that incredible dining room, the upholstery is renewed as fresh every day, the carpets superbly clean. It is one of the few hotels I know where invisible eyes note when you leave your room – you are never, never disturbed. It is also one of the few hotels where I make a practice of going to bed with the wine list – just so I can drift off into nirvana. As long as the ghosts of Ritz and Escoffier maintain their presence, as long as the Place Vendôme remains, while we wish to have standards to respect, then the Ritz is still living.

LANCASTER HOTEL, 7 Rue de Berri, 75008 Paris

★ TELEPHONE: 359.90.43
★ CABLES: Otelancast Paris
★ TELEX: Loyne 640991
★ IN OPERATION: since 1925
★ RESERVATIONS: Prestige Hotels, London/Scott Calder International, New York/Zennith, Toronto and Montreal/John Miller, Sydney
★ ROOMS: 33 doubles 14 singles
★ SUITES: 10
★ RESTAURANTS: 1 – meals can be taken outside during fine weather
★ BARS: 1
★ DISCOTHEQUE: no
★ SHOPS: none
★ CONFERENCE ROOMS: 1
★ BANQUETING ROOMS: 1

★ STANDARD BEDROOM SIZE: 14–30 m²
★ PRIVATE BALCONIES: yes – with penthouse suites
★ SWIMMING POOL: no
★ GARDENS: yes
★ NO. OF STAFF: 85
★ ROOM SERVICE: 07.00–24.00
★ ORIENTATION: south-west
★ CREDIT CARDS: American Express, Eurocard, Master Charge, Access and Diners Club
★ OWNING COMPANY: S.A. Hotel Lancaster
★ GENERAL MANAGER: John Sinclair
★ DISTANCE TO SHOPS: walking distance
★ DISTANCE FROM AIRPORT: 35 km

The Lancaster, long established and now owned by Britain's Savoy group, is very chic in French terms and for some people it is like having their own Paris town house. It is small, gentle, well bred, intimate and it only impresses those who are no longer easily impressed. Some of the rooms are quite small, others very acceptable in size but what matters is the fact that they are all furnished individually with very fine French furniture and well chosen paintings. They are immaculately kept and the young and intelligent management knows from the records what each guest likes. What I like is the feeling that once in this hotel the world outside can get up to all the capers it wants – the Lancaster remains as an oasis of good living, fate cannot harm me. I also love the restaurant, especially in the good weather months when it creeps into the sweet and pretty private garden. The food is excellent even for France. A mere gentle stroll away from the Champs Élysées, the Lancaster is indeed a very desirable residence.

Le Poët-Laval

LES HOSPITALIERS, Le Poët-Laval, 26160 La Bégude de Mazenc, Drôme

★ TELEPHONE: (75) 46 22 32
★ CABLES: no
★ TELEX: no
★ IN OPERATION: 14 years
★ RESERVATIONS: direct
★ ROOMS: 18 doubles 1 single
★ SUITES: 1
★ RESTAURANTS: 3 – one is on the terrace during the summer only
★ BARS: 1
★ DISCOTHEQUE: no
★ SHOPS: 1 – a boutique, open in summer only
★ CONFERENCE ROOMS: 1 (50)
★ BANQUETING ROOMS: none
★ STANDARD BEDROOM SIZE: 25 m^2
★ PRIVATE BALCONIES: no – but the suite has a terrace

★ SWIMMING POOL: yes – fresh water, 14 × 6.5 m
★ RECREATIONAL ACTIVITIES: no – but tennis and horse riding nearby
★ GARDENS: terraces
★ NO. OF STAFF: 25
★ ROOM SERVICE: 07.30–23.00
★ ORIENTATION: south, with a view of the valley and the Alps
★ CREDIT CARDS: Diners Club, American Express and Eurocard
★ OWNING COMPANY: Yvon Morin
★ GENERAL MANAGER: Yvon Morin (Proprietor)
★ DISTANCE TO SHOPS: 3 km
★ DISTANCE FROM AIRPORT: 60 km (Valence); 160 km (Lyon)

Turn east as you drive through Montelimar, drive for half an hour and you are in the gorgeous, sunshiny country of the Drôme. Look left and there, on top of a precipitous hill, is one of those half-ruined villages of which there are so many. This one used to belong to the Knights of St. John of Jerusalem. What you do not know and cannot possibly know unless someone tells you is that right up there, among the crumbling stones, is one of France's best and most unusual small country hotels – Les Hospitaliers. It blends so well with its surroundings that one can hardly see it. Its owners, Monsieur and Madame Morin, spent years rebuilding old houses, building new ones out of old stone, digging into solid rock for foundations and plumbing, making a swimming pool where no swimming pool has any right to be. The result is miraculous – a place of poignant beauty and infinite peace. There are terraces everywhere, overlooking twenty miles of paradise. The new rooms are vast, exceedingly well furnished and most comfortable and with bathrooms to match. In the evening, M. Morin presides over two dining rooms where he provides classic French cuisine, agreeably punctuated by unusual personal variations. France's greatest guidebook gives Les Hospitaliers a mere passing glance. They should look closer.

St. Paul-de-Vence

MAS D'ARTIGNY, 06570 Saint Paul

★ TELEPHONE: (93) 32 84 54
★ CABLES: no
★ TELEX: 470601 Artimas F
★ IN OPERATION: since May 1973
★ RESERVATIONS: direct
★ ROOMS: 81
★ SUITES: 29
★ RESTAURANTS: 1 – and terrace for lunch in the summer
★ BARS: 1 – and terrace
★ DISCOTHEQUE: on request
★ SHOPS: 1 – also a hairdresser and 2 art galleries
★ CONFERENCE ROOMS: 6 (10 to 250)
★ BANQUETING ROOMS: 1 (150)
★ STANDARD BEDROOM SIZE: 30 m^2
★ PRIVATE BALCONIES: yes – most rooms
★ RECREATIONAL ACTIVITIES: tennis, pétanque

★ SWIMMING POOL: yes – fresh water, 25 m long, and 21 private pools for the apartments, approx. 20 m^2
★ GARDENS: yes – also private gardens to each small swimming pool
★ NO. OF STAFF: 100
★ ROOM SERVICE: 07.00–22.00
★ ORIENTATION: most rooms face south
★ FURTHER DEVELOPMENTS: a 7-room villa, with sitting room and private pool, now in operation
★ CREDIT CARDS: none
★ OWNING COMPANY: Sté Grandes Étapes Internationales
★ GENERAL MANAGER: J. C. Scordel
★ DISTANCE TO BEACH: 9 km
★ DISTANCE TO SHOPS: 9 km
★ DISTANCE FROM AIRPORT: 12 km

It needed guts and a good deal of ready money as well as a lot of imagination to pick a hillside facing St. Paul de Vence and build on it the newest luxury hotel on the Riviera. The French tycoon who created the Mas d'Artigny (and a few others too) had all of these things and that gifted entrepreneurial flair which demands and gets the best. Mas d'Artigny is superb, luxurious and fitted out at great expense, both of money and talent. You can have a suite in the main building or a garden-level suite with your own private swimming pool. Decor is modern-Provençal, and all the rooms are extremely comfortable and facing those scented hills of Provence with the sea in the far distance. Considering the size of the place, service is good and nothing is too much trouble. As for the food, it is superior but in the cheerful, friendly way of the South. In style, space, decor and amenities, Mas d'Artigny is one of the few European hotels that manages to equal the best American resort.

Saint Péray

CHÂTEAU DU BESSET, Saint-Romain-de-Lerps, 07130 Saint-Péray

★ TELEPHONE: (75) 58.52.22
★ CABLES: no
★ TELEX: 345261 F
★ IN OPERATION: since 1974
★ RESERVATIONS: direct
★ ROOMS: 6
★ SUITES: 4
★ RESTAURANTS: 2
★ BARS: 1
★ DISCOTHEQUE: no
★ SHOPS: no
★ CONFERENCE ROOMS: 1 (10 to 60)
★ BANQUETING ROOMS: no
★ STANDARD BEDROOM SIZE: 70 m^2
★ PRIVATE BALCONIES: none

★ SWIMMING POOL: heated pool, 15 × 18 m
★ RECREATIONAL ACTIVITIES: tennis, boules, riding and walking in park
★ GARDENS: large park
★ NO. OF STAFF: 21
★ ROOM SERVICE: 7.00–21.30
★ ORIENTATION: views of the park
★ CREDIT CARDS: American Express and Visa
★ OWNING COMPANY: Monsieur and Madame Gozlan
★ GENERAL MANAGER: Monsieur Thenard
★ DISTANCE TO SHOPS: 10 km
★ DISTANCE FROM AIRPORT: 19 km

As everyone knows, France is not short of châteaux, some of which might just pass off. But not this one. The Château du Besset is not only authentic fifteenth century in structure but its divinely inspired owners have furnished it with treasures which took years to find. It is such a rare place that people come here, having booked months ahead, from all over the world – all that just to stay in one of the ten rooms, each one of which is furnished in a different period: Louis XIV, Napoleonic, Louis XVI, Medici etc. Their windows open on one of France's sweetest landscapes, the Ardèche country just a few miles west of Valence across the Rhône. Le Besset is so discreet, so private, so cleverly hidden away that it almost takes a detective to find it. Some of the greatest hoteliers and chefs in the world have come here and been made speechless at so much good taste, so much beauty, so much good living. There is a vast French-style garden plus a great park. The chef de cuisine, Monsieur Delanné, is as unique as the Château – he cooks the way others paint pictures, with his own brushstrokes. Messrs Gault and Millau, those high priests of the good (French) life, call the Château du Besset *la plus belle folie du monde* and although I know of one or two others I am not going to disagree with them.

St. Tropez

HOTEL BYBLOS, Avenue Paul Signac, 83990 Saint Tropez

- ★ TELEPHONE: (94) 970004
- ★ CABLES: Byblos
- ★ TELEX: 470235
- ★ IN OPERATION: since 1969
- ★ RESERVATIONS: direct and Air France offices, worldwide; also through travel agencies
- ★ ROOMS: 56 doubles 13 singles
- ★ RESTAURANTS: 1 and terraces
- ★ BARS: 1
- ★ DISCOTHEQUE: yes – and 'Les Caves du Roy' nightclub in the summer
- ★ SHOPS: 3 – fashion and jewellery, beauty parlour and hairdressing salon
- ★ CONFERENCE ROOMS: 1 (130)
- ★ BANQUETING ROOMS: 1 (up to 100)
- ★ STANDARD BEDROOM SIZE: 25 m^2
- ★ PRIVATE BALCONIES: yes – some rooms

- ★ GARDENS: yes
- ★ SWIMMING POOL: yes – fresh water, heated, outdoor
- ★ RECREATIONAL ACTIVITIES: sauna and massage in the hotel, with clubs nearby for tennis, golf and horse riding
- ★ NO. OF STAFF: 120
- ★ ROOM SERVICE: around the clock
- ★ ORIENTATION: most rooms face gardens, swimming pool and sea
- ★ CREDIT CARDS: American Express, Diners Club, Visa and Carte Bleue
- ★ OWNING COMPANY: S.A. Byblos
- ★ GENERAL MANAGER: Claude Marret
- ★ DISTANCE TO BEACH: 1 km
- ★ DISTANCE TO SHOPS: walking distance
- ★ DISTANCE FROM AIRPORT: 100 km (Nice)

This hotel that really does not look like a hotel opened just over a decade ago, to a lot of astonishment and some sneers from the trade. It would never work, they said. Well, try to get in now. The Byblos has succeeded beyond the wildest expectations and for St. Tropez (which never pretended to be Palm Beach) it is also exactly right. Basically, it is a huddle of delicious little Provençal houses around a fine swimming pool. The gardens are lovingly tended. For this kind of holiday hotel, the service is 100 per cent above the average (I have never heard of a single complaint). It is a gay, convivial hotel custom-built for the beautiful people to meet and show off their new husbands/wives/ what have you. Favourable mention must be made of the Provençal cooking – aioli, Bouillabaisse, and the rest.

Talloires

HOTEL L'ABBAYE, 74290 Talloires

- ★ TELEPHONE: (50) 674088
- ★ CABLES: Abbaye Tallories
- ★ TELEX: 385307
- ★ IN OPERATION: since 1885
- ★ RESERVATIONS: direct
- ★ ROOMS: 32
- ★ SUITES: 2
- ★ RESTAURANTS: 2
- ★ BARS: 1
- ★ DISCOTHEQUE: no
- ★ SHOPS: none
- ★ CONFERENCE ROOMS: 2 (12 to 20)
- ★ BANQUETING ROOMS: 1 (up to 120)
- ★ STANDARD BEDROOM SIZE: 18 m²
- ★ PRIVATE BALCONIES: yes
- ★ SWIMMING POOL: no – but private pontoon on lake
- ★ GARDENS: yes
- ★ NO. OF STAFF: 35
- ★ ROOM SERVICE: around the clock
- ★ ORIENTATION: rooms face lake
- ★ CREDIT CARDS: American Express, Diners Club, Eurocard and Visa
- ★ OWNING COMPANY: Claude Tiffenat
- ★ GENERAL MANAGER: Jean Tiffenat
- ★ DISTANCE TO BEACH: on the lake
- ★ DISTANCE TO SHOPS: 250 m
- ★ DISTANCE FROM AIRPORT: 45 km (Geneva); 15 km (Annecy)

To sit on a summer's day on the terrace of this hotel under the centuries-old trees and to look at the white boats silently gliding on the blue waters of the most beautiful lake in France reminds one that this is indeed the land of *la douceur de vivre*. No doubt the Benedictine monks who began to build the place nearly a thousand years ago must have thought this was a good place to contemplate and praise the Lord. Praise should be reserved for the management too for having preserved this, one of the finest country hotels in France and keeping it as it should be – quiet, serene, beautifully mellow and so smooth that one hardly realizes it is a hotel at all. This takes genius, and family genius at that, because strangers would be bound to spoil it. The Abbaye has a gorgeous interior cloister lined with fine antiques, splendidly furnished rooms – in the former monkish cells – and sun-sapped gardens to remove you from unpleasant reality. A spot so beautiful that it has been celebrated in ballads and poems and novels, the Abbaye is what a country hotel should be and yet curiously it is French and not English – they who claim most often they know what the country is all about. Food here has always been great – and now there is a new and intimate winter restaurant.

Vence

CHÂTEAU DU DOMAINE ST. MARTIN, Route de Coursegoules, 06140 Vence

- ★ TELEPHONE: (93) 58 02 02
- ★ CABLES: Domartin
- ★ TELEX: 470282
- ★ IN OPERATION: 23 years
- ★ RESERVATIONS: direct
- ★ ROOMS: 15 doubles
- ★ SUITES: 10
- ★ RESTAURANTS: 1
- ★ BARS: 1
- ★ DISCOTHEQUE: no
- ★ SHOPS: none
- ★ CONFERENCE ROOMS: 1 (15)
- ★ BANQUETING ROOMS: none
- ★ STANDARD BEDROOM SIZE: 40 m²
- ★ PRIVATE BALCONIES: yes
- ★ SWIMMING POOL: yes – fresh water, heated
- ★ RECREATIONAL ACTIVITIES: tennis
- ★ GARDENS: yes
- ★ NO. OF STAFF: 50
- ★ ROOM SERVICE: 07.00–21.30
- ★ ORIENTATION: south
- ★ CREDIT CARDS: American Express, Carte Bleue and Eurocard
- ★ OWNING COMPANY: Famille Geneve
- ★ GENERAL MANAGER: Miss A. Brunet
- ★ DISTANCE TO BEACH: 15 km
- ★ DISTANCE TO SHOPS: 25 km
- ★ DISTANCE FROM AIRPORT: 20 km

To all those who want to stay in the Côte d'Azur but without the company of the Joneses, the Smiths and the Duponts, this hotel must be among the first choices. First of all it does not look like a hotel – more of a Provençal village with houses dotted all over the verdant hillsides. Secondly, it does not cater for the passing trade. Thirdly, it is superbly managed. It has a thirty-five-acre park dominating the landscape all the way down to the coast and, above all, it has peace and tranquillity. You will never be crowded here – there aren't enough people! You can have a normal room or, much better, one of the lovely cottages where rooms and suites are charmingly decorated and maintained with great care. The view from the restaurant makes you spend your time looking from the panorama down to your plate and wonder which should come first. The food is delicate and beautifully presented and the service is top class. Domaine St. Martin is a place with personality and charm.

Vonnas

LA MÈRE BLANC, 01540 Vonnas, Ain

★ TELEPHONE: (74) 500010
★ CABLES: no
★ TELEX: 380776
★ IN OPERATION: since 1872
★ RESERVATIONS: direct
★ ROOMS: 21 doubles 4 singles
★ SUITES: 6
★ RESTAURANTS: 1
★ BARS: 1
★ DISCOTHEQUE: no
★ SHOPS: 2
★ CONFERENCE ROOMS: 1 (50)
★ BANQUETING ROOMS: 1 (100)
★ STANDARD BEDROOM SIZE: 20 m^2

★ PRIVATE BALCONIES: yes
★ SWIMMING POOL: yes – fresh water, 15 × 7.5 m
★ RECREATIONAL ACTIVITIES: tennis
★ GARDENS: yes
★ NO. OF STAFF: 45
★ ROOM SERVICE: 07.00–23.00
★ ORIENTATION: facing the Veyle River
★ CREDIT CARDS: Diners Club and American Express
★ OWNING COMPANY: Blanc family
★ GENERAL MANAGER: Georges Blanc
★ DISTANCE TO SHOPS: immediate
★ DISTANCE FROM AIRPORT: 60 km

Don't come here expecting a grand, grand hotel. This is an 'auberge', one of the finest in France, which I only discovered recently and obviously a bit late, since it has been in the hands of four generations of the same country family. It is a delightful, fresh-looking place in this small, flower-decked village and next to a pretty river. Rooms are clean, very well planned (most of them are new) and pleasantly furnished with good country pieces – no Régence, no Boulle. Bathrooms work very well and there is every single small comfort you might wish. Service is fast and efficient and the little interior courtyard where you sit for your pre-lunch champagne-framboise is quite delightful. But it is when you pass the portals of the restaurant that the very special quality of this house strikes you – La Mère Blanc is one of the finest country restaurants in the whole of France, masterminded by fourth-generation Georges Blanc with a long tradition behind him. Being a young man, he has put his own stamp on the food; *nouvelle cuisine* and all that but totally individual. The quality is matchless as is the length of the wine list – I expect to hear much good about this place from satisfied customers.

GERMANY

Assmannshausen

HOTEL KRONE, Rheinuferstrasse 10, 6220 Rud. Assmannshausen

★ TELEPHONE: 06722-2036
★ CABLES: Krone
★ TELEX: no

★ IN OPERATION: since 1541
★ RESERVATIONS: direct
★ ROOMS: 50 doubles 32 singles

★ SUITES: 2
★ RESTAURANTS: 2
★ BARS: 1
★ DISCOTHEQUE: no
★ SHOPS: none
★ CONFERENCE ROOMS: 2 (20 to 60)
★ BANQUETING ROOMS: 1 (80)
★ STANDARD BEDROOM SIZE: 30–40 m^2
★ PRIVATE BALCONIES: yes – 6 rooms only
★ SWIMMING POOL: yes – fresh water, 6 × 10 m
★ GARDENS: yes
★ NO. OF STAFF: 80
★ ROOM SERVICE: breakfast only
★ ORIENTATION: faces west
★ CREDIT CARDS: American Express, Diners Club, Eurocard, Barclaycard and Visa
★ OWNING COMPANY: privately owned
★ GENERAL MANAGER: Family Hufnagel
★ DISTANCE TO SHOPS: 250 m
★ DISTANCE FROM AIRPORT: 75 km (Frankfurt)

Four centuries ought to be long enough to create a tradition and when that happens in Germany it augurs good living. That is certainly what one gets at the Krone in the charming little Rheingau town of Assmannshausen. I always like to remember a hotel for one particular thing that no other hotel has got and in this case it must be that quite divine terrace restaurant with its vine roof facing the great river. That and the Rheingau and the food makes this place, as the Michelin people say, 'worth a detour'. It is also a charming place to stay – an old beamed and panelled house of great distinction, good solid country furniture and a feeling of genuine welcome which is a rare thing these days. Rooms are very large, beautifully, one should almost say lovingly, furnished and the service is cheerful. But the things that count most at the Krone are the location and the food and wine.

Baden Baden

BRENNER'S PARK HOTEL, An der Lichtentaler Allee, D-7570 Baden-Baden

★ TELEPHONE: (07221) 3530
★ CABLES: Parkhotel Baden-Baden
★ TELEX: 781261
★ IN OPERATION: 111 years
★ RESERVATIONS: The Leading Hotels of the World, London and New York/Preferred Hotels Assoc, Canada
★ ROOMS: 34 doubles 45 singles
★ SUITES: 28
★ RESTAURANTS: 2
★ BARS: 2
★ DISCOTHEQUE: live music
★ SHOPS: none – but the Lancaster Beauty Farm and Römischer Salon
★ CONFERENCE ROOMS: 5 (10 to 120)
★ BANQUETING ROOMS: 2 (30 to 120)
★ STANDARD BEDROOM SIZE: 40–50 m^2
★ PRIVATE BALCONIES: yes
★ SWIMMING POOL: yes – fresh water, 53 × 21 × 5 ft
★ RECREATIONAL ACTIVITIES: sauna, fitness, health programmes, Brenner's spa Lancaster Beauty Farm
★ GARDENS: yes
★ NO. OF STAFF: 210
★ ROOM SERVICE: around the clock
★ ORIENTATION: most rooms face a large private park and the Lichtentaler Allee
★ CREDIT CARDS: none
★ OWNING COMPANY: Brenner Hotel
★ GENERAL MANAGER: Richard Schmitz
★ DISTANCE TO SHOPS: walking distance
★ DISTANCE FROM AIRPORT: 104 km (Stuttgart)

Any traveller's list of the six best hotels in Europe would certainly contain this one. Where Russian grand dukes used to parade their horses (and their *cocottes*) a better class of person is still to be seen. One American friend recently said to me: 'If that's the way they used to live, no wonder there was a world war . . . '. Egalitarian to the end he then proceeded to stay a month at Brenner's Park. The place gets you. It is so beautiful, so beautifully run, so superbly furnished with elegant dark teak German 1880 furniture, so unbelievably efficient that it is a pleasure every minute of the day. Brenner's Park history needs a book to itself – everyone from Edward VII to Paul Getty stayed there and one understands why, because here luxury is everywhere – in the fork you touch, the pillow on your bed, the carpet in the corridor, the wine you drink. Rooms and suites are so enormous that on my first stay it took me an hour to investigate everything. The indoor swimming pool is the most perfect in Europe and, just in case you should look in the mirror and take fright, the famed Lancaster Beauty Farm is next door. Down in this delicious, wooded little pleasure town is the world-famous Kurhaus and the finest, most ornate casino anywhere. Brenner's Park food is a legend – splendidly conceived – and nowhere does silver gleam more brightly. This is another hotel where I tend to go to bed with the wine list – it's the perfect send-off towards another day.

Badenweiler

HOTEL ROMERBAD, D-7847 Badenweiler, West Germany

★ TELEPHONE: 07632-700
★ CABLES: Romerbad
★ TELEX: 77 29 33
★ IN OPERATION: 160 years
★ RESERVATIONS: direct and The Leading Hotels of the World
★ ROOMS: 57 doubles 57 singles
★ SUITES: 11
★ RESTAURANTS: 1
★ BARS: 1
★ DISCOTHEQUE: no
★ SHOPS: none
★ CONFERENCE ROOMS: 3
★ BANQUETING ROOMS: 3
★ STANDARD BEDROOM SIZE: 24 m^2
★ PRIVATE BALCONIES: yes
★ GARDENS: yes – large park overlooking Rhine valley

★ SWIMMING POOL: yes – fresh water, thermal, 1 indoor 8 × 20 m, and 1 outdoor 9 × 25 m
★ RECREATIONAL ACTIVITIES: tennis, sauna, massage, beauty service, boccia, ping pong and children's playhouse
★ NO. OF STAFF: 100
★ ROOM SERVICE: 07.30–24.00
★ ORIENTATION: overlooking Black Forest and Rhine Valley
★ CREDIT CARDS: American Express and Visa
★ OWNING COMPANY: Family Fellmann-Lauer
★ GENERAL MANAGER: Klaus Lauer
★ DISTANCE TO SHOPS: 100 m
★ DISTANCE FROM AIRPORT: 45 km (Basel/Schweiz)

A century and a half of worldly elegance, a family tradition going back that far and all in the frame of the magnificent Black Forest – that is Romerbad, one of the most unusual and most resplendent country hotels in Europe. The huge park dominates the Rhine Valley and the wine-clad hills – a place of intense beauty and charm. The building itself makes you feel secure – half schloss, half private residence, it has a feeling of having grown over the years, blended in and emerged victorious. It is stately and yet curiously intimate. No two rooms are the same and the only thing they share is a high regard for quality, cleanliness and good taste that seems somehow to borrow nothing from anyone. There are two fantastically beautiful swimming pools – one in and one out – and in the lovely *Hofsaal* there are music festivals in spring and autumn. The *Kinder* have a playhouse all to themselves. An aura of good living permeates everything from the food, which is celestially good, to the wine list which is a work of devotion.

Berlin

BRISTOL HOTEL KEMPINSKI BERLIN, Kurfürstendamm 27, 1000 Berlin 15

★ TELEPHONE: 030/88 10 91
★ CABLES: Kempihotel Berlin
★ TELEX: 018-3553
★ IN OPERATION: since 1952

★ RESERVATIONS: The Leading Hotels of the World
★ ROOMS: 287 doubles 71 singles
★ SUITES: 20

★ RESTAURANTS: 3 – Kempinski Restaurant, Grill Room, and Kempinski Eck

★ BARS: 3 – Bristol Bar, Grill Bar and Pool Bar

★ SHOPS: newspaper stand and flower shop in the main lobby

★ CONFERENCE ROOMS: 12 (6 to 600)

★ BANQUETING ROOMS: 12 (6 to 600)

★ STANDARD BEDROOM SIZE: 25 m²

★ PRIVATE BALCONIES: 4 suites on the 6th floor overlooking Kurfürstendamm

★ SWIMMING POOL: yes – fresh water, 8 × 16 m

★ RECREATIONAL ACTIVITIES: sauna and solarium

★ GARDENS: no

★ NO. OF STAFF: 450

★ ROOM SERVICE: 06.30–24.00

★ ORIENTATION: facing Fasanenstrasse and Kurfürstendamm

★ CREDIT CARDS: American Express, Diners Club, Eurocard and Americard

★ OWNING COMPANY: Kempinski Corporation

★ MANAGING DIRECTOR: Hartmut E. Zunk

★ DISTANCE TO SHOPS: walking distance

★ DISTANCE FROM AIRPORT: 15 km

This is Germany at its best, behind a name that has been a Berlin tradition for longer than anyone can remember. I have not been here since the last edition but a friend who arrived, unexpectedly, in mid-morning a while ago told me that the reception manager took her up to her room, asked her to inspect both the bedroom and bathroom to make sure everything was right. Minutes later, piping hot coffee arrived and the housekeeper telephoned to offer her services. I would have expected no less. Everybody seems to speak every language under the sun and nothing is too much trouble. Rooms vary in size but the majority are more than adequate, extremely clean and well kept and no one disturbs you at the wrong time.

The one trouble I find with Kempinski, if trouble it is, is the quantity of food in the two restaurants – one has to be awfully strong-willed to resist the temptation.

I may add that in six years I have not had a single letter of complaint about this hotel – only praise from travellers who know what it is all about.

Bremen

PARK HOTEL, Im Bürgerpark, 2800 Bremen

★ TELEPHONE: 0421/34080

★ CABLES: Parkhotel

★ TELEX: 024-4343

★ IN OPERATION: since 1956

★ RESERVATIONS: Steigenberger Reservation Service

★ ROOMS: 56 doubles 85 singles

★ SUITES: 10

★ RESTAURANTS: 2 – The Park Restaurant and Buten und Binnen Restaurant

★ BARS: 1 – Halai Bar

★ DISCOTHEQUE: live music and dancing in bar

★ SHOPS: 2 – beauty shop and newspaper shop

★ CONFERENCE ROOMS: 7 (up to 400)

★ BANQUETING ROOMS: 7 (up to 400)

★ STANDARD BEDROOM SIZE: 28 m²

★ PRIVATE BALCONIES: yes

★ SWIMMING POOL: no

★ RECREATIONAL ACTIVITIES: bicycling

★ GARDENS: yes

★ NO. OF STAFF: 230

★ ROOM SERVICE: 06.00–24.00

★ ORIENTATION: all rooms face park

★ CREDIT CARDS: American Express, Diners Club and Eurocard

★ OWNING COMPANY: Park Hotel GmbH

★ GENERAL MANAGER: Hans-Hermann Rosin

★ DISTANCE TO SHOPS: 1½ km

★ DISTANCE FROM AIRPORT: 4 km

Probably one of the best hotels in Germany, the Park faces the Bürgerpark, an oasis of green beauty, within minutes from the city centre, and consequently the hotel is quiet and almost countryfied. Though it is comparatively new, this hotel has a gracious, ageless quality which shows in every detail. The rooms are quite large, meticulously clean and springlike and there are many different styles – cheerfully chintzy, soberly timbered or modern without madness. Bathrooms are the last word in German efficiency and indeed so is the service – they never, but never forget anything and once you are typed off as a person you need never worry again. It is all very discreet, very comfortable and immensely reassuring. There is a quite superb heated terrace facing the park and all the Mercedes purr to a stop far from your ears. Food is on a par – don't go there if you are on a diet. The Park is just right for the new breed of Hanseatic merchant adventurers and those who come to meet them.

Friedrichsruhe

WALD UND SCHLOSSHOTEL FRIEDRICHSRUHE, 7111 Friedrichsruhe, Württemberg

- ★ TELEPHONE:07941/7078
- ★ CABLES: no
- ★ TELEX: 74498
- ★ IN OPERATION: since 1953
- ★ RESERVATIONS: Relais et Chateaux, Paris
- ★ ROOMS: 33 doubles 11 singles
- ★ SUITES: 4
- ★ RESTAURANTS: 2
- ★ BARS: 1
- ★ DISCOTHEQUE: no
- ★ SHOPS: none
- ★ CONFERENCE ROOMS: 4 (20, 20, 40 and 100)
- ★ BANQUETING ROOMS: 5 (20, 40, 50, 80 and 100)
- ★ STANDARD BEDROOM SIZE: 18 m^2
- ★ PRIVATE BALCONIES: yes
- ★ SWIMMING POOL: 2 – fresh water,

- indoor and outdoor, 8 × 11 m and 9 × 9 m
- ★ RECREATIONAL ACTIVITIES: sauna, tennis, golf (9-hole), hunting and guided excursions
- ★ GARDENS: no – but surrounded by a large park and forest
- ★ NO. OF STAFF: 70
- ★ ROOM SERVICE: 06.00–24.00
- ★ ORIENTATION: all rooms face the park
- ★ CREDIT CARDS: Master Charge, Diners Club, Visa, American Express, Eurocard and Access
- ★ OWNING COMPANY: privately owned
- ★ GENERAL MANAGER: Mr Lothar Eiermann
- ★ DISTANCE TO SHOPS: 6 km
- ★ DISTANCE FROM AIRPORT: 80 km

The original part of this establishment is a hunting lodge built in the early eighteenth century by a well-known German nobleman. Now, there is a new wing with all possible aid to comfort, but of the two we much prefer the former – gabled, roofed with handsome brick and white-walled. The public rooms are stately, tapestried and very beautiful and the bedrooms have great period charm. The new wing is modern, with amply proportioned rooms which are excellently furnished and serviced. There is a swimming pool and a sauna as well as tennis courts and vistas of great parkland. One can go hunting and fishing in the wooded Württemberg hills and it is near enough to places of great interest like Rothenburg and Heidelberg to make Friedrichsruhe a good centre. The staff are charmingly polite in a very well-bred way and the food more than adequate.

Hamburg

ATLANTIC HOTEL, An der Alster 72, 2000 Hamburg 1

- ★ TELEPHONE: 040-24-80-01
- ★ CABLES: Atlantic Hamburg
- ★ TELEX: 21 63 297
- ★ IN OPERATION: since 1909, renovation 1978/79
- ★ RESERVATIONS: The Leading Hotels of the World/Deutsche Lufthansa, worldwide/J.A.L. Hotel System
- ★ ROOMS: 140 doubles 160 singles
- ★ SUITES: 13

- ★ RESTAURANTS: 1 – Atlantic Grill
- ★ BARS: 1 – Atlantic Bar
- ★ DISCOTHEQUE: no
- ★ SHOPS: 2
- ★ CONFERENCE ROOMS: 18 (5 to 400)
- ★ BANQUETING ROOMS: 18 (5 to 800)
- ★ STANDARD BEDROOM SIZE: 30 m^2
- ★ PRIVATE BALCONIES: yes – some rooms
- ★ SWIMMING POOL: yes – fresh water, 9 × 12 m

★ GARDENS: courtyard
★ NO. OF STAFF: 400
★ ROOM SERVICE: around the clock
★ ORIENTATION: overlooking the Alster Lake
★ CREDIT CARDS: American Express, Diners Club, Bank of America, Eurocard, Visa, Access and Master Charge

★ OWNING COMPANY: Kempinski-AG
★ MANAGING DIRECTOR: Karl Theodor Walterspiel
★ DISTANCE TO SHOPS: 500 m
★ DISTANCE FROM AIRPORT: 15 km; bus stop at hotel

One American I met at this hotel not long ago had begun his first visit to Germany in Hamburg. Looking around at the Atlantic, he was rather stunned. 'Do you know,' he told me, 'that the "Trib" came with my breakfast this morning plus a special teleprinter tearout of last night's closing prices in New York?' The Atlantic, undoubtedly one of the country's great hotels, has that ability to take care of guests that surprises the hardened traveller. Business is business and only the best will do and the Atlantic is a hotel for large diameter wheeler-dealers. Quite convivial at times too but in the sound-proofed rooms you can hear your watch tick. The food would send any health farm addict back to the shrink – the quality, yes, but ah the quantity. There is here an aura of good living which is unmistakable – a whiff of Havana, the heavenly effluvium of Armagnac, Gucci briefcases everywhere and the cool golden sunshine of the finest German wines. The management, headed by one of the great hotel dynasties of Germany, is superb.

HOTEL VIER JAHRESZEITEN, Neuer Jungfernstieg 9-14, 2000 Hamburg 36

★ TELEPHONE: 040/34 94 1
★ CABLES: Jahreszeiten
★ TELEX: 211 629
★ IN OPERATION: since 1897
★ RESERVATIONS: The Leading Hotels of the World
★ ROOMS: 77 doubles 98 singles
★ SUITES: 29
★ RESTAURANTS: 4 – Gourmet 'Restaurant Haerlin', 'Grill', tearoom 'Condi' and late dinner restaurant 'Jahreszeiten-Keller'
★ BARS: 2 – Simbari and Jahreszeiten Keller bars
★ DISCOTHEQUE: live music with international bands
★ SHOPS: 5
★ CONFERENCE ROOMS: 5 (up to 100)
★ BANQUETING ROOMS: 5 (16 to 140)

★ STANDARD BEDROOM SIZE: all rooms vary
★ PRIVATE BALCONIES: yes – on the 5th floor
★ SWIMMING POOL: no
★ GARDENS: no
★ NO. OF STAFF: 400
★ ROOM SERVICE: around the clock
★ ORIENTATION: most rooms face the Alster Lake, others face decorated courtyards
★ CREDIT CARDS: American Express, Diners Club, Eurocard, Master Charge, Access and Bankamericard
★ OWNING COMPANY: privately owned by the A. Haerlin family
★ MANAGING DIRECTOR: Gert Prantner
★ DISTANCE TO SHOPS: walking distance
★ DISTANCE FROM AIRPORT: 11 km

A very fine hotel indeed offering comfort, good taste and the legendary traditions of its owners' three generations' experience. Unlike so many good German hotels elsewhere, the Vier Jahreszeiten does not show off – there is none of that commercial opulence here. It is very quiet, very *distingué* and sensationally serviced – you have a thermometer for your bath water, they move the telephone to your desk during the day and back to the bedside at night and breakfast standards are of the highest. You get the feeling that the coffee has just been roasted for you. The rooms vary in size but all are absolute perfection when it comes to details and overall furnishing and the bathrooms are unusually good. There are some magnificent tapestries and chandeliers and chairs look as if they had been re-upholstered yesterday. The food is splendidly well served and ranks among the best of any hotel in Germany. Vier Jahreszeiten makes its own chocolates and keeps 185,000 bottles of wine in its superb cellar – the wine list reads much better than the ninety-five principles Luther nailed to the church door.

Hinterzarten

PARKHOTEL ADLER, 7824 Hinterzarten, Südschwarzwald

★ TELEPHONE: 07652/711-717
★ CABLES: Adlerhotel
★ TELEX: 07-72692
★ IN OPERATION: since first established by the Riesterer family in 1446
★ RESERVATIONS: direct/The Leading Hotels of the World/Relais et Chateaux
★ ROOMS: 48 double 15 single
★ SUITES: 19
★ RESTAURANTS: 6 – open-air restaurant during the summer
★ BARS: 1
★ DISCOTHEQUE: dancing and musical entertainment by resident house-band
★ SHOPS: Adler Shopping
★ CONFERENCE ROOMS: 2 (40 and 80)
★ BANQUETING ROOMS: 3 (20 to 250)
★ STANDARD BEDROOM SIZE: 28 m^2
★ PRIVATE BALCONIES: yes – and terrace with adequate furnishings
★ SWIMMING POOL: yes – fresh water, 19 × 8 m with underwater massage

★ RECREATIONAL ACTIVITIES: beauty parlour, hairdresser, sauna, solarium, massage, nine-pin bowling, indoor and outdoor tennis, horse riding, all wintersports; golf and watersports in the vicinity
★ GARDENS: yes – with children's playground, fitness course, deer park; game reserve including private duck pond
★ NO. OF STAFF: 90
★ ROOM SERVICE: around the clock
★ ORIENTATION: view of the Black Forest
★ CREDIT CARDS: American Express, Diners Club and Eurocard
★ OWNING COMPANY: A. Riesterer KG
★ GENERAL MANAGERS: H. A. and V. Riesterer
★ DISTANCE TO BEACH: Lake Titisee 4 km
★ DISTANCE TO SHOPS: 200 m
★ DISTANCE FROM AIRPORT: 90 km (Basel or Zürich)

This hotel holds the record for continuous ownership – the same family have owned it for well over 500 years. Sixteenth-century pilgrims and savants have long given way to well-padded tourists, especially at lunchtime when it becomes the focus for Mercedes-borne trenchermen, but at other times the Adler remains what it has been for so long – the quintessence of the really superb German country hotel. It's only a few miles from the shining Titisee, has its own sauna and covered swimming pool and charming gardens. All around are those beautiful hills of the Black Forest. The hotel is very, but *very* refined, furnished with pieces that bridge the centuries and staffed by people who really know what service is. Rooms are quite delightful – most of them different – and so comfortable that you might never want to leave. The trouble basically with the Adler is the food – one has to exercise enormous willpower to resist the succession of mouth-watering dishes. This is an hotel for those who don't have to watch their figure, or their wallet, too closely.

Kronberg

SCHLOSSHOTEL KRONBERG, Hainstrasse 25, 6242 Kronberg/Ts

★ TELEPHONE: 06173-7011
★ CABLES: no
★ TELEX: 0415 424
★ IN OPERATION: since 1954
★ RESERVATIONS: William Tobias, California/David B. Mitchell & Co Inc, New York

★ ROOMS: 20 doubles 29 singles
★ SUITES: 5
★ RESTAURANTS: 2
★ BARS: 1
★ DISCOTHEQUE: no
★ SHOPS: none
★ CONFERENCE ROOMS: 4 (4 to 50)

★ BANQUETING ROOMS: 4 (4 to 250)
★ STANDARD BEDROOM SIZE: 22 m^2
★ SWIMMING POOL: no
★ PRIVATE BALCONIES: 3 bedrooms only –
large terrace in front of the hotel
★ RECREATIONAL ACTIVITIES: 18-hole golf
course around the hotel
★ GARDENS: yes – large park with old trees
★ NO. OF STAFF: 125

★ ROOM SERVICE: 06.30–24.00
★ ORIENTATION: north and south
★ CREDIT CARDS: American Express,
Diners Club, Eurocard and Visa
★ OWNING COMPANY: Kurhessiche
Hausstiftung
★ GENERAL MANAGER: Klaus Fischer
★ DISTANCE TO SHOPS: 2 km
★ DISTANCE FROM AIRPORT: 20 km

This is the only hotel I know where Titians and Holbeins look down at you as you are having dinner. This extraordinary piece of mock-Tudor was built by Queen Victoria's daughter when she was German Empress – one supposes to remind her of home. Mama stayed there, of course, plus most of Europe's crowned heads. The place is a monument to a bygone age, filled with Savonarola chairs, Tuscan chests, Flemish tapestries, French Empire chests, priceless oriental carpets and fireplaces so huge it takes two men to carry a log in. Yet one does not feel overawed, probably because Kronberg has relatively few guests (and many staff) and the atmosphere is that of an outstanding country house. Rooms vary a good deal in size and quality but the average is very high on comfort and elegance. The food, once rather nondescript, has improved a lot lately. And it is in the green Taunus Mountains a mere few miles from Frankfurt (Frankfurt is forgettable anyway). One extremely rich English duke I know stayed there once and remarked: 'It's almost like home.' For us ordinary mortals it is a rare treat.

Lohmar

SCHLOSS AUEL, Wahlscheid, 5204 Lohmar 21

★ TELEPHONE: Overath (02206) 2041/2/3
★ CABLES: no
★ TELEX: 0 887 510
★ IN OPERATION: since 1951
★ RESERVATIONS: direct
★ ROOMS: 17 doubles 4 singles
★ SUITES: 2
★ RESTAURANTS: 4
★ BARS: 1
★ DISCOTHEQUE: no
★ SHOPS: none
★ CONFERENCE ROOMS: 7
★ BANQUETING ROOMS: 7
★ STANDARD BEDROOM SIZE: all very
different
★ PRIVATE BALCONIES: no
★ SWIMMING POOL: yes – fresh water,
5 × 9 m

★ RECREATIONAL ACTIVITIES: tennis and
sauna
★ GARDENS: yes
★ NO. OF STAFF: 25
★ ROOM SERVICE: 07.00–23.00
★ ORIENTATION: east and west
★ CREDIT CARDS: American Express,
Diners Club and Eurocard
★ OWNING COMPANY: privately owned
★ GENERAL MANAGER: Johann Adolf
Freiherr (von la Valette St. Georges)
★ DISTANCE TO SHOPS: 45 minutes by car
to Dusseldorf, 25 km from Cologne and
25 km from Bonn
★ DISTANCE FROM AIRPORT: 20 km

In this age of the ersatz, authenticity is rare indeed and can only be achieved by people who are authentic! Schloss Auel, some of which goes back to the fourteenth century, has been in the hands of the same celebrated family since the eighteenth century and one would be hard put to find a more charming place than this small, intimate, white-painted country castle a few Mercedes minutes away from Cologne. In this hotel there is not a single piece of furniture that looks as if it had not always been there – marvellous country pieces (including a four poster in which Napoleon once slept), beautiful chairs, gorgeous tapestries and a real chapel with a magnificent rococo altar. Most rooms are different but you cannot really go wrong because every one of them is a gem. People are absolutely charming, in a natural and wellborn way, and service comes with old-fashioned German politeness. Also surprising is the standard of food and wine – quite stratospheric for a hotel of this size. If an unkind fate decrees that you have to go to Frankfurt you can take your own revenge and stay here.

Munich

HOTEL BAYERISCHER HOF AND PALAIS MONTGELAS,
Promenadeplatz 2-6, 8000 München 2

- ★ TELEPHONE: 089/21200
- ★ CABLES: Bayerhof
- ★ TELEX: 05/23409
- ★ IN OPERATION: since 1841, destroyed during the second world war and rebuilt
- ★ RESERVATIONS: The Leading Hotels of the World, London and New York/Preferred Hotels, Frankfurt and U.S.A./SRS (Steigenberger Reservation Service), Frankfurt and New York
- ★ ROOMS: 200 doubles 220 singles
- ★ SUITES: 20
- ★ RESTAURANTS: 3 – Grill, Trader Vic's and Palais Keller
- ★ BARS: 3
- ★ DISCOTHEQUE: night club with live music (1 band) and Juliana's Discotheque
- ★ SHOPS: 9 – Palais Boutique, Emilio Pucci, Paintings, Leder Walter, Rudolph Mooshammer, Gallery, Royal Mink, Pelzhaus, jewellery etc

- ★ CONFERENCE ROOMS: 28 (5 to 1500)
- ★ BANQUETING ROOMS: 14 (up to 2000)
- ★ STANDARD BEDROOM SIZE: 22 m^2
- ★ PRIVATE BALCONIES: yes – 41
- ★ SWIMMING POOL: yes – fresh water, $16 \times 9 \times 1.5$ m
- ★ RECREATIONAL ACTIVITIES: sauna, massage and solarium
- ★ GARDENS: grill garden, used in the summer for open-air meals
- ★ NO. OF STAFF: 740
- ★ ROOM SERVICE: 06.00–01.00
- ★ ORIENTATION: Promenadeplatz, quiet back street and courtyard
- ★ CREDIT CARDS: American Express, Diners Club, Carte Blanche and Eurocard
- ★ OWNING COMPANY: Falk Volkhardt
- ★ GENERAL MANAGER: Falk Volkhardt
- ★ DISTANCE TO SHOPS: walking distance
- ★ DISTANCE FROM AIRPORT: 14 km

The Bayerischer Hof and its aristocratic next-door sister, the Palais Montgelas, are a legend around the world. Should you feel off colour, don't worry – there is an oxygen tent in the sauna that will revive you and in one of the suites there is also a his-and-hers bathtub. What fun. This hotel is for people who know what they want and don't have to point to it – quite a lot of those in Germany and Munich, and the Bayerischer Hof is where they come to get some of the starch off their system.

An exceedingly successful hotel and a very busy one, it manages to be everything to everyone – convivial in the Bavarian style and the ultimate in peace and quiet if that's the way you want it. Rooms in the main hotel are elegantly ageless – fresh flowers everywhere and good, solid furniture that stands the test of ages and in the Palais they are positively ducal.

In all my several visits, I have never been able to fault the Bayerischer Hof though one German tycoon once complained within my hearing that the morning toast was too hard. He should see his dentist.

HOTEL VIER JAHRESZEITEN, Maximilianstrasse 17, 8000 München 22

- ★ TELEPHONE: 089/230 390
- ★ CABLES: Jahreszeiten
- ★ TELEX: 52 38 59
- ★ IN OPERATION: 65 years
- ★ RESERVATIONS: The Leading Hotels of the World

- ★ ROOMS: 365
- ★ SUITES: 30
- ★ RESTAURANTS: 2
- ★ BARS: 1
- ★ DISCOTHEQUE: no – but dancing in the bar

★ SHOPS: 3

★ CONFERENCE ROOMS: 8 (20 to 450)

★ BANQUETING ROOMS: 8 (20 to 450)

★ STANDARD BEDROOM SIZE: 24 m²

★ PRIVATE BALCONIES: some

★ SWIMMING POOL: yes – fresh water

★ GARDENS: no

★ NO. OF STAFF: 400

★ ROOM SERVICE: around the clock

★ ORIENTATION: facade faces the Maximilianstrasse

★ CREDIT CARDS: Diners Club, American Express, Bankamericard, Master Charge, Eurocard, Pan Am and Take Off Card

★ OWNING COMPANY: Kempinski Hotels Corporation

★ GENERAL MANAGER: Michael D. Maass

★ DISTANCE TO SHOPS: walking distance

★ DISTANCE FROM AIRPORT: 9 km

This is still one of Germany's great hotel landmarks – I love it and so do many readers. One lady from Seattle wrote: 'When I arrive at the Four Seasons, the whole place really makes me feel that I am back in old Europe . . .' Lovely, dark panelled walls, handsome salons, beautiful antiques and a staff who seem to have been there forever – all this is part of the Vier Jahreszeiten image. There are also the ghosts of the Walterspiel family who once owned it and were the country's greatest gastronomes. Most of the bedrooms have been modernized – if that is the word – with so much intelligent planning and thought for detail that one hardly notices things have changed – apart from the plumbing, of course. It is a very, but very comfortable and aristocratic hotel with a great tradition. The food in the distinguished Walterspiel restaurant attracts Müncheners who, with so much choice around, have a high critical standard.

Oberwesel

BURGHOTEL AUF SCHONBURG, D-6532 Oberwesel/Rhein

★ TELEPHONE: 06744/7027

★ CABLES: no

★ TELEX: no

★ IN OPERATION: 29 years

★ RESERVATIONS: direct

★ ROOMS: 17 doubles 3 singles

★ SUITES: none

★ RESTAURANTS: 3

★ BARS: none

★ DISCOTHEQUE: no

★ SHOPS: none

★ CONFERENCE ROOMS: 2 (18 and 35)

★ BANQUETING ROOMS: 2 (18 and 40)

★ PRIVATE BALCONIES: 4 and a large terrace

★ STANDARD BEDROOM SIZE: 42 m²

★ SWIMMING POOL: no

★ GARDENS: no

★ NO. OF STAFF: 17

★ ORIENTATION: all directions

★ CREDIT CARDS: American Express and Visa

★ OWNING COMPANY: Hüttl family

★ GENERAL MANAGER: Hüttl family

★ DISTANCE TO SHOPS: 1 km

★ DISTANCE FROM AIRPORT: 90 km (Frankfurt); 120 km (Cologne)

Anyone who goes up or down the Rhine at its noblest can see Auf Schonburg. You can't miss it. It sits up there on its hill like an illustration to a fairy tale, a proud statement in stone going back close on a thousand years. And if you think that it is the home of some great German margrave, you are wrong. It's your home and mine and anyone can get to stay there if he is quick about it because Schonburg, big as it is, has few rooms and only a small number can succeed. Which in a way makes it all the more worthwhile since you can have the great beamed halls, the fantastic corridors and the four-poster beds almost to yourself. The brothers Grimm, one feels, must be somewhere around and Schumann's music goes with it better than Wagner's. Both the management and staff are quite charming and most welcoming and theirs is German hospitality at its finest. Food and wines are excellent too – the latter especially if they come from those glorious local vineyards. Also, watch the Rhine panorama in the early morning or at dusk. You'll never forget it.

Trendelburg

BURGHOTEL TRENDELBURG, D-3526 Trendelburg

★ TELEPHONE: 05675-1021
★ CABLES: no
★ TELEX: 0994812
★ IN OPERATION: 30 years
★ RESERVATIONS: direct
★ ROOMS: 18 doubles 5 singles
★ SUITES: 1
★ RESTAURANTS: 4
★ BARS: none
★ DISCOTHEQUE: no
★ SHOPS: none
★ CONFERENCE ROOMS: 2 (10 to 45)
★ BANQUETING ROOMS: 2
★ STANDARD BEDROOM SIZE: 16–30 m^2
★ PRIVATE BALCONIES: no

★ SWIMMING POOL: no
★ RECREATIONAL ACTIVITIES: swimming, tennis and horse riding nearby
★ GARDENS: yes
★ NO. OF STAFF: 24
★ ROOM SERVICE: 07.00–23.00
★ CREDIT CARDS: American Express and Diners Club
★ ORIENTATION: all directions
★ OWNING COMPANY: private
★ GENERAL MANAGER: Mr V. Stockhausen
★ DISTANCE TO SHOPS: 12 km
★ DISTANCE FROM AIRPORT: 190 km (Hanover); 220 km (Frankfurt)

If your fancy turns to a night or two in a real German castle, you couldn't do better than try Trendelburg – only a few miles from Kassel and yet, it would seem, belonging to a different age. It is beautiful, genuine, totally authentic, gently bucolic and so well run by the baronial family who own it that it has become a legend in Germany. A lot of it dates from the thirteenth century and, like all such places, other centuries added their contribution, making Trendelburg into a residence of immense character and charm. There are old timbers everywhere – even the bathrooms are timbered – lovely floors, delightful country antiques and a magnificent vaulted dining room where the food is simply delicious. If you are lucky you might even get the very romantic Wedding Tower Suite which is the pride of this most unusual and welcoming hotel. The plumbing dates from 1979.

Wiesbaden

HOTEL NASSAUER HOF, Kaiser-Freidrich-Platz 3-4, 6200 Wiesbaden

★ TELEPHONE: 06121 1330
★ CABLES: Nassauer Hof, Wiesbaden
★ TELEX: 4186315
★ IN OPERATION: since 1819
★ RESERVATIONS: Preferred Hotels, worldwide/The Leading Hotels of the World, worldwide/Steigenberger Reservation Service, worldwide/JAL, Tokyo, Frankfurt
★ ROOMS: 201
★ SUITES: 19
★ RESTAURANTS: 3 – including one with nouvelle cuisine
★ BARS: 5
★ DISCOTHEQUE: pianist in the Kamin Bar
★ SHOPS: boutiques, souvenir shop, hairdresser
★ CONFERENCE ROOMS: 7 – 30–176 m^2 (10 to 100); 2 executive rooms (20 to 30)
★ BANQUETING ROOMS: 3 (40 to 170)
★ STANDARD BEDROOM SIZE: 30 m^2

★ PRIVATE BALCONIES: some rooms have private balconies
★ SWIMMING POOL: yes – thermal water, 65 m^2
★ RECREATIONAL ACTIVITIES: fitness centre, sauna, massages, sun terrace at top of hotel
★ GARDENS: hotel is located next to the Kurpark
★ NO. OF STAFF: 250
★ ROOM SERVICE: around the clock
★ ORIENTATION: some rooms overlook Kurpark, some overlook indoor garden
★ CREDIT CARDS: American Express, Diners Club, Eurocard, Master Card, Access
★ OWNING COMPANY: Stinnes AG
★ GENERAL MANAGER: Karl Nuser
★ DISTANCE TO SHOPS: hotel is in the centre of town
★ DISTANCE FROM AIRPORT: 30 km (Rhein-Main)

Speaking out of turn, and very rudely, we would confess that we could live quite happily without ever going back to Frankfurt . . . But we would sorely miss Düsseldorf, and Munich and indeed gracious Wiesbaden. And we would miss this city's Nassauer Hof, surely one of the nicest and most civilized city hotels in Germany. Here one even gets one's own country's top people newspaper with breakfast, splendid personalized bathroom soap and courteous and immediate service. Rooms are large enough to please and there is a welcome absence of all that information-trash we dislike so much. Carpets are thick-thick, windows soundproofed, beds solid and always beautifully made. The feeling of good living goes on into the three carefully planned restaurants where the food, German-international, is, happily, never colossal. Simply plain good. The Nassauer Hof is a very efficient hotel indeed and a very pleasant one too – people actually greet you by name when you get off the elevator in the morning. Good morning to you too. If you are in this part of Germany, this is your best address.

Zell

HOTEL SCHLOSS ZELL, 5583 Zell, Mosel

- ★ TELEPHONE: 06542-4084
- ★ CABLES: no
- ★ TELEX: no
- ★ IN OPERATION: since 1948
- ★ RESERVATIONS:
- ★ ROOMS: 9
- ★ SUITES: 1
- ★ RESTAURANTS: 1 – Restaurant Schloss Zell (nouvelle cuisine)
- ★ BARS: none
- ★ DISCOTHEQUE: no
- ★ SHOPS: none
- ★ CONFERENCE ROOMS: none
- ★ BANQUETING ROOMS: none
- ★ STANDARD BEDROOM SIZE: individual (very old castle)
- ★ PRIVATE BALCONIES: 2
- ★ SWIMMING POOL: no
- ★ GARDENS: small garden
- ★ NO. OF STAFF: 10
- ★ ROOM SERVICE: 07.00–22.00
- ★ ORIENTATION: West
- ★ CREDIT CARDS: Visa, Eurocard
- ★ OWNING COMPANY: Maria Bohn (owner)
- ★ GENERAL MANAGER: Peter Bonefas
- ★ DISTANCE TO SHOPS: hotel located in city
- ★ DISTANCE FROM AIRPORT: 100 km

How strange it is that so many houses built by bishops in olden times have now become historic hotels – there are at least seven in this book! They obviously knew how to live well. Schloss Zell, built in the thirteenth century by the Archbishop of Trier, is one of these – a charming and totally authentic old place which now of course is right in the centre of this delightful little wine-making town of Zell. The Schloss is tiny, replete with glorious antiques and furnished with love and care. It shines with good German hospitality and the very small staff soon become friends – they do their job with cheerfulness and charm. The food is exceedingly good for such a small place and of course the wines are out of this world. If you want the best (you'll have to be quick . . .) ask for room number seven – it's a little turret all by itself, all chintzy and bright, and perfect for a honeymoon.

GREAT BRITAIN

Auchterarder

GLENEAGLES HOTEL, Auchterarder, Perthshire, PH3 1NF, Scotland

- ★ TELEPHONE: (076 46) 2231
- ★ CABLES: Glenotel, Auchterarder
- ★ TELEX: 76105
- ★ IN OPERATION: since 1924
- ★ RESERVATIONS: The Leading Hotels of the World
- ★ ROOMS: 212 doubles 42 singles
- ★ SUITES: 20
- ★ RESTAURANTS: 4 – The Strathearn, The Eagle's Nest, Dormy House and Country Club
- ★ BARS: 3 – Cocktail Bar, Dormy House Bar and Country Club
- ★ DISCOTHEQUE: yes – by arrangement – and dancing to live music each evening
- ★ SHOPS: 8
- ★ CONFERENCE ROOMS: 6 (50 to 400)
- ★ BANQUETING ROOMS: 7 (40 to 400)
- ★ STANDARD BEDROOM SIZE: 28 m^2 (double) 13½ m^2 (single)
- ★ PRIVATE BALCONIES: yes – some rooms
- ★ SWIMMING POOL: yes – fresh water, indoor, heated
- ★ RECREATIONAL ACTIVITIES: 4 golf courses, 5 tennis courts, putting green, bowling green, croquet lawn, billiards, fishing, sauna, squash
- ★ GARDENS: yes – 640-acre estate
- ★ NO. OF STAFF: 420
- ★ ROOM SERVICE: around the clock
- ★ ORIENTATION: facing south
- ★ OWNING COMPANY: Arthur Bell & Son Ltd
- ★ CREDIT CARDS: all major credit cards
- ★ GENERAL MANAGER: Mr Peter G. Lederer
- ★ DISTANCE TO SHOPS: 24 km (Perth); 32 km (Stirling) and 72 km (Edinburgh)
- ★ DISTANCE FROM AIRPORT: 88 km (Glasgow); and 64 km (Edinburgh)

I don't know what the Scots will say about it but Gleneagles is changing and its new owners are determined to make it great. This vast pile always was that, a place on its own with tremendous aura, where you could arrive by helicopter if you wished. The sort of place where, traditionally, they iron out the creases in *The Times* before putting it on your breakfast tray. And, of course, Gleneagles meant golf-lunatics coming in from all over the world. I once saw an American visitor with tears in his eyes when he caught sight of the courses – King's and Queen's.

But it had to move with the times and from the hotel's 1000 windows looking over the Perthshire hills to the great pillared hall which I swear is bigger than Piccadilly Circus, the new owners are renovating, initiating, inventing, getting rid of the institutional look and even taking real French food North of the Border (they are spending £40,000 on the kitchens alone). All this plus a huge new leisure complex, an all-year-round affair with squash courts, saunas, jacuzzi pool and solarium (let's hope they import the sun too). I am hoping they won't forget the Gleneagles atmosphere, a blend of grand urbanity and the personal touch which made Gleneagles a much loved place by all those who knew it.

Bath

ROYAL CRESCENT HOTEL, Royal Crescent, Bath, Avon, BA1 2LS

★ TELEPHONE: (0225) 319090
★ CABLES: Royalguest
★ TELEX: 444251
★ IN OPERATION: 43 years – re-opened in June 1979, after complete restoration
★ RESERVATIONS: The Leading Hotels of the World, London and New York
★ ROOMS: 26 doubles 2 singles
★ SUITES: 7 – 3 with four-posters, 2 with spa pools
★ RESTAURANTS: 1
★ BARS: 1
★ DISCOTHEQUE: no
★ SHOPS: none
★ CONFERENCE ROOMS: 2 (up to 30)
★ BANQUETING ROOMS: 2 (up to 20)
★ STANDARD BEDROOM SIZE: 42 m²
★ PRIVATE BALCONIES: no – but private terrace to one room and terrace outside the bar
★ SWIMMING POOL: no

★ RECREATIONAL ACTIVITIES: tennis, swimming, horse riding, and sauna available nearby; horse-drawn coach rides by prior appointment
★ GARDENS: yes
★ NO. OF STAFF: 58
★ ROOM SERVICE: around the clock
★ ORIENTATION: faces the private Royal Crescent lawn overlooking the city of Bath
★ FURTHER DEVELOPMENTS: planning additional rooms and guest facilities in the hotel mews
★ CREDIT CARDS: American Express, Access, Barclaycard and Visa
★ OWNING COMPANY: Blakeney Hotels Ltd
★ GENERAL MANAGER: Malcolm J. M. Walker
★ DISTANCE TO SHOPS: walking distance
★ DISTANCE FROM AIRPORT: 30 km

Having recently returned to the Royal Crescent, my affection and admiration for this unique hotel are undimmed – it is still one of the most interesting and remarkable hotels in Europe. The location of course is matchless – right in the middle of that beautiful Georgian Crescent which is possibly one of the six greatest architectural concepts in Europe. Inside, everything is a feast for the eye, a balm for the soul, for this hotel, totally reconditioned in 1979, is absolutely perfect. From the ashtrays to the paintings and from the four-poster beds to the magnificent ceiling decorations and the carpets which one would love to roll up and take away, the Royal Crescent is an object lesson on how to present a period hotel.

As for the management and staff, they deserve medals for making this small hotel into a home for its guests – everyone is friendly, helpful, happy to oblige and it is a real pleasure to stay here and stroll around this most handsome of small English towns. The food too is worth travelling for – something deliciously adventurous and yet always within the guidelines of intelligent gastronomy. Full marks to this very rare hostelry.

Broadway

THE LYGON ARMS, Broadway, Worcestershire, WR12 7DU

★ TELEPHONE: (0386) 852255
★ CABLES: Lygon Broadway
★ TELEX: 338260
★ IN OPERATION: since the sixteenth century
★ RESERVATIONS: direct/Hotel Representative Inc/Prestige
★ ROOMS: 57 doubles 3 singles
★ SUITES: 3
★ RESTAURANTS: 2 – main restaurant and wine bar
★ BARS: 2
★ DISCOTHEQUE: no
★ SHOPS: 1 – Inn Shop
★ CONFERENCE ROOMS: 4 (10 to 80)
★ BANQUETING ROOMS: 5 (10 to 150)
★ STANDARD BEDROOM SIZE: 31 m^2
★ PRIVATE BALCONIES: yes – some rooms
★ SWIMMING POOL: no

★ RECREATIONAL ACTIVITIES: tennis, golf close by and horse riding and hunting by arrangement
★ GARDENS: yes – secluded formal gardens and orchard
★ NO. OF STAFF: 113
★ ROOM SERVICE: around the clock
★ ORIENTATION: main street, courtyard and garden
★ CREDIT CARDS: American Express, Diners Club, Access, Eurocard, Barclaycard and Carte Blanche
★ OWNING COMPANY: The Lygon Arms Ltd
★ MANAGING DIRECTOR: Kirk Ritchie
★ DISTANCE TO SHOPS: within village
★ DISTANCE FROM AIRPORT: 144 km (Heathrow); 55 km (Birmingham); helicopter pad

In the fourth edition I wrote: 'One of the hardest things in the world to do is to run a good hotel in a location which is invaded twice daily by a gaggle of gawping tourists . . .' And they are still coming to Broadway, one of England's most celebrated villages, and a few lucky ones stay at the Lygon Arms; even fewer sleep in the Great Chamber which was built the year the Mayflower sailed. Both Charles I and Cromwell stayed here – though unfortunately not at the same time or the Civil War may have ended differently. Yet, the most remarkable thing of all is that despite its fame, despite the fact that it is in the heart of England's tourist land, the Lygon Arms has managed to remain so good a hotel. One feels that it must take great willpower not to succumb to the temptation of cashing in on the boom. The Lygon Arms remains itself: well-tempered, gentle, beautifully run and totally devoid of razzmatazz. The people who staff it always seem to have time to answer even the tourist's most stupid questions, to help and direct and to make you feel welcome. Now, even the less interesting rooms in the new wing have been given the Lygon look and the food, as before, is very acceptable.

Chagford

GIDLEIGH PARK, Chagford, Devon, TQ13 8HH

★ TELEPHONE: (06473) 2367/2225
★ CABLES: no
★ TELEX: no
★ IN OPERATION: 7 years
★ RESERVATIONS: David B. Mitchell & Co Inc/Relais et Chateaux
★ ROOMS: 12
★ SUITES: none
★ RESTAURANTS: 1 – menu changes weekly
★ BARS: 1
★ DISCOTHEQUE: no
★ SHOPS: none
★ CONFERENCE ROOMS: none
★ BANQUETING ROOMS: none

★ STANDARD BEDROOM SIZE: 16–50 m^2
★ PRIVATE BALCONIES: 2 rooms have balconies
★ SWIMMING POOL: no
★ RECREATIONAL ACTIVITIES: croquet, grass tennis court, walking on Dartmoor or in the Teign Valley
★ GARDENS: yes
★ NO. OF STAFF: 24
★ ROOM SERVICE: for breakfast and drinks 07.30–24.00
★ ORIENTATION: 8 rooms face valley, 4 face forest
★ CREDIT CARDS: American Express

★ OWNING COMPANY: Owned by Paul and Kay Henderson
★ GENERAL MANAGER: Paul Henderson
★ DISTANCE TO SHOPS: 30 km (Exeter)
★ DISTANCE FROM AIRPORT: 270 km (Heathrow); 30 km (Exeter)

How does a young American lady cook running a remote country hotel in England manage to get a star rating in the Michelin Guide? To find out you will have to travel on potholed roads deep inside hedgerows to this remarkable small hotel – Gidleigh Park. It had long intrigued me and, pressed by some good hotel friends, I eventually found my way there. I have not regretted it. When Paul and Kay Henderson took over the tumbled-down house on the edge of Dartmoor, they wanted to create something that had never been done before: an English country house hotel with French food and American plumbing – at least this is what they modestly say and they have succeeded beyond their wildest dreams, since Gidleigh Park is now acclaimed all over the world. The place is charming, warm, intimate, personal and totally unexpected. The house is lovingly furnished, mostly with good, unassuming country antiques and superbly kept, with fresh flowers everywhere and a great deal of proprietorial attention. You just let yourself live. And, of course, eat if your figure will stand it. Kay Henderson's cooking is special. One can only describe it as French in inspiration with international accents. The wine list is the best of all the small hotels I know. Gidleigh Park must not be missed.

Chelwood

HUNSTRETE HOUSE HOTEL, Chelwood, Nr Bristol, Avon, BS18 4NS

★ TELEPHONE: (07618) 578
★ CABLES: Hunstrete House Hotel
★ TELEX: 449540
★ IN OPERATION: 6 years
★ RESERVATIONS: direct or David B. Mitchell & Co Inc
★ ROOMS: 19
★ SUITES: 2
★ RESTAURANTS: 2
★ BARS: 1
★ DISCOTHEQUE: no
★ SHOPS: none
★ CONFERENCE ROOMS: 1 (5 × 6 m)
★ BANQUETING ROOMS: 1 (30)
★ STANDARD BEDROOM SIZE: 24 m^2
★ PRIVATE BALCONIES: none
★ SWIMMING POOL: 1 – outdoor, fresh water, heated

★ RECREATIONAL ACTIVITIES: tennis court, croquet, swimming; riding, fishing, golf nearby
★ GARDENS: yes
★ NO. OF STAFF: 45
★ ROOM SERVICE: 07.20–23.30
★ ORIENTATION: east, south and west
★ CREDIT CARDS: American Express, Carte Blanche, Barclaycard and Visa
★ OWNING COMPANY: Mr F. J. and Mrs T. Dupays (resident proprietors)
★ GENERAL MANAGER: Sharron Love
★ DISTANCE TO SHOPS: 13 km (Bath); 13 km (Bristol)
★ DISTANCE FROM AIRPORT: 140 km (Heathrow)

It is when I find a hotel like Hunstrete House that I realize how lucky foreign visitors are – for them this is the best of England while for us who live in this sceptred isle, a quick weekend is all we can manage. Hunstrete is delightful, totally English and Georgian to boot – a very handsome house with a walled garden, croquet lawn and splendid countryside all around, plus the nearness of such places as Bath and Glastonbury, Longleat, Wilton House and many other stately homes. The house is delightfully individual with most bedrooms done up in a different style and lovingly furnished with good pieces and splendid furnishings. In the public rooms, you feel at home because you could be a guest of the family and the whole atmosphere is just that – a private party for a few fortunate people. Fortunate too because the food, presented here by a chef from Normandy, is one of the high points. Putting Gallic pride aside, he ha managed to combine the best of both countries and things like salmon from the Wy for instance are worth the journey. If you are aiming for the West Country, this coul well be the right choice.

Dedham

MAISON TALBOOTH, Dedham, Colchester, Essex, CO7 6HN

★ TELEPHONE: (0206) 322367
★ CABLES: no
★ TELEX: no
★ IN OPERATION: 14 years
★ RESERVATIONS: direct
★ ROOMS: 9 doubles
★ SUITES: 1
★ RESTAURANTS: 1 – Le Talbooth Restaurant, sixteenth-century timbered house
★ BARS: 1 – plus private bar in each room
★ DISCOTHEQUE: no
★ SHOPS: none
★ CONFERENCE ROOMS: 2 (20 in each)
★ BANQUETING ROOMS: 1 (20)
★ STANDARD BEDROOM SIZE: 25–30 m^2
★ PRIVATE BALCONIES: yes
★ SWIMMING POOL: no
★ GARDENS: yes

★ NO. OF STAFF: 10 in the hotel and 25 in the restaurant
★ ROOM SERVICE: 07.00–24.00
★ ORIENTATION: hotel faces north, but suites face all directions
★ FURTHER DEVELOPMENTS: construction of tennis court; private yacht hire
★ CREDIT CARDS: American Express, Barclaycard, Visa, Access and Diners Club
★ OWNING COMPANY: Le Talbooth (Dedham) Ltd
★ GENERAL MANAGER: G. M. W. Milsom (Proprietor)
★ DISTANCE TO BEACH: 30 km
★ DISTANCE TO SHOPS: 10 km (Colchester)
★ DISTANCE FROM AIRPORT: 80 km (Norwich); 120 km (Heathrow); 60 km (Southend)

There are twin identities here. One is Le Talbooth, one of England's most celebrated country restaurants lodged in a spectacularly beautiful house that Constable once painted. I like to eat there and discreetly steal the menu to remind me of past delights. Then, half a mile away, is Maison Talbooth – an admirable small country house hotel. Britain's best hotel guide (they are lucky – they only cover one country . . .) gives it the fifth-highest rating in this particular category. Maison Talbooth is a good place to know, largely because it is the creation of one man.

No two rooms are alike. What is similar is the touch – a tremendous effort to lift this once undistinguished Victorian house into something special. Furniture is excellently chosen. The beds are beautiful and wallpapers and colour schemes are exactly what you might pick yourself. Bathrooms are great fun, too. There are fresh flowers everywhere and fruit and drinks too and, when breakfast comes, it really makes you feel like facing the new day. Service is impeccable.

All this, with the high gastronomy down the road and the Constable country all around, with its wide skies, great trees and soft, blurry horizons, means that Talbooth is a name to put in your diary.

The Terrace at the Dedham Vale Hotel and the Pier Fish Restaurant at Harwich are both worth a visit.

Dunblane

CROMLIX HOUSE, Dunblane, Perthshire, FK15 9JT

★ TELEPHONE: (0786) 822125
★ CABLES: no
★ TELEX: no
★ IN OPERATION: 3 years
★ RESERVATIONS: Abercrombie and Kent International Inc, Illinois, U.S.A., London, UK
★ ROOMS: 11
★ SUITES: 7
★ RESTAURANTS: 2
★ BARS: none

★ DISCOTHEQUE: no
★ SHOPS: none
★ CONFERENCE ROOMS: 1 – 60 m^2 (20)
★ BANQUETING ROOMS: 1 – 60 m^2 (24)
★ STANDARD BEDROOM SIZE: 32 m^2
★ PRIVATE BALCONIES: none
★ SWIMMING POOL: no
★ RECREATIONAL ACTIVITIES: shooting in season, riding, tennis, fishing
★ GARDENS: yes
★ NO. OF STAFF: 15–20

★ ROOM SERVICE: 07.00–23.00

★ ORIENTATION: some rooms overlook the estate and some overlook the Ochil Hills

★ CREDIT CARDS: Access, Visa, American Express, Diners Club

★ OWNING COMPANY: Cromlix House Ltd

★ GENERAL MANAGER: Stephen Coupe

★ DISTANCE TO SHOPS: 15 km (Dunblane)

★ DISTANCE FROM AIRPORT: 60 km (Edinburgh)

Edward VII stayed here. No doubt he liked the shooting. And the 5000 acres of stunning Scottish countryside plus all the rituals of a great country house. We do too and since Cromlix has lately become a hotel (if you can call it that . . .) we don't mind at all being part of it. The estate has been in the hands of the same family for 400 years (newcomers really) but the present house, imposing and beautifully sited in its manicured parkland, only goes back to 1880. Public rooms, and bedrooms too, are quite special – vast and lofty, with superb furnishings that one cannot find nowadays and magnificent carpets and curtains. Everywhere looks lived in, happily by people who know how to behave. And if the chef comes to ask them what they would really like for dinner, they don't mind giving it some intelligent thought. There is no menu here – you just ask and ye are given, a meal that you are likely to remember. As for the wine list, you might even take it to bed with you since it will leave you thinking great thoughts. And with all that, Scotland's greatest golf courses are near at hand. It's not really worth going anywhere else – everything is at Cromlix House.

East Grinstead

GRAVETYE MANOR, Nr East Grinstead, West Sussex, RH19 4LJ

★ TELEPHONE: Sharpthorne (0342) 810567

★ CABLES: no

★ TELEX: 957239

★ IN OPERATION: 25 years

★ RESERVATIONS: direct

★ ROOMS: 12 doubles 2 singles

★ SUITES: no

★ ROOMS: 1

★ BARS: 1

★ DISCOTHEQUE: no

★ SHOPS: none

★ CONFERENCE ROOMS: 1 (14)

★ BANQUETING ROOMS: 1 (16)

★ STANDARD BEDROOM SIZE: 30 m^2

★ PRIVATE BALCONIES: no

★ SWIMMING POOL: no

★ RECREATIONAL ACTIVITIES: trout fishing, croquet, tennis, squash, golf and horse riding can be arranged locally

★ GARDENS: yes – 20 acres created by William Robinson, pioneer of the English natural garden

★ NO. OF STAFF: 52

★ ROOM SERVICE: 07.00–23.30

★ ORIENTATION: rooms face garden and forest

★ CREDIT CARDS: no credit cards are accepted

★ OWNING COMPANY: Gravetye Manor Hotel Ltd

★ GENERAL MANAGER: Peter Herbert (Resident Proprietor)

★ DISTANCE TO BEACH: 50 km

★ DISTANCE TO SHOPS: 8 km

★ DISTANCE FROM AIRPORT: 19 km

One of the oddities about writing this book is that when I sit in my study looking over the gentle Sussex Downs, I can almost hear the soft pop of the champagne corks down at Gravetye Manor, a mere two miles away. Alas, this proximity to the finest food in South-East England does me little good (apart from the occasional self-indulgence of course). Trouble is, people ring me up from far and wide accusing me of suggesting temptations in which they have little hope of indulging because they cannot get into Gravetye. Such is the price of fame for a country house hotel that has a worldwide reputation.

Gravetye, especially in the summertime when you can have your pre-dinner Pol Roger sitting in the superb gardens, is a way of life one can get used to. This lovely mellow 400-year-old stone house, beautifully but not ostentatiously furnished, is sheer delight. Rooms are countryfied, gentle and beautifully kept and service is quiet and expert. But what counts here is the food – truly original, beautifully balanced and ecstatically fine. I often take French friends to Gravetye just to show them that Britain too can produce great meals and to a man they remark that, of course, the superb wines are French. Quite. Gravetye is an experience that you owe to yourself but, please, don't telephone me!

Fort William

INVERLOCHY CASTLE, Fort William, Inverness-shire, Scotland

★ TELEPHONE: (0397) 2177/8
★ CABLES: Inverlochy Castle
★ TELEX: no
★ IN OPERATION: for 15 years
★ RESERVATIONS: direct
★ ROOMS: 13 doubles 1 single
★ SUITES: 2
★ RESTAURANTS: 2
★ BARS: none
★ DISCOTHEQUE: no
★ SHOPS: none
★ CONFERENCE ROOMS: none
★ BANQUETING ROOMS: none
★ STANDARD BEDROOM SIZE: variable
★ PRIVATE BALCONIES: no
★ SWIMMING POOL: no

★ RECREATIONAL ACTIVITIES: tennis, trout fishing, billiards, horse riding and golf nearby
★ GARDENS: yes
★ NO. OF STAFF: 50
★ ROOM SERVICE: around the clock
★ ORIENTATION: rooms face loch or mountain
★ CREDIT CARDS: Access and Barclaycard
★ OWNING COMPANY: Mr & Mrs J. Hobbs
★ GENERAL MANAGER: Michael Leonard
★ DISTANCE TO BEACH: 40 km
★ DISTANCE TO SHOPS: 5 km
★ DISTANCE FROM AIRPORT: 109 km (Inverness); 160 km (Glasgow)

Not long ago, I asked a German friend which country hotel he liked best in Britain and he looked at me as if I had taken leave of my senses. 'Inverlochy Castle of course!' he said. Quite. The fame of this great Scottish folly is now worldwide and it needs no endorsement from me. As far as I know, it is the largest hotel building I can recall for the smallest number of guests – never more than about twenty-seven people in a vast grey pile overlooking Loch Linnhe, framed by masses of rhododendrons and vistas of parkland. From the fantastic great hall with its painted ceiling one ascends – that's the right word – to bedrooms of ducal splendour filled with lovely fabrics and, does one dare say it, homely furniture (ie the kind you'd like to have at home . . .). Food has always been one of Inverlochy's great pluses – nothing mass produced or frozen here – everything is fresh, natural and absolutely succulent. Chef François Huquet makes sure it gets the treatment it deserves.

Hambleton

HAMBLETON HALL HOTEL AND RESTAURANT, Hambleton, Oakham, Rutland, Leicestershire, LE15 8TH

★ TELEPHONE: (0572) 56991
★ CABLES: no
★ TELEX: 342888 Hamble
★ IN OPERATION: since July 1980
★ RESERVATIONS: David B. Mitchell & Co Inc
★ ROOMS: 15
★ SUITES: none
★ RESTAURANTS: 1
★ BARS: 1
★ DISCOTHEQUE: no

★ SHOPS: none
★ CONFERENCE ROOMS: 1 – small, boardroom-style (10 to 15)
★ BANQUETING ROOMS: none
★ STANDARD BEDROOM SIZE: 30 m^2
★ PRIVATE BALCONIES: no
★ SWIMMING POOL: no
★ RECREATIONAL ACTIVITIES: hard tennis court, fishing and sailing available by prior arrangement on Rutland Water, golf courses within 10 miles, shooting

and hunting in season by prior
arrangement
★ GARDENS: yes
★ NO. OF STAFF: 40
★ ROOM SERVICE: 07.30–23.30
★ ORIENTATION: most rooms face south
★ CREDIT CARDS: American Express,
Access, Visa and Diners Club

★ OWNING COMPANY: Hart Hambleton Ltd
★ GENERAL MANAGER: Jan-Willem Bos
★ DISTANCE TO SHOPS: Peterborough 22
km, Nottingham 29 km, Leicester 25 km
★ DISTANCE FROM AIRPORT: 30 km (East
Midlands)

There have been some resounding successes in the line-up of English country house hotels in the last few years (and a few failures too – if you read this edition against the previous one . . .). Hambleton Hall has certainly made it, within four years of opening. Most people we know agree that it is quite charming: a mellow and impressive Victorian country house (Noël Coward and other witty characters stayed there), it stands proudly on its own little peninsula right in the middle of Rutland Water, a setting that is as English as they come, with beautiful gardens and gracious vistas. Once inside, you could say that Queen Victoria never had it so good because the look, the furnishings and the fittings are Victorian brought up to date – gorgeous antique furniture, marvellous fireplaces, fresh flowers everywhere and original and quite beautiful carpets and curtains. Rooms are large, easy-going and very restful. As for the food, it is worth a long detour – fresh, imaginative and charmingly presented by a staff who know how to look after guests. Hambleton Hall is of course privately owned – and it shows. It is more like the country home you would love to own.

London

THE BERKELEY, P.O. Box 590, Wilton Place, Knightsbridge, London, SW1X 7RL

★ TELEPHONE: 01-235 6000
★ CABLES: Silentium London
★ TELEX: 919252 Berkly G
★ IN OPERATION: since 1972
★ RESERVATIONS: The Leading Hotels of
the World
★ ROOMS: 132
★ SUITES: 27
★ RESTAURANTS: 2 – The Buttery and main
hotel restaurant
★ BARS: 1
★ DISCOTHEQUE: yes
★ SHOPS: 4 – hairdressing, bookshop,
cinema and flower shop
★ CONFERENCE ROOMS: none
★ BANQUETING ROOMS: 3 (10 to 200)
★ STANDARD BEDROOM SIZE: 24 m²

★ PRIVATE BALCONIES: yes
★ SWIMMING POOL: yes – fresh water,
18 × 30 ft, 4 ft deep
★ RECREATIONAL ACTIVITIES: sauna and
massage department
★ GARDENS: no, but small roof garden
★ ROOM SERVICE: around the clock
★ ORIENTATION: hotel faces south, west
and north with views over Hyde Park
★ CREDIT CARDS: Master Charge, Eurocard,
Access, Visa and American Express
★ OWNING COMPANY: The Berkeley Hotel
Co Ltd
★ GENERAL MANAGER: Mr Stefano
Sebastiani
★ DISTANCE TO SHOPS: walking distance
★ DISTANCE FROM AIRPORT: 30 km

Old Father Time is fast catching up with those, like me, who remember the heyday of the old Berkeley, that gentle bastion of Englishness – Noël Coward, debutantes, country parsons and maiden aunts. Yet when one visits the new Berkeley these days it is strange to see so many characteristics of the progenitor – the almost countryfied decor, the real fireplace, the doorknobs and even the entire Lutyens Room, transported, bit by bit one would imagine, around Hyde Park Corner. Strange too how the present Berkeley, quite apart from being up to date (which the old one certainly was not) has already acquired a face of its own – housing those few people left in Britain one could call gentlemen. I love the mirrors at the Berkeley, each seemingly made for its spot, and the gorgeous carpets and the lightness of the decor. The rooms are very

English – much as a gentleman would wish, yet tremendously practical and comfortable. As for the public rooms, there is a lot of marble and crystal around but in no way are they vulgar – vulgarity being the very antithesis of this kind of hotel. Service is like that too – not at all obsequious, just friendly and competent as in a good English club. The food, in The Buttery which is almost always full, is an indication that the best Berkeley culinary traditions have been passed on. Country parsons can't afford it now and debs are fewer, but somehow one feels Noël Coward would love it.

CLARIDGE'S HOTEL, Brook Street, London, W1A 2JQ

★ TELEPHONE: 01-629 8860
★ CABLES: Claridges London
★ TELEX: 21872
★ IN OPERATION: since 1855
★ RESERVATIONS: The Leading Hotels of the World
★ ROOMS: 205
★ SUITES: 57
★ RESTAURANTS: 2
★ BARS: none – drinks in foyer
★ DISCOTHEQUE: no
★ SHOPS: 4 – theatre agency, travel agency, ladies' and gentlemen's hairdressing and florist shop
★ CONFERENCE ROOMS: none

★ BANQUETING ROOMS: 4 (50 to 250)
★ STANDARD BEDROOM SIZE: 24 m^2
★ PRIVATE BALCONIES: no
★ SWIMMING POOL: no
★ GARDENS: no
★ NO. OF STAFF: 450
★ ROOM SERVICE: around the clock
★ ORIENTATION: north and west
★ CREDIT CARDS: Eurocard, Master Charge, Visa and American Express
★ OWNING COMPANY: Claridge's Hotel Ltd
★ GENERAL MANAGER: B. Lund Hansen
★ DISTANCE TO SHOPS: walking distance
★ DISTANCE FROM AIRPORT: 30 km

As everyone knows, the well-bred Englishman knows instinctively how to deal with social equals and inferiors and since, in his opinion, he has no superiors, that part of it does not bother him. The same can be said of Claridge's. Never was there a hotel that tried less hard to compete and simply did not bother about publicity. I am not even sure there is such a thing as a reservation service here – Claridge's people just know you are coming. There is no bar – that's vulgar. There is no dial on the room telephone. Just lift, speak and unto you shall be given. Waiters aren't waiters here – they are footmen and share the same elegant detachment with their clientele. To be happy at Claridge's, you must *belong*, and if you do, Claridge's is heaven. Even the four-man orchestra will strike up your favourite tune when you walk into the lounge except, of course, that here it is called the sitting-room ('lounge' is non-U). No one ever forgets anything and even if your particular eccentricity is eating fish and chips out of a newspaper (one English marquess I know does it all the time), Claridge's will provide an old copy of the *Daily Mirror*, salt, pepper, and vinegar. A superb hotel, surprisingly modern in its equipment, it is so adept at dealing with any, but any situation, that even the Soviet Prime Minister departed happy in the knowledge that he had seen something of the best of England.

THE CONNAUGHT HOTEL, Carlos Place, Mayfair, London, W1Y 6AL

★ TELEPHONE: 01-499 7070
★ CABLES: Chataigne
★ TELEX: no
★ IN OPERATION: since 1896
★ RESERVATIONS: The Leading Hotels of the World
★ ROOMS: 76
★ SUITES: 24
★ RESTAURANTS: 2

★ BARS: 1
★ DISCOTHEQUE: no
★ SHOPS: none
★ CONFERENCE ROOMS: none
★ PRIVATE DINING ROOMS: 2 (10 and 20)
★ STANDARD BEDROOM SIZE: 25 m^2
★ PRIVATE BALCONIES: no
★ SWIMMING POOL: no
★ GARDENS: no

★ NO. OF STAFF: 300
★ ROOM SERVICE: 07.30–23.30
★ ORIENTATION: all rooms face Mayfair location
★ CREDIT CARDS: Eurocard, Master Charge and Access

★ OWNING COMPANY: Connaught Hotel Ltd
★ MANAGING DIRECTOR & GENERAL MANAGER: Paolo Zago
★ DISTANCE TO SHOPS: walking distance
★ DISTANCE FROM AIRPORT: 30 km

The Connaught is not a hotel. It is home – the kind of house that the management assume you normally live in. It is the most distinctive, the most original, the most select of London's great hotels. Although it does march with the times, it makes quite sure that it is not noticed and just goes serenely on with a kind of half-familiar, half-deferential attitude that is unique. This is its speciality and nobody does it better. It is the kind of hotel where you can be quite sure that if a certain piece of furniture was in this spot last time you came, it will still be there. It shines with refined good living, politeness, old-fashioned charm and quite superb service and management. Some people don't like it. Like the young foreign executive who, at the next table to mine, recently ordered a hamburger. The head waiter looked at him without the slightest hint of patronage and replied: 'I am so very sorry, sir, that is off today.' Rooms are completely dateless and superbly comfortable and the service so highly personalized that once you have been a guest, your tiniest quirk of behaviour or habit is known to all. The Connaught is a club for people who are no longer easily impressed. As for the food (hamburger apart) it is probably the finest hotel food in London.

THE DORCHESTER HOTEL, Park Lane, London, W1A 2HJ

★ TELEPHONE: 01-629 8888
★ CABLES: Dorchotel
★ TELEX: 887704
★ IN OPERATION: since April 1931
★ RESERVATIONS: Regent Hotels International
★ ROOMS: 351
★ SUITES: 66
★ RESTAURANTS: 2
★ BARS: 2 – including lobby/lounge
★ DISCOTHEQUE: Piano Bar
★ SHOPS: none – but hairdressers and barbers, with a bookstall and showcases
★ CONFERENCE ROOMS: 2 (90 to 500)
★ BANQUETING ROOMS: 4 (32 to 500)
★ STANDARD BEDROOM SIZE: 30 m^2

★ PRIVATE BALCONIES: yes
★ SWIMMING POOL: no
★ GARDENS: no
★ NO. OF STAFF: 600
★ ROOM SERVICE: around the clock
★ ORIENTATION: south and west overlooking Hyde Park
★ CREDIT CARDS: American Express, Diners Club, Access, Barclaycard, Eurocard and Master Charge
★ OWNING COMPANY: Regent Hotels International
★ MANAGING DIRECTOR: vacant
★ DISTANCE TO SHOPS: walking distance
★ DISTANCE FROM AIRPORT: 30 km

Judging by the frequent changes of ownership in the past decade, everybody seems to want the Dorchester! Happily, this chequered career does not seem to have changed the management style in the last few years and now that this famous London landmark is in the excellent Regent International stable, it will probably even improve. The change in recent times has been spectacular, but quiet and underplayed. There is less noise, less bustle, less of the in-and-out rush into Park Lane, and a quiet efficiency reigns everywhere. The staff – many changes here – is now excellently trained and most helpful. The quality of the food at the Dorchester under the illustrious chef, Anton Mosimann, is the greatest change of all. Mmm. Rooms are as before but nicely revamped and the hotel has great presence. It is not a place one can ignore.

HYATT CARLTON TOWER, 2 Cadogan Place, London, SW1

★ TELEPHONE:01-235 5411
★ CABLES: no
★ TELEX: 21944 CTOWER G
★ IN OPERATION: 21 years
★ RESERVATIONS: Hyatt Worldwide Reservations
★ ROOMS: 228 (including 17 studies)
★ SUITES: 31
★ RESTAURANTS: 3 – The Chelsea Room, The Rib Room, Chinoiserie
★ BARS: 2 – The Rib Room Bar, The Chelsea Lounge
★ DISCOTHEQUE: no – but piano bar during cocktail hours in both bars
★ SHOPS: 4 – newsagent, jeweller, florist, barber
★ CONFERENCE ROOMS: 3 (352 m² to 3174 m²)

★ BANQUETING ROOMS: 3 (18 to 240)
★ STANDARD BEDROOM SIZE: 17 m²
★ PRIVATE BALCONIES: most rooms
★ SWIMMING POOL: no
★ RECREATIONAL ACTIVITIES: health club (sauna and gym), tennis courts, jogging
★ GARDENS: yes
★ NO. OF STAFF: 390
★ ROOM SERVICE: around the clock
★ ORIENTATION: south, south-west, west
★ CREDIT CARDS: all major credit cards
★ OWNING COMPANY: Proteus Ltd Management: Hyatt International Corporation
★ GENERAL MANAGER: Manfred Toennes
★ DISTANCE TO SHOPS: walking distance
★ DISTANCE FROM AIRPORT: 30 km

Statistics show that more foreign travellers come through London than any other capital city so perhaps I might be forgiven for adding an extra hotel to my listing. In my opinion the Carlton Tower is making it into the big league and now that it has been taken over by a substantial worldwide chain from people who had little interest in the hotel business, I predict a new lease of life.

Its situation, with windows overlooking the green of Cadogan Gardens, could not be better. From here, one can actually walk to Harrods – that Aladdin's Cave of the good life – or to the King's Road – great too but not so good. Carlton Tower rooms are easy on the eye, functional and many have been brought up to date decor-wise. The staff are fine and helpful, the tower suites are highly recommendable. As for the food, don't go near the famed Rib Room unless you want to end up looking like Henry the Eighth! Slimmer, more choosy people should make for the first floor Chelsea Room where the continental menu is fine continental, beautifully balanced and perfect in execution. Welcome to the Carlton Tower.

THE RITZ HOTEL, Piccadilly, London, W1V 9DG

★ TELEPHONE: 01-493 8181
★ CABLES: Ritzel London
★ TELEX: 267200
★ IN OPERATION: since 1906
★ RESERVATIONS: Cunard, New York/Utell Reservations, worldwide/Loews

Representation International, U.S.A./Swire Travel, Hong Kong/H.R.C., Italy
★ ROOMS: 77 doubles 45 singles
★ SUITES: 16

★ RESTAURANTS: 1 – the Ritz Restaurant, Louis XVI style

★ BARS: 2 – the Bar at the Ritz and the Palm Court Lounge

★ DISCOTHEQUE: no – but resident trio in restaurant and dancing on Friday and Saturday nights. Cabaret every Wednesday evening at 11.00 p.m. in the restaurant

★ SHOPS: menswear shop, newsagent, florist, ladies' and gentlemen's hairdressing

★ CONFERENCE ROOMS: 2 (26 to 40)

★ BANQUETING ROOMS: 2 (26 to 40)

★ STANDARD BEDROOM SIZE: 35 m^2

★ PRIVATE BALCONIES: yes – some but small

★ SWIMMING POOL: no

★ GARDENS: yes – the Italian garden, small and private

★ NO. OF STAFF: 280

★ ROOM SERVICE: around the clock

★ ORIENTATION: north facade faces Piccadilly, west facade faces Green Park, south facade faces Westminster Abbey and St Margaret's Church and east facade faces Arlington Street

★ FURTHER DEVELOPMENTS: six new superior suites – all individually designed and air-conditioned, overlooking Green Park

★ CREDIT CARDS: all major credit cards

★ OWNING COMPANY: Trafalgar House Group

★ GENERAL MANAGER: Michael Duffell

★ DISTANCE TO SHOPS: walking distance to Bond Street, Jermyn Street, Regent Street and Knightsbridge

★ DISTANCE FROM AIRPORT: 30 km (Heathrow)

The top hotel in London according to Britain's most hard-to-please guide and who am I to disagree? I have always loved this hotel, Cesar Ritz's last brainchild, though I must admit that at times in the past my affections took a good deal of buffeting. The Ritz had hard times. Not any more. Its *fin de siècle* grandeur, its gilt angels and nymphs climbing up the walls, clusters of chandeliers and vast vistas of palatial lobbies plus that incomparable restaurant overlooking the park – they are all still with us. But now the plumbing works, some of the oldest old pensioners have been nicely retired, the management is new and efficient and those great corridors which had not been repainted since Lily Langtry came around the corner are back in their original splendour. It was really like cleaning up an old painting and it has worked – to the point where the most difficult people appear happy and contented. One thing has not changed: the illustrious Ritz wine list, one of the greatest in the world. At the moment the Ritz is going through a culinary revolution (find out for yourself . . .) and I think it would be invidious to comment on it at this stage.

THE SAVOY HOTEL, P.O. Box 189, London, WC2R 0BP

★ TELEPHONE: 01-836 4343

★ CABLES: Savotel London

★ TELEX: 24234

★ IN OPERATION: since 1889

★ RESERVATIONS: The Leading Hotels of the World

★ ROOMS: 200

★ SUITES: 46

★ RESTAURANTS: 2 – River Restaurant, Savoy Grill

★ BARS: 2 – the famous American Bar, Thames Foyer

★ DISCOTHEQUE: no – but music and dancing nightly from Monday to Saturday in River Restaurant

★ SHOPS: shopping arcade, florist, news kiosk, ladies' and gentlemen's hairdressing

★ CONFERENCE ROOMS: 8 specializing in private parties

★ BANQUETING ROOMS: 4 (up to 500)

★ STANDARD BEDROOM SIZE: 28 m^2

★ PRIVATE BALCONIES: no

★ SWIMMING POOL: no

★ GARDENS: adjacent Embankment Gardens

★ NO. OF STAFF: 550

★ ROOM SERVICE: around the clock

★ ORIENTATION: rooms face the river, street and courtyard

★ CREDIT CARDS: Eurocard, Master Charge, American Express and Visa

★ OWNING COMPANY: The Savoy Hotels PLC

★ MANAGING DIRECTOR & GENERAL MANAGER: Willy B. G. Bauer

★ DISTANCE TO SHOPS: adjacent, Covent Garden nearby

★ DISTANCE FROM AIRPORT: 29 km

With so many rumours flying about, plus a headline-making financial dogfight, the Savoy has had a bad press in recent years and, in such things as decor, it still has some way to go to recover all its former glory. But things are happening and, staying there recently, I had to admit that it is still one of the great hotels of the world – a place of suave urbanity and continuing tradition as the nursery of great hotel folk. Service simply cannot be faulted: hot coffee and sandwiches at two a.m., a man who is quite willing to park your car (in London?) and a front desk staff for whom nothing is too much trouble. The food, slightly 'off' for a while, is back on top and I thought that, especially in the famous Grill, it could hardly be bettered. In the third edition I wrote: 'Unlike so many London hotels the Savoy is not a club – it's a real hotel, working, buzzing with life, intensely practical and very highborn'. I stick to my guns and as long as financial finagling does not interfere with management, the Savoy is still on.

New Milton

CHEWTON GLEN HOTEL, New Milton, Hampshire, BH25 6QS

★ TELEPHONE: Highcliffe (04252) 5341

★ CABLES: no

★ TELEX: 41456

★ IN OPERATION: 18 years

★ RESERVATIONS: The Leading Hotels of the World/Scott Calder/Prestige

★ ROOMS: 33 doubles

★ SUITES: 11

★ RESTAURANTS: 1

★ BARS: 1

★ DISCOTHEQUE: no

★ SHOPS: 1

★ CONFERENCE ROOMS: 1 (8 to 45)

★ BANQUETING ROOMS: 2 (8 to 90)

★ STANDARD BEDROOM SIZE: 23 m^2

★ PRIVATE BALCONIES: 3 on first floor; 6 ground floor rooms with terrace

★ SWIMMING POOL: yes – fresh water, outdoor, heated, 40 × 20 ft

★ RECREATIONAL ACTIVITIES: tennis with golf and horse riding nearby

★ GARDENS: yes – 30 acres of parkland

★ NO. OF STAFF: 90

★ ROOM SERVICE: around the clock

★ ORIENTATION: main facade faces south

★ CREDIT CARDS: Diners Club, American Express, Barclaycard, Access and Eurocard

★ OWNING COMPANY: Skan Developments

★ GENERAL MANAGER: David M. Brockett

★ DISTANCE TO BEACH: 2 km

★ DISTANCE TO SHOPS: 2 km

★ DISTANCE FROM AIRPORT: 12 km (Hurn); 170 km (Heathrow)

The fame of this hotel is now so wide that it is both indecent and obvious to add even the most feeble of endorsements. Chewton Glen remains what it has been for some years – the best or at least one of the two or three best country house hotels in Britain and I have heard people rave about it all over the world. It's a very distinguished country mansion set amidst acres of lovely parkland. Walk inside and you immediately feel that here you are going to live the way you have always wanted to – bedrooms that are palatial and yet not showy, public rooms aglow with fine taste, and service so charming and willing that you hardly ever have to ask for anything. It is a 'lived-in' place, mature, elegant and superbly comfortable and its creation has been a work of art. The food, if anything, is even better – imaginative, fresh and glowing and terribly bad for one's figure. Like one or two other hotels I know, the wine list is marvellous bedside reading. Chewton Glen deserves every bit of praise it gets.

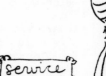

Penrith

SHARROW BAY COUNTRY HOUSE HOTEL, Lake Ullswater, Penrith, Cumbria, CA10 2LZ

★ TELEPHONE: Pooley Bridge (08536) 301
★ CABLES: no
★ TELEX: no
★ IN OPERATION: 36 years
★ RESERVATIONS: Relais et Chateaux/David Mitchell & Co Ltd
★ ROOMS: 25
★ SUITES: 4
★ RESTAURANTS: 2 – one smoking, one non-smoking
★ BARS: none
★ DISCOTHEQUE: no
★ SHOPS: none
★ CONFERENCE ROOMS: 1 (about 12)
★ BANQUETING ROOMS: none
★ STANDARD BEDROOM SIZE: 42 m²
★ PRIVATE BALCONIES: 1 room

★ SWIMMING POOL: no
★ RECREATIONAL ACTIVITIES: activities available around the hotel: fell walking, pony trekking, fishing and lake swimming
★ GARDENS: yes
★ NO. OF STAFF: 41
★ ROOM SERVICE: 07.30–23.00
★ ORIENTATION: most rooms have lake and/or hill views
★ CREDIT CARDS: none
★ OWNING COMPANY: private – Mr Francis Coulson and Mr Brian Sack
★ GENERAL MANAGER: Nigel R. Lawrence
★ DISTANCE TO SHOPS: 12 km
★ DISTANCE FROM AIRPORT: 160 km (Manchester)

'If you know Sharrow Bay, you use it as a yardstick for all English country hotels . . .' So says a friend of ours. Alas, we have only just recently been there and now we know what we have been missing all these years – a simply gorgeous, well-weathered greystone house with its walls literally on Lake Ullswater, and run by people who understand the meaning of personal comfort. Good taste it has aplenty but it is never of the show-off variety – simple, beautiful furniture and porcelain everywhere, well-chosen carpets and curtains and, from your bedroom window, one of the finest and most scenic views in England. Tea is served in the drawing room and is a ritual. After all that the food could come as an anti-climax. Instead, it is the top of the dream – food so beautiful, so finely cooked and so well displayed that it surely deserves all the accolades it has had. In our view, Sharrow Bay has one extra distinction: it has two restaurants, one for smokers and one for non-smokers and since, for our sins, we favour the weed, it is the one time when we don't feel guilty about it. A great idea.

North Stoke

THE SPRINGS HOTEL, North Stoke, Nr Wallingford, Oxfordshire, OX9 6BE

★ TELEPHONE: Wallingford (0491) 36687
★ CABLES: no
★ TELEX: 849794 Spring G
★ IN OPERATION: 10 years
★ RESERVATIONS: direct
★ ROOMS: 23
★ SUITES: 5
★ RESTAURANTS: 1 – Lakeview Restaurant
★ BARS: 1 cocktail bar
★ DISCOTHEQUE: no
★ SHOPS: none
★ CONFERENCE ROOMS: 3 – 40 m² (18); 50 m² (28); 60 m² (32)
★ BANQUETING ROOMS: as conference rooms
★ STANDARD BEDROOM SIZE: 28 m²

★ PRIVATE BALCONIES: 2 rooms have balconies, 3 rooms have shared terrace
★ SWIMMING POOL: yes – fresh water, heated April to October
★ RECREATIONAL ACTIVITIES: croquet, putting green, two touring bicycles, tennis, sauna
★ GARDENS: 5 acres of grounds surround the hotel
★ NO. OF STAFF: 30
★ ROOM SERVICE: around the clock
★ ORIENTATION: most of the rooms overlook the lake or gardens
★ CREDIT CARDS: American Express, Diners Club, Access, Visa, Master Charge

★ OWNING COMPANY: The Springs Hotel
   (Wallingford) Ltd
★ GENERAL MANAGER: Richard Young
★ DISTANCE TO SHOPS: Wallingford 5 km,
   Oxford 24 km

★ DISTANCE FROM AIRPORT: 45 km
   (Heathrow)

Four years ago a German gentleman who is not unknown in the hospitality business passed by this place, liked it and bought it. And that of course was the start of an involvement that is slowly turning a not very impressive country house hotel into a superlative one. We have no doubt that The Springs will make it – it has already received enough 'gongs' to make it certain. The building faces a natural springs lake in the middle of some quite divine countryside and I feel that anyone who knows Oxfordshire will agree with me. Public rooms are charming and welcoming and bedrooms vast and comfortable, with good taste beginning to wind its way up and down the corridors into the furthest corners. What is interesting in many ways is the curious blend of German efficiency and that slightly nonchalant Englishness which visitors like so much. The staff are fine – polite, helpful and extremely well trained and will certainly make you want to stay longer. There is a lived-in atmosphere which is rare and very pleasant – it does not feel like a hotel. The dining room overlooking the lake serves food that goes from the good to the brilliant. Try the smoked salmon – they smoke it themselves.

Taunton

THE CASTLE HOTEL, Castle Green, Taunton, Somerset, TA1 1NF

★ TELEPHONE: Taunton (0823) 72671
★ CABLES: Castle Hotel
★ TELEX: 46488 Castle G
★ IN OPERATION: about 300 years
★ RESERVATIONS: direct or Prestige Hotels
   (Tom Eden Associates)/Scott Calder
   International, U.S.A.
★ ROOMS: 22 doubles 18 singles
★ SUITES: 1 – the Bow Suite
★ RESTAURANTS: 1
★ BARS: 1 – The Rose Room
★ DISCOTHEQUE: no
★ SHOPS: none
★ CONFERENCE ROOMS: 2 (up to 100)
★ BANQUETING ROOMS: 3 (up to 125)
★ STANDARD BEDROOM SIZE: variable
★ PRIVATE BALCONIES: no
★ SWIMMING POOL: no
★ RECREATIONAL ACTIVITIES: no – but
   tennis, golf, horse riding etc, easily
   arranged

★ GARDENS: yes – the Norman Garden –
   featuring remains of ancient Norman
   keep, moat wall and a unique square
   Norman well
★ NO. OF STAFF: 75
★ ROOM SERVICE: around the clock
★ ORIENTATION: west over Castle Green,
   with some rooms overlooking the
   Norman Garden
★ CREDIT CARDS: Diners Club, American
   Express, Access, Barclaycard, Eurocard
   and Master Charge
★ OWNING COMPANY: The Castle Hotel
   (Taunton) Ltd (private)
★ EXECUTIVE MANAGER: the Chapman
   family and Mr David Prior
★ DISTANCE TO SHOPS: 2 minutes' walk
★ DISTANCE FROM AIRPORT: 217 km
   (Heathrow); 64 km (Bristol Lulsgate)

Virtue, hard work and quality rewarded – it is nice to know that this kind of thing still happens. I was delighted some time ago to hear that The Castle had finally been awarded a Michelin star. I never doubted that it would – one day. The star of course is for food and young chef Christopher Oakes fully deserves it for his imaginative cooking. But the hotel deserves an accolade too for being by far the best hotel in this part of England. Everybody knows it and loves it, an historic old place taken over a few years ago by a gifted hotel family who have transformed it into a haven of comfort, good taste and *savoir faire*. The rooms are delightfully comfortable, easy on the eye and very well furnished and the bathrooms are great. The place has an atmosphere of quiet good living which is worth travelling for. People are nice to you, they often anticipate your requirements and are delighted to help and it is a pleasure to be there. Full marks for success.

Thornbury

THORNBURY CASTLE, Thornbury, Avon, BS12 1HH

★ TELEPHONE: (0454) 412647/418511
★ CABLES: no
★ TELEX: 449986 Castle G
★ IN OPERATION: restaurant since 1966; bedrooms since 1982
★ RESERVATIONS: Prestige Hotels, London/Scott Calder International, New York/Martins of Winchester, New South Wales, Australia/Carte Blanche Tours, Johannesburg, South Africa
★ ROOMS: 11
★ SUITES: 1
★ RESTAURANTS: 1
★ BARS: none
★ DISCOTHEQUE: no – piano some evenings
★ SHOPS: none
★ CONFERENCE ROOMS: 1 (25)
★ BANQUETING ROOMS: none
★ STANDARD BEDROOM SIZE: 10–64 m^2

★ PRIVATE BALCONIES: no
★ SWIMMING POOL: no
★ RECREATIONAL ACTIVITIES: croquet; fishing, riding and golf can be arranged nearby
★ GARDENS: yes
★ NO. OF STAFF: 40
★ ROOM SERVICE: 07.00–23.00 for breakfast and drinks
★ ORIENTATION: most rooms face south
★ CREDIT CARDS: American Express, Access, Visa, Diners Club, Carte Blanche
★ OWNING COMPANY: Mr Kenneth Bell
★ GENERAL MANAGER: Fernando Asensio
★ DISTANCE TO SHOPS: Bristol 20 km; Bath 40 km
★ DISTANCE FROM AIRPORT: 160 km (Heathrow)

The gastronomic fame of Thornbury Castle is such that writing about it is rather like knocking on St. Peter's door, Kenneth Bell, its creator, being one of Britain's three or four greatest cooks. We might be forgiven, though, for only listing it now, since Thornbury only became a hotel two years ago – so now you can sleep there and eat there. And what sleep, what food! This vast sixteenth century pile is one of the country's greatest showplaces and, of course, Henry VIII slept here (some say he chopped off Buckingham's head just to lay his hands on Thornbury). Be that as it may, Mr Bell has invested into the hotel part what he always had in the kitchen – superb taste, nothing but the best and a feeling for time and place which is rare. Bedrooms are vast and luxurious, gently countryfied and all look upon the divine gardens. Bathrooms are sumptuous. Kenneth Bell has now abdicated from the kitchen (some of the time) and handed over to the gifted Timothy Cheevers but of course the great tradition remains. Thornbury is not just any hotel, or any castle for that matter – it is an experience that remains with you forever.

Turnberry

TURNBERRY HOTEL, Turnberry, Ayrshire, Scotland, KA26 9LT

★ TELEPHONE: 06553 202
★ CABLES: Turnberry, Scotland
★ TELEX: 777779
★ IN OPERATION: 77 years
★ RESERVATIONS: UK – Orient Express, Sea Containers House, 20 Upper Ground, London; USA – RSI/BTH INC
★ ROOMS: 85 doubles 40 singles

★ SUITES: 6
★ RESTAURANTS: 2
★ BARS: 2
★ DISCOTHEQUE: no – music for dancing 2/3 times per week during season
★ SHOPS: 1 – boutique and 6 showcases
★ CONFERENCE ROOMS: 4 (150, 125, 35 and 20)

★ BANQUETING ROOMS: 4 (300, 150, 30 and 15)
★ STANDARD BEDROOM SIZE: 20—30 m^2
★ PRIVATE BALCONIES: a few
★ SWIMMING POOL: yes – fresh water
★ RECREATIONAL ACTIVITIES: 2 championship 18-hole golf courses, tennis, pitch & putt and putting
★ GARDENS: yes – 500 acres
★ NO. OF STAFF: 200
★ ROOM SERVICE: around the clock
★ ORIENTATION: mainly west, but also south and east facing the sea

★ FURTHER DEVELOPMENTS: an air-conditioned conference suite with simultaneous translation facilities and other modern aids
★ CREDIT CARDS: American Express, Diners Club, Barclaycard/Visa, Access, Master Charge
★ OWNING COMPANY: Seaco Hotels Ltd
★ GENERAL MANAGER: C. J. Rouse
★ DISTANCE TO BEACH: 1/5 km
★ DISTANCE TO SHOPS: 20 km
★ DISTANCE FROM AIRPORT: 70 km

Everything that Orient-Expressed James Sherwood touches turns to gold – that's only right since this intelligent, enterprising American is a multi-millionaire. Not very long ago he took over the venerable Turnberry and I am sure that here too one is going to be surprised at the result. As long as he does not change those two priceless golf courses, 'Ailsa' and 'Arran' he will be forgiven. A vast, airy place of great renown, Turnberry did need a bit of get-up-and-go and it is getting it now. Money is being poured in and although it is only at an intermediate stage of revamping I feel sure the end product will be great – look at Mr Sherwood's Italian pads, Cipriani and the Villa San Michele. . . . He and his people will have a tough job getting rid of Turnberry's institutional feel and an even harder one to make its food really worth writing about. All they need is time.

Worcester

THE ELMS HOTEL, Abberley, Nr Worcester, WR6 6AT

★ TELEPHONE: (029 921) 666
★ CABLES: no
★ TELEX: 337105
★ IN OPERATION: since 1946
★ RESERVATIONS: Prestige Hotels, Great Britain/Wandana Travel, Australia/Carte Blanche Tours Ltd, South Africa/Scott Calder International, U.S.A.
★ ROOMS: 21 doubles 4 singles
★ SUITES: 2
★ RESTAURANTS: 1 – Regency style, seating 80
★ BARS: 1 – the Library Bar
★ DISCOTHEQUE: no
★ SHOPS: none – 3 show cases
★ CONFERENCE ROOMS: 2 (10 and 40)
★ BANQUETING ROOMS: 2 (10 and 40)
★ STANDARD BEDROOM SIZE: 24—30 m^2
★ PRIVATE BALCONIES: 2
★ SWIMMING POOL: no

★ RECREATIONAL ACTIVITIES: tennis, croquet and putting in the grounds; horse riding, golf and fishing nearby
★ GARDENS: 10 acres of parkland and 10 acres of formal gardens
★ NO. OF STAFF: 45
★ ROOM SERVICE: around the clock
★ ORIENTATION: the rear of the hotel and the majority of the gardens face south
★ CREDIT CARDS: Barclaycard/Visa, American Express, Diners, Access, Eurocard, Master Charge and Carte Blanche
★ OWNING COMPANY: Celebrated Country Hotels
★ GENERAL MANAGER: Rita Mooney
★ DISTANCE TO SHOPS: 10 miles (Worcester)
★ DISTANCE FROM AIRPORT: 45 km Birmingham (Elmdon)

Beset as they are by urbanization, instant food and service problems, inhabitants of this sceptred isle often wonder why so many foreign visitors keep coming back. One of the reasons could be our rich heritage of gorgeous country house hotels. The Elms is one of them, gracious, serene, well brought up and with an air of timelessness. It is near enough to the Cotswolds, the Shakespeare country, Worcester Cathedral and, if you like that sort of thing, the tomb of King John, to offer plenty to see.
Queen Anne did not build the place but the stamp of her times is upon it – handsome

facades and noble proportions looking over manicured English lawns. Bedrooms are country house size, lovingly furnished with period pieces. Public rooms are both stately and comfortable. Above all, this is a hotel with personality – that of the owner who manages it – and the staff really make you welcome. The food is English and very good – there are new dishes every day. The wine selection is better than most.

GREECE
Athens

ASTIR PALACE ATHENS, Corner of Panepistimiou and Vas. Sofias Avenues, Athens Centre

* ★ TELEPHONE: 01 364 3112-8
* ★ CABLES: Astirathen
* ★ TELEX: 222380 APAT GR
* ★ IN OPERATION: since August 1983
* ★ RESERVATIONS: any Astir office/Robert Warner Inc, New York/Traveline Inc, Toronto/Cruise & Coach Corp, Sydney
* ★ ROOMS: 75
* ★ SUITES: 28 plus 2 VIP suites
* ★ RESTAURANTS: 2 – Asteria Coffee Shop, Apokalypsis Restaurant
* ★ BARS: 1
* ★ DISCOTHEQUE: no
* ★ SHOPS: none
* ★ CONFERENCE ROOMS: symposium room – 130 m² (50 to 150)
* ★ BANQUETING ROOMS: 2 – 200 m² (160 to 250)

* ★ STANDARD BEDROOM SIZE: 27 m²
* ★ PRIVATE BALCONIES: no
* ★ SWIMMING POOL: no
* ★ RECREATIONAL ACTIVITIES: none
* ★ GARDENS: no
* ★ NO. OF STAFF: 144
* ★ ROOM SERVICE: around the clock
* ★ ORIENTATION: facing main avenues and overlooking city
* ★ CREDIT CARDS: Diners Club, Eurocard, Access, Master Card, JCB, Visa and American Express
* ★ OWNING COMPANY: Astir Hotel Co Inc
* ★ GENERAL MANAGER: Mr Christos Capsis
* ★ DISTANCE TO BEACH: 15 km
* ★ DISTANCE TO SHOPS: walking distance to city centre
* ★ DISTANCE FROM AIRPORT: 12 km

In the hotel business if your name is Astir you have to be careful – reputation and prestige as well as quality are the highlights of the game for this, the best hotel company in Greece. What to do with a fairly small site right on the corner of Constitution Square was a problem but they have solved it by building what is, in my view, one of the best small city-centre hotels in Europe. It is cool, elegant, beautifully soundproofed on this particularly noisy bit of Athens and above all, it does not shock with its modernity – although speaking for myself, I would change the chandeliers in the restaurant. Just one of those things. But then, close to one's table, is part of the ancient walls of Athens so that makes up for everything. Bedrooms are very spacious, well designed and with plenty of space to put bits and pieces on – not always the case in new hotels. Bathrooms are splendid and service is instant. Refined city luxury might be the best description for this new Astir flagship.

THE ATHENS HILTON, 46 Vassilissis Sofias Avenue, Athens

* ★ TELEPHONE: 722-0201 or 722-0301
* ★ CABLES: Hiltels-Athens
* ★ TELEX: 21-5808
* ★ IN OPERATION: since April 1963
* ★ RESERVATIONS: Hilton International
* ★ ROOMS: 250 doubles 181 twins 21 studios
* ★ SUITES: 23

* ★ RESTAURANTS: 5 – Byzantine Cafe, Trattoria, Taverna Ta Nissia, Supper Club and Pool Snack Bar
* ★ BARS: 2
* ★ DISCOTHEQUE: no – but live music
* ★ SHOPS: 14
* ★ CONFERENCE ROOMS: 5 (5 to 2000)
* ★ BANQUETING ROOMS: 5 (5 to 2000)

★ STANDARD BEDROOM SIZE: 32–35 m²
★ PRIVATE BALCONIES: yes – all rooms with seating facilities
★ SWIMMING POOL: yes – fresh water, 1 for adults, 12 × 25 m, and 1 for children
★ RECREATIONAL ACTIVITIES: sauna and golf, tennis and other activities by arrangement nearby
★ GARDENS: no
★ NO. OF STAFF: 680
★ ROOM SERVICE: around the clock

★ ORIENTATION: rooms overlook the Acropolis to the west and Mounts Hymettus and Pentelicon to the east
★ CREDIT CARDS: American Express, Carte Blanche and Master Charge
★ OWNING COMPANY: Ioniki Hotel Enterprises Ltd
★ GENERAL MANAGER: Hugo Langer
★ DISTANCE TO BEACH: 12 km
★ DISTANCE TO SHOPS: walking distance
★ DISTANCE FROM AIRPORT: 13 km

If only all Hiltons were like this one! At least it shows they can do it when they try and here they have succeeded beyond one's wildest expectation. This is, for the moment, the finest city hotel in Greece – extremely well designed on an original plan, imposing without knocking your eye out, with a decor that leaves all other Hiltons in the shade. Everything goes apace. One of my first calls in the Greek capital is always dinner at the Hilton's Taverna Ta Nissia which I think is one of the two or three best hotel restaurants in the Mediterranean. What's more, it is strongly Greek as well as American. Views from the rooms are sensational – Hymettus on one side and the Acropolis on the other. The hotel has a range of extremely good shops, the staff are friendly and not at all blasé with so many visitors and the service is very well organized. I find the rooms exceptionally pleasing – large, nicely air-conditioned, furnished with easy-going taste. I have never found fault with this very remarkable hotel.

Corfu

ASTIR PALACE CORFU, Kommeno Bay, Corfu

★ TELEPHONE: 91481-490/340
★ CABLES: Koxu GR
★ TELEX: 332169 Koxu GR
★ IN OPERATION: since 1977
★ RESERVATIONS: Astir Hotel Co Inc,
Athens, London, Brussels, Rome/Robert
F. Warner Inc, New York/Traveline Inc,
Toronto/Cruise and Coach Corp Pty,
Sydney
★ ROOMS: 274 doubles 26 singles
★ SUITES: 8
★ BUNGALOWS: 124
★ RESTAURANTS: 3
★ BARS: 3
★ DISCOTHEQUE: yes
★ SHOPS: news stand, beauty parlour
★ CONFERENCE ROOMS: 2 (80 to 350)
★ BANQUETING ROOMS: 2 (60 to 600)

★ STANDARD BEDROOM SIZE: 25 m^2
★ PRIVATE BALCONIES: yes
★ SWIMMING POOL: yes – sea water
★ RECREATIONAL ACTIVITIES: water skiing,
surfing, sailing, tennis, golf course
16 km from hotel
★ GARDENS: yes
★ NO. OF STAFF: 320
★ ROOM SERVICE: 07.00–23.00
★ ORIENTATION: all rooms and bungalows
with sea view
★ CREDIT CARDS: all major credit cards
★ OWNING COMPANY: Astir Hotel Co Inc
★ GENERAL MANAGER: George Louisidis
★ DISTANCE TO BEACH: walking distance to
three sandy beaches
★ DISTANCE TO SHOPS: 10 km Corfu town
★ DISTANCE FROM AIRPORT: 12 km

In an island already over-populated with hotels of all kinds but mostly indifferent, any newcomer had to be special – and the Astir Palace, with its illustrious parentage, is that. The lobby is large enough to hold a presidential convention which is a waste of space on a small island. But Greek niceness overtakes all and I never complained at what I saw. Many of the rooms are in individual cottages with private verandahs decorated in the efficient space style so necessary in a resort. In the main building the rooms are more sober but cool and very pleasant. The hotel stands on a lovely olive-clad hillside, has gardens and a very handsome swimming pool. Over and above this, the genuine Greek charm and hospitality take over – people smile, joke and manage to combine decorum with friendly informality. This would be my choice in Corfu.

Crete

ASTIR PALACE ELOUNDA, Elounda, Crete

★ TELEPHONE: 41580-5
★ CABLES: Starhotel GR
★ TELEX: 262215 Asco GR
★ RESERVATIONS: Astir Hotel Co Inc,
Athens, London, Brussels, Rome/Robert
F. Warner Inc, New York/Traveline Inc,
Toronto/Cruise and Coach Corp Pty,
Sydney
★ ROOMS: 210 doubles 10 singles
★ BUNGALOWS: 80 doubles
★ RESTAURANTS: 2
★ BARS: 3
★ DISCOTHEQUE: yes
★ SHOPS: boutique and newsagents
★ CONFERENCE ROOMS: 1 (274 to 450)
★ BANQUETING ROOMS: 2 (400 to 600)
★ STANDARD BEDROOM SIZE: 20 m^2
★ PRIVATE BALCONIES: majority of sea view
rooms

★ SWIMMING POOLS: 2 sea water, one
indoors
★ RECREATIONAL ACTIVITIES: water skiing,
surfing, 2 floodlit tennis courts, table
tennis, pedaloes, sailing, cinema
★ GARDENS: yes
★ NO. OF STAFF: 250
★ ROOM SERVICE: 07.00–23.00
★ ORIENTATION: most rooms face the sea
★ CREDIT CARDS: all major credit cards
★ OWNING COMPANY: Astir Hotel Co Inc
★ GENERAL MANAGER: Alex Kimissis
★ DISTANCE TO BEACH: walking distance to
2 small private sandy beaches
★ DISTANCE TO SHOPS: 15 minutes' walk to
Elounda and 8 km to Aghios Nicolaos
★ DISTANCE FROM AIRPORT: 64 km

Crete has long been famous as an ante-room to heaven. How it was regarded in antiquity – the centre of the known world – reaffirms one's conviction that all change is bad and that the good old days were best.

There are two beaches at Elounda and innumerable little coves spread over about twenty acres. It is modern without being in the least offensive, good-looking, convenient and above all fresh and clean.

The rooms, happily, are cool in hot summers, well designed, with nice, practical Greek furniture and hangings. There is a good-sized balcony which is ideal for breakfast à deux and service is fast and reliable. Public rooms are impressive and to have dinner in the arched, al fresco restaurant is to really live a little. Highly recommended by many readers of this guide, this hotel is one of the best of the resort category among the Greek islands.

ELOUNDA BEACH HOTEL, Elounda, Aghios Nikolaos, Crete

★ TELEPHONE: 0841-41412/3
★ CABLES: Elotel
★ TELEX: 0262192 EL GR
★ IN OPERATION: 11 years
★ RESERVATIONS: direct
★ ROOMS: 226 doubles 30 singles
★ SUITES: 45
★ RESTAURANTS: 4
★ BARS: 3
★ DISCOTHEQUE: nightclub
★ SHOPS: 5
★ CONFERENCE ROOMS: 5 (40 to 250)
★ BANQUETING ROOMS: 5 (30 to 250)
★ STANDARD BEDROOM SIZE: 15–18 m^2
★ PRIVATE BALCONIES: yes
★ SWIMMING POOL: yes – salt water, 36 × 12 m

★ RECREATIONAL ACTIVITIES: 2 floodlit tennis courts, water skiing, sailing, pedaloes, canoes, day trips and fishing trips in the hotel kaiki, ping-pong, billiards, TV lounge, card room and sauna
★ GARDENS: yes
★ NO. OF STAFF: 300
★ ROOM SERVICE: 07.00–23.00
★ ORIENTATION: most rooms face the sea
★ CREDIT CARDS: American Express and Diners Club
★ OWNING COMPANY: Ilios S.A.
★ GENERAL MANAGER: Peter T. Palashis
★ DISTANCE TO BEACH: walking distance
★ DISTANCE TO SHOPS: 3 km
★ DISTANCE FROM AIRPORT: 60 km

In a most scenic island – Crete – the Gulf of Mirabello is the most scenic spot, great craggy mountains going down to a sea so blue you cannot credit it. And there, not far from Aghios Nikolaos is the Elounda Beach, a very modern hotel which not long ago won the first prize as Greece's most beautiful new hotel. It is certainly handsome and very well thought out. What I like most are the charming, Cretan-style bungalows spread along the shore – each one very private, very rustic in a charming way and extremely comfortable. There is a good, if rather small, beach, a splendid poolside restaurant and a very amusing open-air Greek nightclub. For a holiday hotel, service is above the average and so is the food.

Lemnos

AKTI MYRINA HOTEL, Island of Lemnos

★ TELEPHONE: (0276) 22681/2/3/4
★ CABLES: Aktimyr Lemnos
★ TELEX: 0297173 Myri GR
★ IN OPERATION: since 1964; renovated 1970
★ RESERVATIONS: Robert F. Warner, New York/The Best of Greece, Great Britain
★ BUNGALOWS: 125
★ SUITES: 15

★ RESTAURANTS: 4
★ BARS: 3
★ DISCO CLUB: yes
★ SHOPS: 1 – boutique
★ CONFERENCE ROOMS: 1 (up to 80)
★ BANQUETING ROOMS: 1 (up to 80)
★ STANDARD BEDROOM SIZE: 20 m^2
★ PRIVATE BALCONIES: yes – terraces with small gardens

★ SWIMMING POOL: yes – open air, heated, sea water
★ RECREATIONAL ACTIVITIES: 3 championship Supertan tennis courts, volleyball, table tennis, mini-golf, water skiing, sailing, windsurfing, pedaloes, canoes, fishing boats and excursions to other islands by hotel-owned caique
★ GARDENS: yes
★ NO. OF STAFF: 130

★ ROOM SERVICE: 07.00–23.00
★ ORIENTATION: south-west, facing the sea
★ CREDIT CARDS: American Express, Diners Club and Visa
★ OWNING COMPANY: Akti Myrina S.A.
★ GENERAL MANAGER: George Papadam
★ DISTANCE TO BEACH: on the beach
★ DISTANCE TO SHOPS: 2 km
★ DISTANCE FROM AIRPORT: 23 km

Having recently had the pleasure of re-visiting this holiday hotel, I would not hesitate to name it as the best in the Greek islands and one of the six or seven finest resort hotels in the Mediterranean. If only people would take lessons from Akti Myrina. . . . It is sophisticated and yet totally unstuffy; superbly serviced but without ostentation and as for the food, it has to be seen, and tasted, to be believed – varied, interesting and extremely well presented. At noon, one lunches at a beachside buffet and at night people gather in a little square for drinks while deciding which of the three restaurants to patronize. Riches indeed. Akti Myrina is a gaggle of stone cottages leading to a very pretty sandy beach and each one has its own little private terrace where one can sit facing the sun. Rooms are big – to – biggish, simply but intelligently furnished and easy on the eye. Above all, there is an atmosphere of wellbeing and of happy relaxation which, these days, are worth their weight in gold. Altogether a very beautiful holiday place. Full marks.

Nauplion

HOTEL XENIA COMPLEX, Nauplion

★ TELEPHONE: 0752/28981-2-3
★ CABLES: Hotel Xenia, Nauplion
★ TELEX: no
★ IN OPERATION: since 1962
★ RESERVATIONS: Greek Tourist Offices
★ ROOMS: 88 doubles 18 singles
★ SUITES: 3 and 54 bungalows
★ RESTAURANTS: 2
★ BARS: 3
★ DISCOTHEQUE: yes
★ SHOPS: 5
★ CONFERENCE ROOMS: 1 (150)
★ BANQUETING ROOMS: 2 (200 and 250)
★ STANDARD BEDROOM SIZE: 20 m^2
★ PRIVATE BALCONIES: yes

★ SWIMMING POOL: yes – fresh water, 180 m^2
★ GARDENS: yes
★ NO. OF STAFF: 150
★ ROOM SERVICE: 07.00–23.00
★ ORIENTATION: facing the sea
★ CREDIT CARDS: Diners Club
★ OWNING COMPANY: National Tourist Organization of Greece
★ GENERAL MANAGER: Nikolaos Smyrniotakis
★ DISTANCE TO BEACH: 300 m
★ DISTANCE TO SHOPS: 200 m
★ DISTANCE FROM AIRPORT: 150 km (Athens)

The Government-run Xenia chain in Greece went into business to provide good, clean, utilitarian hotels where commercial operators feared to tread but I have a feeling that in the new, hilltop part of the Nauplion Xenia, it has also been trying to show off what it could achieve. The result is extremely impressive. Up the road from the old Xenia is this luxury cottages-and-suites complex, right by the ancient fortress and the care taken with the planning on this august site is remarkable. Rooms are modern – in fact the last word – and done up with a very high sense of quality – good timber, fine textiles, functional furniture that is a pleasure to see. Very good design everywhere and a good deal of privacy, with superb terraces overlooking this gorgeous little city, once the first capital of independent Greece. Everything is cool, gently understated and yet very carefully organized. The staff as usual in Greece are friendliness personified and the food, if not great, is very acceptable. The above of course applies only to the Xenia Palace part of the complex.

Rhodes

GRAND HOTEL ASTIR PALACE, Akti Miaouli, Rhodes

- ★ TELEPHONE: 26284 (20 lines)
- ★ CABLES: Grandrhodes
- ★ TELEX: 292121 GHSP GR
- ★ IN OPERATION: since 1962
- ★ RESERVATIONS: Astir Hotel Co Inc, Athens, London, Brussels, Rome/Robert F. Warner Inc, New York/Traveline Inc, Toronto/Cruise and Coach Corp Pty, Sydney
- ★ ROOMS: 320 doubles 56 singles
- ★ SUITES: 12
- ★ RESTAURANTS: 4
- ★ BARS: 3
- ★ DISCOTHEQUE: Night Club Isabella
- ★ SHOPS: shopping arcade, news stand, tailors, gifts and beauty parlour
- ★ CONFERENCE ROOMS: 3 (75 to 450)
- ★ BANQUETING ROOMS: 3 (100 to 500)
- ★ STANDARD BEDROOM SIZE: 20 m^2
- ★ PRIVATE BALCONIES: yes
- ★ GARDENS: yes
- ★ SWIMMING POOLS: 2 – outdoor sea water, indoor fresh water
- ★ RECREATIONAL ACTIVITIES: floodlit tennis court, sauna, gym, table tennis, casino
- ★ NO. OF STAFF: 300
- ★ ROOM SERVICE: 07.00–23.00
- ★ ORIENTATION: majority of rooms face the sea
- ★ CREDIT CARDS: all major credit cards
- ★ OWNING COMPANY: Astir Hotel Co Inc
- ★ GENERAL MANAGER: Panos Skendros
- ★ DISTANCE TO BEACH: across the road
- ★ DISTANCE TO SHOPS: 1 km
- ★ DISTANCE FROM AIRPORT: 15 km

Like starlings, tourists only spoil their own perch and its vicinity and the splendidly beautiful island of Rhodes still has much to offer to those who are willing to go off the track. Yet, after trying the obvious holiday haunts it is always a great pleasure to return to the Astir Palace which, in my view, is the most civilized hotel in Rhodes. In the Greek Islands the best hotels are usually close to the water. Here is a hotel that maintains a grand hotel style translated into an unlikely location. Rooms are good, fairly simple but perfectly comfortable and kept beautifully clean. There is a nightclub and a casino and two swimming pools, one in and one out, both of which are unusually well looked after. What is more, the food here is well above the average standard for hotels in Greece.

Vouliagmeni

ASTIR PALACE HOTEL AND BUNGALOWS, Vouliagmeni Beach

- ★ TELEPHONE: 896 0211 (20 lines)
- ★ CABLES: Bungotel Vouliagmeni
- ★ TELEX: 215013 ASPA GR
- ★ IN OPERATION: since 1967
- ★ RESERVATIONS: any Astir office/Robert Warner Inc, New York/Traveline Inc, Toronto/Cruise & C. ach Corp, Sydney
- ★ ROOMS: 123 doubles 12 singles
- ★ SUITES: 20
- ★ APARTMENTS: 8
- ★ BUNGALOWS: 77
- ★ RESTAURANTS: 3
- ★ BARS: 2
- ★ DISCOTHEQUE: yes – The Nine Muses
- ★ SHOPS: 10
- ★ CONFERENCE ROOMS: 4 (33 to 500)
- ★ BANQUETING ROOMS: 6 (60 to 450)
- ★ STANDARD BEDROOM SIZE: 20 m^2
- ★ PRIVATE BALCONIES: all rooms
- ★ SWIMMING POOL: 3 outdoor sea water/1 indoor fresh water
- ★ RECREATIONAL ACTIVITIES: tennis, mini golf, water skiing, surfing, sauna, health care, yachting harbour, golf course (5 km away)
- ★ GARDENS: yes
- ★ NO. OF STAFF: 60
- ★ ROOM SERVICE: around the clock
- ★ ORIENTATION: majority of rooms face the sea
- ★ CREDIT CARDS: all major cards
- ★ OWNING COMPANY: Astir Hotel Company Inc
- ★ GENERAL MANAGER: Mr C. Stergiopoulos
- ★ DISTANCE TO BEACH: walking distance
- ★ DISTANCE TO SHOPS: 3 km
- ★ DISTANCE FROM AIRPORT: 15 km

This is now part of a new and shining hotel complex (there are two other super luxury hotels) and together they are the best address in the vicinity of the Greek capital. This one, the older sister, is extremely well run and very sophisticated. It is large and busy and one is never bored here because there is so much to do, but it is also a cool, elegant, dignified place where one is treated as a guest and not as a day-tripper and the staff are quite charming and very experienced and obliging. If you can obtain one of the top floor suites, do, because there is nothing to touch them in Greece – superb space and furnishings, great views and complete privacy. The food is Greek and international and you also have a choice of eating places, especially if you take in the two neighbouring hotels as well. Weekends of course see a rather noisy lot of Athenians to whom this is almost a second home but, being Greeks, the personality element is not lacking.

HONG KONG

THE HONG KONG MANDARIN, 5 Connaught Road, Central, G.P.O. Box 2623

- ★ TELEPHONE: 5-220111
- ★ CABLES: Mandarin Hongkong
- ★ TELEX: HX 73653
- ★ IN OPERATION: since 1963
- ★ RESERVATIONS: The Leading Hotels of the World, worldwide
- ★ ROOMS: 437 doubles 49 singles
- ★ SUITES: 58
- ★ RESTAURANTS: 5 – Mandarin Grill, Man Wah Chinese Restaurant, Pierrot, Clipper Lounge and The Mandarin Coffee Shop
- ★ BARS: 3 – Captains, Chinnery and Harlequin Bar
- ★ DISCOTHEQUE: no – but dancing to a live band in the Captains Bar
- ★ SHOPS: 28
- ★ CONFERENCE ROOMS: 4 (60 to 400)
- ★ BANQUETING ROOMS: 4 (30 to 300)
- ★ STANDARD BEDROOM SIZE: 26.4 m^2
- ★ PRIVATE BALCONIES: yes – most rooms

- ★ SWIMMING POOL: yes – fresh water, $10 \times 5 \times 2.5$ m
- ★ RECREATIONAL ACTIVITIES: sauna, solarium, massage and whirlpools at the Mandarin Health Centre; arrangements can be made for golf, tennis and water skiing
- ★ GARDENS: no
- ★ NO. OF STAFF: 1200
- ★ ROOM SERVICE: around the clock
- ★ ORIENTATION: best rooms face north and east harbour, others south and west
- ★ CREDIT CARDS: Amexco, Visa, Diners Club, Carte Blanche and Master Charge
- ★ OWNING COMPANY: Mandarin International Hotels Ltd
- ★ GENERAL MANAGER: Peter French
- ★ DISTANCE TO BEACH: 10 km
- ★ DISTANCE TO SHOPS: walking distance
- ★ DISTANCE FROM AIRPORT: 9 km

'One of the six best hotels in the world.' That is what I wrote about the Mandarin in the last edition and I have a feeling that if I pass any more flowery compliments readers will become suspicious – and yet I must because the Mandarin always manages to surprise me by getting even better. In big things and little things. Take ashtrays for instance. On my last visit, I suddenly noticed that here, any ashtray resting on a glass or marble table holds little rubber pads underneath to avoid noise and scratching. Somebody had to think of that one and this is the Mandarin all over – here hotelkeeping becomes an art form and the interested guest is always a student. In this miraculous city where fortunes are made overnight, this hotel remains utterly civilized, totally unperturbed by the noise and bustle and becomes in a way the very image of Hong Kong as it should be – the place where the finest in the West meets the best in the East.

Rooms and suites are truly magnificent and even if you are only a modest VIP you reach them from Kaitak in the hotel's Rolls. The famous Grill is the most polished international restaurant in the East and as for the Chinese Man Wah Room, with its superb decor, you simply cannot know what Chinese food is like until you have tried it. Now, the Pierrot Restaurant brings a delicate French touch to the gastronomic round. Yet, in the end, it is the service that counts: at the Mandarin you never see a dirty ashtray, never carry a parcel, never wait for a lift – it's that kind of a place. In the last edition, I wrote that when a Mandarin general manager leaves, there is only one place for him to go: heaven. I was wrong. The dear man has only been promoted. May all his future Mandarins be of such celestial excellence.

THE PENINSULA HOTEL, Salisbury Road, Kowloon

★ TELEPHONE: 3-666251
★ CABLES: Penhote Hong Kong
★ TELEX: 43821 PEN HX
★ IN OPERATION: since 1928
★ RESERVATIONS: Cathay Pacific Airways, worldwide/Steigenberger Reservation Service/Preferred Hotels Association, worldwide/HORIS Hotel Reservation and Information System (Swissair)
★ ROOMS: 190
★ SUITES: 20
★ RESTAURANTS: 4
★ BARS: 1
★ DISCOTHEQUE: yes and live music in Gaddi's, The Verandah and The Lobby
★ SHOPS: 80 – a variety of exclusive European designers boutiques, offering leatherware, jewellery, antiques, airline and travel agent counters, book shop etc
★ STANDARD BEDROOM SIZE: 43 m^2

★ PRIVATE BALCONIES: no
★ SWIMMING POOL: no
★ GARDENS: no
★ NO. OF STAFF: 600
★ ROOM SERVICE: around the clock
★ ORIENTATION: main facade faces harbour
★ CREDIT CARDS: American Express, Bankamericard, Diners Club, Master Charge, Carte Blanche and OTB
★ OWNING COMPANY: The Hongkong & Shanghai Hotels Ltd
★ GENERAL MANAGER: Urs Aeby
★ DISTANCE TO BEACH: 10 km
★ DISTANCE TO SHOPS: walking distance
★ DISTANCE FROM AIRPORT: 6.5 km
★ TRANSPORTATION: by reservation. The hotel maintains a fleet of nine Rolls Royce Silver Shadow II saloons

Before it vanished into the history books, the British Empire invented the Pen which remains one of the great landmarks of the hotel world, standing with dignified hauteur on the edge of Kowloon with glimpses of that fantastic Hong Kong Island skyline. People often ask me how it is that I can have such affection and admiration for two hotels in the same city. The answer is simple – I like Asprey's and Tiffany's too. The Peninsula is a special place and my heart warms to it when one of those tiny bellboys in a white uniform ushers me into that holy of holies, the Pen's world famous lobby. It takes your breath away – latterday Victoriana with frills – and the place where 'taipans', Swiss bankers and Hollywood stars rub shoulders.

Rooms at the Pen are enormous and stately and when one thinks of what they used to be like, they are surely one of the most successful hotel rebirths in the world. Service is matchless – carried out by people and not computers – and even the return of your laundry is a ceremony. Another ceremony of course is Gaddi's which many believe is the finest continental restaurant East of Suez, with traditional cuisine in the grand manner.

The Peninsula has enormous style and great personality. Of course I know people who, in Hong Kong, would never even think of staying anywhere else while some Mandarins would never move from the other shore. That's human nature. For myself as a perennial traveller, the fact that these two great hotels face each other across the water and speak a different language is one of the miracles of Hong Kong.

THE REGENT, Salisbury Road, Kowloon

★ TELEPHONE: 3-7211211
★ CABLES: Regentel
★ TELEX: HX 37134
★ IN OPERATION: since 1980

★ RESERVATIONS: any Regent International Hotel or sales office, worldwide
★ ROOMS: 542
★ SUITES: 60

★ RESTAURANTS: 4

★ BARS: 3

★ DISCOTHEQUE: live music and dancing nightly in the Mezzanine Lounge

★ SHOPS: 15

★ CONFERENCE ROOMS: 7 (5 to 1000)

★ BANQUETING ROOMS: 7 (5 to 800)

★ STANDARD BEDROOM SIZE: 30 m²

★ PRIVATE BALCONIES: some rooms and suites have private balconies overlooking the harbour

★ SWIMMING POOL: yes

★ RECREATIONAL ACTIVITIES: health centre for men and women

★ GARDENS: yes

★ NO. OF STAFF: 1300

★ ROOM SERVICE: around the clock

★ ORIENTATION: 70% of rooms overlook Hong Kong harbour and 30% overlook the pool terrace and garden

★ CREDIT CARDS: all major credit cards

★ OWNING COMPANY: Regent International Hotels

★ GENERAL MANAGER: Rudolf Greiner

★ DISTANCE TO BEACH: hotel built on harbour front

★ DISTANCE TO SHOPS: hotel located in the centre of Kowloon

★ DISTANCE FROM AIRPORT: 4 km (Kai Tak)

All the time this hotel was rising on the Kowloon skyline, old Hong Kong hands could be heard tut-tutting. In a city with two of the most famous hotels in the world, what could a third one do? First appearances were deceptive – rather monolithic and all that. Now, the Hong Kong Regent is passing its fourth birthday and there is no longer any doubt, in my mind, at any rate – this hotel has to be seen and sampled to be believed. One glides into a sea of reddish-brown granite to face the vastest windows I have personally ever seen – looking across that fantastic harbour to the Hong Kong island profile (money piled upon money). Rooms are vast, cool, elegant and regally furnished and here, too, you have that view: the greatest Cinerama reel in the world. In the bathroom you don't need it – the bathtub is enough: triangular, pink too, sunken and big enough for a conversation piece for two. Everything gleams and glitters, not with false fronts but with real, solid luxury. It's the same with service: press the bell and an immaculately dressed room boy is at your service. Food is technicolour and immensely varied and as for that fresh look, the hotel spends 160 dollars a day on flowers. No, it's not a bad third cousin.

HUNGARY

Budapest

BUDAPEST HILTON, 1014 Budapest, Hess Andras Ter 1-3

★ TELEPHONE: 853-500

★ CABLES: Hiltels – Budapest

★ TELEX: 225984/BPHI H

★ IN OPERATION: since January 1977

★ RESERVATIONS: Hilton International

★ ROOMS: 295

★ SUITES: 28

★ RESTAURANTS: 4 – Kalocsa Dining Room, Coffee Shop, Margareta Espresso, Fishermen's Bastion wine cellar and restaurant

★ BARS: 2

★ DISCOTHEQUE: no

★ SHOPS: 10 – boutique, beauty parlour, barber, florist, gift shop, news stand, optical shop, tourist offices, photo shop and airline office

★ CONFERENCE ROOMS: 8 (12 to 700)

★ BANQUETING ROOMS: 8 (12 to 400)

★ STANDARD BEDROOM SIZE: 27.6 m²

★ PRIVATE BALCONIES: no

★ SWIMMING POOL: no

★ RECREATIONAL ACTIVITIES: casino, tennis and swimming nearby

★ GARDENS: yes

★ NO. OF STAFF: 600

★ ROOM SERVICE: around the clock

★ ORIENTATION: all directions

★ CREDIT CARDS: Carte Blanche, American Express, Master Charge, Eurocard, Diners Club, Hilton Hotels, Bankamericard

★ OWNING COMPANY: Danubius Hotel & Spa Co

★ GENERAL MANAGER: Dr Karoly Biro

★ DISTANCE TO SHOPS: walking distance

★ DISTANCE FROM AIRPORT: 21 km

If I had not seen it with my own eyes I would not have believed it – the Hilton Corporation have taken over a few old walls and a baroque facade in the heart of old Buda, digging it out, building with great discretion and coming up with a magnificent hotel. I doff my deerstalker in salute. This is about the only hotel I like on the dark side of Europe. It shines with good taste, intelligent planning, respect for the past and, so rare in chain hotels, an eye for real beauty. Sit in the elegant lobby and through the glass wall you can see a 700-year-old Dominican church with a marvellous, partly reconstructed cloister. The Codex Bar has been dug out of a fifteenth-century printing shop. Then, miracle of miracles, the rooms are Hilton-sized, fresh and clean and done up in a way that makes you admire ingenuity. There is surely nothing old fashioned about the Budapest Hilton and yet its architectural roots are so deep in the past that there is not a single jarring note. This hotel is enough to make the government of Hungary rejoin the Austro-Hungarian Empire.

INDIA

Agra

HOTEL MUGHAL SHERATON, Taj Ganj, Agra 282 001

- ★ TELEPHONE: 64701
- ★ CABLES: WELCOTEL AGRA
- ★ TELEX: 0565 – 210
- ★ IN OPERATION: since November 1976
- ★ RESERVATIONS: direct or Sheraton Corporation
- ★ ROOMS: 200
- ★ SUITES: 2
- ★ RESTAURANTS: Nauratna, Tajbano, Bagh-e-Bahar (night club) and Samovar
- ★ BARS: 1
- ★ DISCOTHEQUE: no
- ★ SHOPS: 7
- ★ CONFERENCE ROOMS: 3 (20 to 200)
- ★ BANQUETING ROOMS: 3 (25 to 175)
- ★ STANDARD BEDROOM SIZE: 29 m^2
- ★ PRIVATE BALCONIES: no
- ★ SWIMMING POOL: yes – fresh water, 218 m^2

- ★ RECREATIONAL ACTIVITIES: croquet, mini-golf, tennis, archery, horse carriage, camel and elephant rides, health club and beauty parlour; sightseeing tours to sites of historical interest can be arranged
- ★ GARDENS: yes
- ★ NO. OF STAFF: 400
- ★ ROOM SERVICE: around the clock
- ★ ORIENTATION: all rooms have a view either of the gardens, swimming pool or the Taj Mahal
- ★ CREDIT CARDS: Diners Club, Bank of America and American Express
- ★ OWNING COMPANY: I.T.C. Ltd
- ★ GENERAL MANAGER: Mr Nripjit Singh Chawla
- ★ DISTANCE TO SHOPS: 3 km
- ★ DISTANCE FROM AIRPORT: 9 km

If Shah Jahan came back to life and wanted to build another Taj Mahal, he could not because all the marble has been used inside this hotel. This haven of coolness and good taste is one of the most remarkable hotels in India – conceived on an unusually clever architectural theme, with gardens and pool in the middle and long corridor fingers going off in all directions. The lobby is a revelation: amid all this marbled magnificence, the fatigue, the heat and the sometimes overwhelming feel of India all fall off you like scales. If you are lucky enough to have a suite – say the Raja Man Singh for instance – prepare yourself for more: this is presumably how the Moguls lived, with cushions everywhere, great canopied bed and swing seats hanging from the ceiling. The great pity of it is that people only stay a day or two – to see the Taj. This hotel deserves much more – it is friendly, tremendously hospitable, unflappable even when faced with multi-tongued tourists. Service glides about and the food, both Indian and international, is above average.

Bombay

HOTEL OBEROI TOWERS, Nariman Point, Bombay 400 021

★ TELEPHONE: 2024343
★ CABLES: Obhotel
★ TELEX: OII 4153/OII 4154 OBBY IN
★ IN OPERATION: 10 years
★ RESERVATIONS: Loews Reservations Inc, London, New York, Los Angeles, Tokyo, Frankfurt/Oberoi Hotels (I)Pvt Ltd, New York, Sydney, Jakarta
★ ROOMS: 700
★ SUITES: 48
★ RESTAURANTS: 6 – Continental, Indian, French, Polynesian and two coffee shops
★ BARS: 3
★ DISCOTHEQUE: yes – plus live music in two restaurants
★ SHOPS: 300 – barber shop, beauty salon, bank, drugstore, travel agency, books, post office, handicrafts, textiles, gifts etc

★ CONFERENCE ROOMS: 11 (50 to 3000)
★ BANQUETING ROOMS: 11 (30 to 700)
★ STANDARD BEDROOM SIZE: 26 m^2
★ PRIVATE BALCONIES: no
★ SWIMMING POOL: yes – fresh water
★ RECREATIONAL ACTIVITIES: arrangements for sailing, riding, tennis, squash, golf and sightseeing
★ GARDENS: terraced garden at the pool
★ NO. OF STAFF: 1500
★ ROOM SERVICE: around the clock
★ ORIENTATION: seafront and inland
★ CREDIT CARDS: Amex, Diners Club, Bank of America, Barclaycard/Visa, Carte Blanche, Eurocard, Access, Andhra Bancard
★ OWNING COMPANY: East India Hotels Ltd
★ GENERAL MANAGER: Mr Anil Madhok
★ DISTANCE TO SHOPS: 2 km
★ DISTANCE FROM AIRPORT: 25 km

Although it obviously does not have its neighbours' nostalgic feel, this hotel is India's mostest – the biggest (it's the second tallest building in Bombay), the most up to date, the most international, the best equipped. Name it and Oberoi Towers have got it – an enormous and very attractive lobby with eleven shimmering Indian chandeliers, express elevators, a Lancers' Bar where the waiters come straight out of the pages of Kipling, an authentic Polynesian restaurant, an equally fair continental restaurant and one of the most attractive and tempting round-the-clock Coffee Shops we have ever seen. Plus thirty-five storeys of rooms and suites overlooking the greeny-blue Arabian sea. Plus a swimming pool seemingly suspended on the fourth floor. The decor is grand/modern, in very good taste and the furnishings are excellently chosen and well maintained. It is a hotel that rules over teeming, business-mad Bombay like a signpost to the future and anyone who ever thought Indians could not design and run such a place ought to come here for lessons. Service, the hallmark of this company, is outstanding – when, at one a.m., we accidentally broke our room key inside the lock, guess what? They had a locksmith on duty around the clock. But of course.

THE TAJ MAHAL HOTEL AND THE TAJ MAHAL INTERCONTINENTAL, Apollo Bunder, Bombay 400 039

★ TELEPHONE: 2023366
★ CABLES: Tajgroup Bombay
★ TELEX: 11-2442 TAJB IN and 11-6175 TAJB IN
★ IN OPERATION: 78 years
★ RESERVATIONS: Inter-Continental Hotels Corp, New York/Utell International, worldwide/Horis Hotel Reservation and Information System (Swissair)/The Leading Hotels of the World
★ ROOMS: 555 doubles 25 singles
★ SUITES: 45
★ RESTAURANTS: 6 – Tanjore, Golden

Dragon, Rendezvous, Shamiana, Sea Lounge and Ballroom
★ BARS: Harbour Bar and Apollo Bar
★ DISCOTHEQUE: yes – also a dance band in the Rendezvous Restaurant and Indian classical dances and music every night in the Tanjore Restaurant
★ SHOPS: 24 – shopping arcade on the ground floor selling books, records, carpets, handicrafts, jewellery, shoes, leathergoods, textiles; boutiques, tobacconists etc
★ CONFERENCE ROOMS: 9 (20 to 800)

★ BANQUETING ROOMS: 11

★ STANDARD BEDROOM SIZE: 26 m² (new wing) and 31 m² (old wing)

★ PRIVATE BALCONIES: yes – most rooms

★ SWIMMING POOL: yes – fresh water

★ RECREATIONAL ACTIVITIES: health club with sauna, also tennis and golf arranged on request

★ GARDENS: yes

★ NO. OF STAFF: 1640

★ ROOM SERVICE: around the clock

★ ORIENTATION: rooms face the sea or swimming pool area

★ CREDIT CARDS: American Express, Diners Club, Master Charge and Carte Blanche

★ OWNING COMPANY: Indian Hotels Co Ltd

★ GENERAL MANAGER: Mr J. D. F. Lam

★ DISTANCE TO BEACH: 18 km

★ DISTANCE TO SHOPS: walking distance

★ DISTANCE FROM AIRPORT: 20 km

Although it now has competition this is still India's most celebrated hotel. It has age and tradition, modernity, fantastic good taste and super-efficient service. It has been a landmark of the sub-continent for a long time – at least its fanciful Indo-Saracenic half has, and now that it also possesses a really elegant tower block, most world travellers passing through the portals of the Taj and trying out its delights are full of praise. The Taj is the Taj and I do not think it can ever really be imitated. You have a choice of a room in the old galleried wing or one, equally good in a different way, in the new wing. I would choose the old wing with its grand staircases, its Indian curlicues, its magnificent ceilings and the windows looking on to the Gateway to India. I once had a suite there that had 42 pieces of furniture in it. Service is impeccable and the Taj has the highest staff-to-guest ratio in Asia, possibly the world. It's a world of its own, moving fast if you so wish or at the sedate pace of the Orient if that's what you like best. With six restaurants, one never goes hungry or looking for a change elsewhere – I adore those Sunday buffets in the Grand Ballroom, also the Chinese food and the decor in the Indian restaurant. The Taj is a hotel for real connoisseurs.

Calcutta

HOTEL OBEROI GRAND, 15 Jawaharlal Nehru Road, Calcutta 700 013

★ TELEPHONE: 230181
★ CABLES: Obhotel
★ TELEX: 7248, 7854
★ IN OPERATION: 100 years
★ RESERVATIONS: Loews Reservations London, New York, Tokyo, Frankfurt, Los Angeles/Oberoi Hotels(I) Pvt Ltd New York, Sydney, Jakarta
★ ROOMS: 300
★ SUITES: 27
★ RESTAURANTS: 3 – Polynesian, Moghul Room (Indian/Mughlai food), Garden Cafe
★ BARS: 2
★ DISCOTHEQUE: yes – live and recorded music
★ SHOPS: yes – shopping arcade with curio, chemist, handicrafts, jewellery
★ CONFERENCE ROOMS: 6 (20 to 800)

★ BANQUETING ROOMS: 6 (20 to 800)
★ STANDARD BEDROOM SIZE: 30.3 m^2
★ PRIVATE BALCONIES: all rooms face the pool
★ SWIMMING POOL: yes – fresh water
★ RECREATIONAL ACTIVITIES: close circuit television in all rooms
★ GARDENS: yes – around the pool
★ NO. OF STAFF: 800
★ ROOM SERVICE: around the clock
★ ORIENTATION: east and west
★ CREDIT CARDS: Amex, Diners Club, Visa, Master Charge, Andhra Bancard, Central Card, Oberoi Hotels Card
★ OWNING COMPANY: East India Hotels Ltd
★ GENERAL MANAGER: Mr Satish Kumar
★ DISTANCE TO SHOPS: in centre of city
★ DISTANCE FROM AIRPORT: 16 km

It stands foursquare on Chowringhee, Calcutta's legendary main street, opposite the Maidan and looking rather like a tropical version of King's Cross Station. That's the Grand, one of India's most famous and oldest grand hotels and one that drips with history, nostalgia and the ghosts of people and things past. As soon as you step inside its beautiful period lobby with its flower-laden round table and the white and gold reception desk, you know that you are in for grace, beauty and elegance. The Grand is basically the living history of British India – now nicely Indianized of course and it has witnessed every major event of the past century. Rooms are lofty and cool, extremely well furnished in a good, unostentatious way and beautifully serviced by a veritable army of staff. At night especially, with all the lights on, the Grand positively glitters. Don't let its age fool you though – this hotel has been and is constantly being renovated, polished up and trimmed around: the management shows great care in this – care of the Grand and care of you. Food is diverse and there is a charming coffee shop. As the man said, they don't make them like that any more.

Goa

FORT AGUADA BEACH RESORT, Sinquerim, Bardez, Goa 403515

★ TELEPHONE: 4408/4409
★ CABLES: Fortaguada-Goa
★ TELEX: 0194-206 Taj In
★ IN OPERATION: since 1974
★ RESERVATIONS: The Taj Group of Hotels/Utell International, worldwide
★ ROOMS: 120
★ SUITES: none but 24 terrace rooms
★ RESTAURANTS: 2
★ BARS: 3
★ DISCOTHEQUE: yes – and live music
★ SHOPS: 5
★ CONFERENCE ROOMS: 2 (60 to 250)
★ BANQUETING ROOMS: no
★ STANDARD BEDROOM SIZE: 26 m^2

★ PRIVATE BALCONIES: yes – most rooms, 32 cottages
★ SWIMMING POOL: yes – fresh water
★ GARDENS: yes
★ RECREATIONAL ACTIVITIES: tennis, cycling, target practice with airguns, basketball, volleyball, sailing, fishing, rowing and various indoor games
★ NO. OF STAFF: 270
★ ROOM SERVICE: 07.00–23.00
★ ORIENTATION: all rooms face the sea
★ CREDIT CARDS: Diners Club, American Express and Bankamericard
★ FURTHER DEVELOPMENTS: an additional one hundred cottages in a coconut grove

with its own restaurant, bar and swimming pool
★ OWNING COMPANY: Indian Resort Hotels Ltd

★ GENERAL MANAGER: Mr Salil Dutt
★ DISTANCE TO BEACH: 100 m
★ DISTANCE TO SHOPS: 20 km
★ DISTANCE FROM AIRPORT: 46 km

Only a decade or so ago if one had suggested that you should go to India for a beach holiday you would have no doubt called the padded wagon. But the hippy trail led to Goa and tourists followed after when people began building small beach hotels, mostly around Madras and finally, seven years ago, the prestigious Taj Group took the plunge and built Fort Aguada. Expensively built on this rather remote but matchless beach, very well conceived and expertly managed, at Fort Aguada you can watch the hippies at the other end of the beach in comfort. For all those who love India, especially those relics of the former European presence, Goa is marvellous. It's Indian and it is also charmingly Portuguese (they still sing fado and make wine . . .). As for the hotel, it is more than acceptable. Rooms are fairly large, airy and cool and the furnishings have been chosen with care though obviously one does not spend much time inside with all that beach and magnificent coconut grove close by. If you like the local food, with or without the Portuguese overtones, you'll be very happy here. All in all, Goans are the best cooks in India.

Jaipur

THE RAMBAGH PALACE, Jaipur 302 005

★ TELEPHONE: 75141
★ CABLES: Rambagh
★ TELEX: 36 254-RBAG IN
★ RESERVATIONS: Taj Mahal Hotel, Bombay/The Taj Group of Hotels/Utell International, worldwide
★ ROOMS: 105
★ SUITES: 12
★ RESTAURANTS: 2
★ BARS: 1
★ DISCOTHEQUE: yes
★ SHOPS: 15
★ CONFERENCE ROOMS: 4 (30 to 300)
★ BANQUETING ROOMS: 2 (150 to 300)
★ STANDARD BEDROOM SIZE: variable
★ PRIVATE BALCONIES: yes
★ SWIMMING POOL: yes – fresh water, 75 × 45 m

★ RECREATIONAL ACTIVITIES: squash and golf, with horse riding on request, beauty parlour
★ GARDENS: yes
★ NO. OF STAFF: 250
★ ROOM SERVICE: around the clock
★ ORIENTATION: most of the rooms overlook beautiful gardens
★ FURTHER DEVELOPMENTS: additional rooms and coffee shop
★ CREDIT CARDS: Diners Club, American Express and Bankamericard
★ OPERATING COMPANY: The Rambagh Palace Hotel Pvt Ltd
★ GENERAL MANAGER: Vikram Singh
★ DISTANCE TO SHOPS: 3 km
★ DISTANCE FROM AIRPORT: 11 km

Psychiatrists everywhere should send their patients being treated for identity crises to this hotel. At Rambagh on special days, they send a ceremonial elephant to meet you at the gate. At the majestic pace that only an elephant can offer, you reach the splendid terrace where the gorgeous liveried staff await you with garlands of flowers and a cool 'nimbu-pani' (lime juice and water). The welcome at this immense and stately pile, all turrets and cupolas and galleries and gardens with peacocks strutting about, will turn the sickest nonentity into an instant maharajah. Rambagh was the home of Jaipur's own ruling prince, of course – no imitations. Rooms here vary a lot – some are somewhat spartan so do ask to see yours first.
The best are awe-inspiring with pre-1930 London bathrooms, with Oriental touches everywhere that have an unmistakable Bombay/Maple's touch so typical of princely India. The dining room with its painted ceiling is magnificent and so is the Chinese Room. The numberless staff are everywhere, smiling and cheerful, padding along miles of corridors. Rambagh's panache is the stuff of romance but the storybook never

tells you what the prince and princess had for dinner – which perhaps is just as well since food is not Rambagh's great point and the man who comes here for gastronomy should stay home. Who cares? All around you lies the fabled Pink City and that is surely worth travelling for.

Madras

TAJ COROMANDEL HOTEL, 17, Nungam-Bakkam High Road, Madras 600 034

★ TELEPHONE: 848888

★ CABLES: Hotelorent

★ TELEX: 041-7194

★ IN OPERATION: since 1975

★ RESERVATIONS: Taj Group of Hotels, New York/Utell International, worldwide/The Leading Hotels of the World

★ ROOMS: 225

★ SUITES: 27

★ RESTAURANTS: 3 – the Mysore, the Golden Dragon and the Pavilion (coffee shop)

★ BARS: 1

★ DISCOTHEQUE: no – but live music in Coffee Shop every night except Mondays

★ SHOPS: 18

★ CONFERENCE ROOMS: 2 (75 and 110)

★ BANQUETING ROOMS: 2 (75 to 1500)

★ STANDARD BEDROOM SIZE: 42 m^2

★ PRIVATE BALCONIES: only three suites have private terraces

★ SWIMMING POOL: yes – fresh water, 18 × 9 m

★ GARDENS: no

★ NO. OF STAFF: 520

★ ROOM SERVICE: around the clock

★ ORIENTATION: all rooms overlook the city

★ FURTHER DEVELOPMENTS: plans for a health club, sauna and a discotheque

★ CREDIT CARDS: Diners Club, American Express, Visa, Bankamericard and Master Charge

★ OWNING COMPANY: Oriental Hotels Ltd

★ GENERAL MANAGER: Mr Maneck B. Patel

★ DISTANCE TO BEACH: 6 km

★ DISTANCE TO SHOPS: 1½ km

★ DISTANCE FROM AIRPORT: 13 km

In the imposing pace of competition from princely palaces one might be forgiven the thought that it is hardly worth much effort when it comes to erecting a large modern hotel. But at the Taj Coromandel – by now the finest modern hotel in southern India – so successful were the architects and designers, it is now a famous feature of that so little known part of the sub-continent. Superbly elegant, with very fine and colourful decor, the public rooms like the Indian restaurant or its Chinese counterpart shine with that glittering Eastern appeal which is really overwhelming when it is done in such good taste. Colour schemes are very clever – running into the reds and golds in the public rooms and to the pale blue and cool greens in the bedrooms which are vast and sumptuously furnished. The suites are maharajah-sized. Service, as always in India, is ready and smiling while the variety and quality of the very hot food native to the region are the opposite of boring. Mahabalipuram and Kanchipuram are not far away: a visit to both is obligatory.

Mysore

LALITHA MAHAL PALACE HOTEL, Mysore 570011

★ TELEPHONE: 23650

★ CABLES: Tourism Mysore

★ TELEX: 0846 217

★ IN OPERATION: 10 years

★ RESERVATIONS: Ashok Reservations Service, New Delhi/John Miller, Australia/Air India Offices,

worldwide/Government of India Tourist Information Offices

★ ROOMS: 48

★ SUITES: 6

★ RESTAURANTS: 1

★ BARS: 1

★ DISCOTHEQUE: no

- ★ SHOPS: 3
- ★ CONFERENCE ROOMS: 1 (140 m²)
- ★ BANQUETING ROOMS: 1 (50 to 150)
- ★ STANDARD BEDROOM SIZE: 20 m²–55 m²
- ★ PRIVATE BALCONIES: yes – terraces
- ★ SWIMMING POOL: 1 – fresh water
- ★ RECREATIONAL ACTIVITIES: tennis, billiards, card room, badminton, table tennis, darts, chess and golf (1 km away)
- ★ GARDENS: yes – including tropical garden
- ★ NO. OF STAFF: 100
- ★ ROOM SERVICE: 07.00–23.00
- ★ ORIENTATION: east and west
- ★ CREDIT CARDS: American Express, Diners Club and ITDC
- ★ OWNING COMPANY: India Tourism Development Corporation Ltd
- ★ GENERAL MANAGER: V. M. Rao
- ★ DISTANCE TO SHOPS: 5 km
- ★ DISTANCE FROM AIRPORT: 225 km

In olden days, when they had too much money and not much to spend it on, India's erstwhile maharajahs built themselves palaces, preferably along the lines of those they believed Western monarchs had. This one is a mad and delicious hybrid, with touches of Buckingham Palace, King's Cross Station and some North of England county hall. The result is, to say the least, an eyeful and it's fun just being there – in a room the size of which will make you blink, a restaurant that looks faintly Ritz-ish and a staircase just like Francis Josef used to have. Located here, in this marvellous city of Mysore, it should not be missed by all those who enjoy the incongruities of the sub-continent. What's more, you are also treated like a maharajah. There is a man in full, vaguely military uniform who greets you at the front steps of this immense spun-sugar place, regiments of staff running up and down the corridors and vast grounds full of tropicana. A good swimming pool, too. The whole place is clean, resplendent and a very good effort in sailing on a new tack. The food, as long as it is Indian, is excellent. When it pretends to be what Indians term 'Continental', it requires a sense of humour to be appreciated. But if this is the way maharajahs used to live, I think I can stand it for a few days.

New Delhi

HOTEL OBEROI INTER-CONTINENTAL, Dr Zakir Hussain Marg, New Delhi

- ★ TELEPHONE: 699571
- ★ CABLES: INHOTELCOR/OBHOTEL
- ★ TELEX: 2372, 3829
- ★ IN OPERATION: since 1965
- ★ RESERVATIONS: Oberoi Hotels (I) Pvt Ltd, New York/Loews Representatives, New York, Los Angeles and London
- ★ ROOMS: 330
- ★ SUITES: 17
- ★ RESTAURANTS: 5 – The Taj, Coffee Shop, Cafe Chinois, Moghul Room and Cafe Expresso
- ★ BARS: 2
- ★ DISCOTHEQUE: yes
- ★ SHOPS: yes
- ★ CONFERENCE ROOMS: 1 (up to 1000)
- ★ BANQUETING ROOMS: 1 (800 to 1000)
- ★ PRIVATE BALCONIES: some
- ★ SWIMMING POOL: yes
- ★ RECREATIONAL ACTIVITIES: Health Club facilities
- ★ GARDENS: yes
- ★ NO. OF STAFF: 1043
- ★ ROOM SERVICE: around the clock
- ★ ORIENTATION: east and west
- ★ CREDIT CARDS: American Express, Bankamericard, Diners Club, Carte Blanche
- ★ OWNING COMPANY: East India Hotels Ltd
- ★ GENERAL MANAGER: J. S. Parmar
- ★ DISTANCE TO CITY CENTRE: 3.5 km
- ★ DISTANCE FROM AIRPORT: 16 km

This hotel was, in its time, a pioneer – the first modern hotel to be built in the Indian capital. Now, after twenty years and the arrival of many competitors, it is nice to record that its fame has not been tarnished. Many world travellers like it because of the absence of razzmatazz, its solid and enduring quality which is constantly brought up to date and above all its better-than-average staff. Here every client has a name – not just a number – and people remember not just what you drink but how you would like your ashtrays placed in the room. Smiles are the rule and when it comes to food, the Oberoi Intercontinental variety is by far the best in any New Delhi hotel – splendid buffets and well-planned dinner menus – it's the only hotel in India I know where people have heard that one serves hot food on hot plates. Makes a change. The rooms are adequate to very good, sensibly furnished and bathrooms work like a dream – suites are vast and right for tycoons. There are gardens and a very good swimming pool. Altogether a very good address in a city where hotels shine with marble and fail in the little things.

THE TAJ MAHAL HOTEL, Number One Mansigh Road, New Delhi 110011

- ★ TELEPHONE: 38 61 62
- ★ CABLES: Tajdel
- ★ TELEX: 31 3604 Tajd IN
- ★ IN OPERATION: since 1978
- ★ RESERVATIONS: The Taj Group of Hotels, New York/Utell International, worldwide/The Leading Hotels of the World
- ★ ROOMS: 70 doubles 200 singles
- ★ SUITES: 28
- ★ RESTAURANTS: 4 – House of Ming, Haveli, Machan and Casa Medici
- ★ BARS: 1
- ★ DISCOTHEQUE: yes
- ★ SHOPS: Khazana Shopping Centre run by the hotel
- ★ CONFERENCE ROOMS: 5 (85 to 550)
- ★ BANQUETING ROOMS: 5 (85 to 550)
- ★ STANDARD BEDROOM SIZE: 30 m^2
- ★ PRIVATE BALCONIES: yes
- ★ SWIMMING POOL: yes – fresh water
- ★ GARDENS: yes
- ★ NO. OF STAFF: 860
- ★ ROOM SERVICE: around the clock
- ★ ORIENTATION: east and west
- ★ CREDIT CARDS: American Express, Diners Club and Bankamericard
- ★ OWNING COMPANY: The Indian Hotels Co Ltd
- ★ GENERAL MANAGER: Mr Ravi Dubey
- ★ DISTANCE TO SHOPS: walking distance
- ★ DISTANCE FROM AIRPORT: 10 km

The illustrious company that built this hotel has a ceaseless urge to find the best so it is no wonder that the Delhi Taj is a talking point among habitual travellers. It is one of the most magnificent, the most costly, the most *soigné* new hotels in the whole of India and when you know that they even grow their own basil to get the pizzas exactly right, you will gather that no effort has been spared. It has been built of pink sandstone outside and it seems to be 100 per cent marble inside – cool, supremely beautiful and so elegant that one feels like a latter-day Moghul emperor. Public rooms, as usual in this chain, are superbly designed and here and there are works of art such as only India can produce. Bedrooms and studios are stunningly lovely, with pale, fresh colours, lots of storage space and shining bathrooms. The restaurants, especially the Chinese one, are quite superb and the so-called coffee shop is a work of art. Obviously, as a new hotel, it needs 'wearing in' but with superb management and a willing staff, this won't take long and the Delhi Taj is already taking its place among the great hotels of the world.

Srinagar

HOTEL OBEROI PALACE, Gupkar Road, Srinagar-190001, Jammu & Kashmir

- ★ TELEPHONE: 75617/8 – 71241/2
- ★ CABLES: Obhotel
- ★ TELEX: 375-201 LXSR IN
- ★ IN OPERATION: since 1955
- ★ RESERVATIONS: LRI worldwide/Stinnes, Frankfurt
- ★ ROOMS: 55 doubles 28 singles
- ★ SUITES: 19 (incl 2 presidential)
- ★ RESTAURANTS: 2
- ★ BARS: 2
- ★ DISCOTHEQUE: yes
- ★ SHOPS: 8

★ CONFERENCE ROOMS: 3 (up to 50)
★ BANQUETING ROOMS: 4 (up to 120)
★ STANDARD BEDROOM SIZE: 30 m^2
★ PRIVATE BALCONIES: no
★ SWIMMING POOL: no one can swim in the Dal lake facing the hotel
★ RECREATIONAL ACTIVITIES: golf, badminton, table tennis, horse riding and TV/video lounge
★ GARDENS: yes
★ NO. OF STAFF: 250
★ ROOM SERVICE: around the clock
★ ORIENTATION: rooms face gardens and lake
★ FURTHER DEVELOPMENTS: a swimming pool, restaurant and tennis courts
★ CREDIT CARDS: American Express, Diners Club, Eurocard, Visa
★ OWNING COMPANY: The East India Hotels Ltd
★ GENERAL MANAGER: Mr Nirwan Kumar
★ DISTANCE TO SHOPS: 3 km
★ DISTANCE FROM AIRPORT: 16 km

The Hindu maharajah of Muslim Kashmir used to live here. It could not be said that he denied himself anything. One drives along Dal Lake, the Pearl of Kashmir, and there in a setting fit for mountain gods is this great pile of a place set among exotic gardens, with fountains playing and staff in glittering livery who consider it a favour to carry your bags. One hesitates to walk in over those fine silk Bokhara carpets dating from the eighteenth century but apparently they are much more hard-wearing than the nylon variety. Rooms and suites vary in size but most of them are princely in size and furnishings, with lots of those little Oriental whatnots which obviously have their use – if only one knew what it is. The staff are everywhere at attention – like a multicoloured battalion of willing soldiers. Down the garden path on the lake, brilliantly hued shikaras wait to glide you along to the world-famous Shalimar Gardens, and those Utopian valleys of Gulmarg and Pahalgam are a short drive away. Like everywhere in India, food is somewhat *fantaisiste* – running from the very good to the odd. Whatever you do, insist on a room in the palace itself. The new wing is for travel agents.

Udaipur

LAKE PALACE HOTEL, Pichola Lake, Udaipur 313001

★ TELEPHONE: 3241/2/3/4/5
★ CABLES: Lakepalace
★ TELEX: 33-203 LPAL IN
★ IN OPERATION: since 1961
★ RESERVATIONS: via Taj Mahal Hotel, Bombay/Utell International, worldwide
★ ROOMS: 85
★ SUITES: 6
★ RESTAURANTS: 1
★ BARS: 1
★ DISCOTHEQUE: no
★ SHOPS: 6
★ CONFERENCE ROOMS: 2 (60 and 300)
★ BANQUETING ROOMS: 2 (60 and 300)
★ STANDARD BEDROOM SIZE: 28 m^2
★ PRIVATE BALCONIES: yes – some rooms
★ SWIMMING POOL: yes – fresh water
★ GARDENS: yes
★ NO. OF STAFF: 140
★ ROOM SERVICE: around the clock
★ ORIENTATION: all rooms face the lake
★ CREDIT CARDS: American Express and Diners Club
★ OWNING COMPANY: The Lake Palace Hotels & Motels (P) Ltd
★ GENERAL MANAGER: Mr Deepak Dutt
★ DISTANCE TO SHOPS: 1 km
★ DISTANCE FROM AIRPORT: 20 km

Many people, myself included, believe that the Lake Palace is the most beautiful hotel building in the world. A former maharajah's palace, it occupies every inch of a tiny island in the middle of Udaipur's sacred lake and at times, especially at dawn, it looks like some Oriental dream floating on a silvery mirror. It has towers, cupolas, tiny miradors, fountains playing and a decor of such astonishing beauty and authenticity that it grips your heart. Very, very romantic, especially if you can have one of the corner rooms. Everywhere are frescoed walls and delicate marble screens and there is even a swimming pool under the mango trees. One has to go ashore by boat to visit that marvellously colourful city of Udaipur which has enormous appeal. In the hotel alas, whoever designed the new dining room dropped a stitch or two – it isn't what it should be. Neither is the food but who needs to eat when there is so much to feast the eye?

INDONESIA
Bali
HOTEL BALI OBEROI, Legian Beach, P.O. Box 351, Denpasar, Bali

- ★ TELEPHONE: 25581
- ★ CABLES: Balioberoi
- ★ TELEX: 35125 OBHOTELDPR
- ★ IN OPERATION: since 1978
- ★ RESERVATIONS: Loews Representation International/Utell/Oberoi Hotels (India)/S.T.R. Frankfurt
- ★ ROOMS: 60 lanai cottages
- ★ SUITES: 13 villas, 1 presidential villa with private swimming pool and 1 Istana Suite with personal valets
- ★ RESTAURANTS: 2
- ★ BARS: 1
- ★ DISCOTHEQUE: no
- ★ SHOPS: 4
- ★ CONFERENCE ROOMS: 1 (60)
- ★ BANQUETING ROOMS: none
- ★ STANDARD BEDROOM SIZE: 5 × 4 m
- ★ PRIVATE BALCONIES: yes
- ★ SWIMMING POOL: yes – fresh water 25 × 12 m
- ★ RECREATIONAL ACTIVITIES: table tennis, pool table, indoor games, surfing, floodlit tennis court, sauna, massage, daily video films and frequent Balinese dances at hotel's open-air amphitheatre
- ★ GARDENS: 30 acres; additionally each villa has its own private garden courtyard
- ★ NO. OF STAFF: 200
- ★ ROOM SERVICE: around the clock
- ★ ORIENTATION: all directions
- ★ CREDIT CARDS: American Express, Diners Club, Visa, Mastercharge
- ★ OWNING COMPANY: P. T. Widja Putra Karya
- ★ GENERAL MANAGER: Mr Kamal Kant Kaul
- ★ DISTANCE TO BEACH: on the beach
- ★ DISTANCE TO SHOPS: 4 km
- ★ DISTANCE FROM AIRPORT: 9 km

Rumour has it that all those adventurous people who knew Bali when it was Bali are now moving over to the next door island of Lombok. Maybe. For myself, I will still go to Bali if only to stay at the Bali Oberoi because, when it comes to it, it is unbeaten in the exotic stakes. It's small and charming and on Legian Beach, well away from the tourist traps of Sanur. Here you have your own private villa or lanai suite and splendiferous gardens. Even your bathroom has a garden (one of only two hotels in the world I know that have that . . .) and if you want service just hit the gong out front and a smiling Balinese room-boy will appear as if by magic. The beach is a mile long and immaculate. The hotel decor is Balinese but modern, genuine and in excellent taste. For a while this excellent hotel looked a little down at heel but now it has been re-vamped and re-born. The food is international – acceptable – and Indonesian, which is fine once you get used to it. From there, go inland towards the intensely green paddyfields and the haughty mountains and you will find the real Bali. But the Bali Oberoi is now the only base.

Jakarta
THE JAKARTA MANDARIN, P.O. Box 3392, Jakarta

- ★ TELEPHONE: 321307
- ★ CABLES: Mandahotel Jkt
- ★ TELEX: 45755 Manda Jkt
- ★ IN OPERATION: since 1979
- ★ RESERVATIONS: The Leading Hotels of the World
- ★ ROOMS: 450 doubles/twin
- ★ SUITES: 19
- ★ RESTAURANTS: 5 – The Spice Garden, The Club Room, The Marquee Coffee Shop, The Clipper Lounge and Pelangi Terrace

★ BARS: 3

★ DISCOTHEQUE: live music in bar

★ SHOPS: 6

★ CONFERENCE ROOMS: 2 (5 to 480)

★ BANQUETING ROOMS: 2 (5 to 800)

★ STANDARD BEDROOM SIZE: 36.5 m^2

★ PRIVATE BALCONIES: no

★ SWIMMING POOL: yes – fresh water, 150 m^2

★ RECREATIONAL ACTIVITIES: physical fitness centre and sauna, jogging track, air-conditioned squash courts

★ GARDENS: no

★ NO. OF STAFF: 825

★ ROOM SERVICE: around the clock

★ ORIENTATION: facing the Welcome Monument and the main avenue of Jakarta

★ CREDIT CARDS: Carte Blanche, American Express, Eurocard, Diners Club, Visa and Mandarin

★ OWNING COMPANY: Mandarin International Hotels Ltd

★ GENERAL MANAGER: Daniel P. McCafferty

★ DISTANCE TO BEACH: approximately 3 hours' drive

★ DISTANCE TO SHOPS: 10 minutes to main department store

★ DISTANCE FROM AIRPORT: 10 km (Kemayoran Domestic Airport); 17 km (Halim International Airport)

Mandarin hotels are not built. They just appear by magic, and now there are two more in this book. Like Rolls Royce bringing out a new model, a Mandarin is a long time coming but unbeatable because the prestige, investment courage and expertise of this company are very rare in the world today. The Jakarta Mandarin has two authentic stone Sumatra statues topped by golden canopies in the lobby. Their stiff remote gaze in formalized attitude is the reverse of the impression made by this hotel whose welcome is unrivalled. It's the kind of hotel where even the lowly chairs in the coffee shop have been custom-made to the right design. Rooms and suites are palatial – gorgeously upholstered furniture, teak-fronted wardrobes, superb lighting, a proper writing desk as well as a three-mirror dressing table and everywhere splendid Indonesian materials. The Royal Orchid Restaurant, one of five, is magnificently decorated in rich browns, greens and gold and the cooking is commensurate with well cared for French cheeses. What really counts in the end is Mandarin service, probably the best in the world today – trained, intelligent, attentive, but above all trained. Nothing succeeds like success, of course, and the Mandarin Group is expanding very fast in the far East. Can they keep it up? My own bet is on them.

IRAQ
Baghdad

HOTEL AL RASHEED, P.P. Box 8070, Baghdad

★ TELEPHONE: 8871300

★ CABLES: Rashtel

★ TELEX: 213204 Rashid IK 213205 Rashid IK

★ IN OPERATION: one year

★ RESERVATIONS: Loews Reservations Inc, London, New York, Tokyo, Frankfurt, Los Angeles/Oberoi Hotels (I)Pvt Ltd New York, Sydney, Jakarta

★ ROOMS: 380

★ SUITES: 52 – 26 standard suites 26 presidential suites

★ RESTAURANTS: 6 – Coffee Shop, Grillroom, National Restaurant, Night Club, Barbeque, Al Zahir

★ BARS: 4

★ DISCOTHEQUE: yes – live music

★ SHOPS: 4 – pastry shop, florist, general store, handicrafts

★ CONFERENCE ROOMS: 2 (79 m^2)

★ BANQUETING ROOMS: 1 (600)

★ STANDARD BEDROOM SIZE: 18.23 m^2

★ PRIVATE BALCONIES: no

★ SWIMMING POOL: yes – fresh water, heated

★ RECREATIONAL ACTIVITIES: casino, bowling alley, tennis courts

★ GARDENS: yes – very large

★ NO. OF STAFF: 800

★ ROOM SERVICE: around the clock

★ ORIENTATION: north and east

★ CREDIT CARDS: American Express

★ OWNING COMPANY: Oberoi Hotels (I)Pvt Ltd
★ GENERAL MANAGER: Mr Madan Misra
★ DISTANCE TO SHOPS: 2 km
★ DISTANCE FROM AIRPORT: 18 km

Here is a capital city, Baghdad, that very much needed a hotel like the Al Rasheed – up to date with no half measures and yet without too much of the false glitter so often seen in Arab world hotels. It is well designed and intelligently furnished with a care that shows in every chair, every carpet, every bathroom. One feels that there is solidity here – not just flash. The lobby is a marbled oasis of cool comfort (which one needs after this frenetic city). There is a beautifully designed Arabic restaurant where one of the world's most interesting gastronomic experiences is available on a decor background that won't give you indigestion. There is a good and amusing nightclub and, if you are at a loose end, you can also lose (or maybe win) at the built-in casino and let off steam by going bowling. The Al Rasheed is not at all a bad try when it comes to new hotels and if you are in this part of the world, take our tip: it's the best.

ISRAEL

Caesarea

DAN CAESAREA GOLF HOTEL, Caesarea

★ TELEPHONE: 063-62266
★ CABLES: Cedan
★ TELEX: 04-46216
★ IN OPERATION: 11 years
★ RESERVATIONS: Dan Hotels Group, London/Israel Hotel Representatives, New York
★ ROOMS: 105
★ SUITES: 6
★ RESTAURANTS: 3 – Dining Room, Coffee Shop and Swimming Pool Bar
★ BARS: 2
★ DISCOTHEQUE: yes
★ SHOPS: 2 – boutique and newspapers and gifts
★ CONFERENCE ROOMS: 1 (100 to 150)
★ BANQUETING ROOMS: 1 (350)
★ STANDARD BEDROOM SIZE: 22 m^2
★ PRIVATE BALCONIES: yes
★ SWIMMING POOL: yes – fresh water, L-shaped, 800 m^2

★ GARDENS: yes
★ NO. OF STAFF: 150
★ ROOM SERVICE: 07.00–24.00
★ RECREATIONAL ACTIVITIES: tennis, gymnasium, sauna and turkish bath, volleyball and cycling; also golf, horse riding and skin diving nearby
★ ORIENTATION: Half the rooms face the sea, the other half the swimming pool and gardens
★ CREDIT CARDS: Diners Club, American Express, Eurocard and Bankamericard
★ OWNING COMPANY: Dan Hotels Corporation Ltd
★ GENERAL MANAGER: David Ellenbogen
★ DISTANCE TO BEACH: 1½ km
★ DISTANCE TO SHOPS: 2 km
★ DISTANCE FROM AIRPORT: 80 km

Having heard some so-so reports about this hotel, I was glad to have a chance to return there when I was in Israel a while back and all I can say is that my correspondents must have been unlucky in some respect. I found the Dan Caesarea extremely good, as it was when I first saw it – cool and practical, with pleasant balconies and very good room service and a host of services that one does not always find in Israel. There is a very good swimming pool, a magnificent 18-hole golf course and the gardens are very *soigné*. The food is really quite good (bearing in mind that most Israelis are not gastronomes). The Romans, whose capital this was, knew all about the right places and Caesarea is well worth visiting for its antiquities and especially the superb aquaduct and the theatre. One is never very far from other sights and come to think of it, this is about the only country hotel in Israel where I would feel happy.

Jerusalem

KING DAVID HOTEL, King David Street, Jerusalem

- ★ TELEPHONE: 02-221111
- ★ CABLES: Kindotel
- ★ TELEX: 25228
- ★ IN OPERATION: since 1931
- ★ RESERVATIONS: Israel Hotel Representatives, New York/Dan Hotels Group, London and Zurich/The Leading Hotels of the World
- ★ ROOMS: 258
- ★ SUITES: 29
- ★ RESTAURANTS: 4
- ★ BARS: 1
- ★ DISCOTHEQUE: no
- ★ SHOPS: 8 – jewellery, gifts, drugstore, travel agent, fashion boutique and art gallery
- ★ CONFERENCE ROOMS: 7 (20 to 230)
- ★ BANQUETING ROOMS: 7 (12 to 250)
- ★ STANDARD BEDROOM SIZE: 25 m^2
- ★ PRIVATE BALCONIES: yes
- ★ SWIMMING POOL: yes – fresh water, 25 × 13 m
- ★ RECREATIONAL ACTIVITIES: tennis and sauna
- ★ GARDENS: yes
- ★ NO. OF STAFF: 300
- ★ ROOM SERVICE: around the clock
- ★ ORIENTATION: facing gardens, pool and Old City
- ★ FURTHER DEVELOPMENTS: plans to add an extra 100 rooms and a banqueting hall to accommodate 600 persons
- ★ CREDIT CARDS: Amexco, Diners Club, Visa and Master Charge
- ★ OWNING COMPANY: Dan Hotels Corporation
- ★ GENERAL MANAGER: Mr Yossi Heksch
- ★ DISTANCE TO SHOPS: 1 km
- ★ DISTANCE FROM AIRPORT: 50 km

There are hotels in this world (Raffles in Singapore, Shepherds in Cairo among many) whose names are legendary. This list includes the King David though it achieved fame once too often by being blown up during Israel's birthpangs. Then it was rebuilt, in a somewhat less extroverted, antiquarian mood, but managed to find its persona again through hard work, good management and the fact that it is in this unique city. It is palatially vast, cool and distinguished and its political importance has given way to top flight tourism and state visitors. Rooms are very well laid out and the public rooms could hold any international conference with ease. The food is international, perhaps a little plain as befits a nation with curiously Spartan habits. What I like most about it, however, is the sense of tradition and the quality of the service – people are happy to see you, happy to help and so glad you came.

KING SOLOMON SHERATON, 32 King David Street, Jerusalem 94101

- ★ TELEPHONE: (02) 241433
- ★ CABLES: no
- ★ TELEX: 26434
- ★ IN OPERATION: since May 1981
- ★ RESERVATIONS: International reservations system operating at Sheraton Hotels, worldwide
- ★ ROOMS: 111

★ SUITES: 14 junior 16 de luxe
2 diplomatic 1 presidential
★ RESTAURANTS: 4 – The Cafe, The
Carvery, Lobbylounge and The
Teppanyaki. All restaurants kosher.
Japanese Restaurant opening shortly
★ BARS: 1
★ DISCOTHEQUE: piano in Lobbylounge
★ SHOPS: 8 – duty free shop, jewellery,
Judaic art, King Solomon boutique, gift
shop, news stand, florist and bank
★ CONFERENCE ROOMS: none
★ BANQUETING ROOMS: 1 (up to 12)
★ STANDARD BEDROOM SIZE: 25 m²
★ PRIVATE BALCONIES: 27 private balconies
or terraces, including all suites

★ SWIMMING POOL: yes – fresh water,
14 × 6.5 m
★ GARDENS: no
★ NO. OF STAFF: 150
★ ROOM SERVICE: around the clock
★ ORIENTATION: all suites and many rooms
face Jerusalem's Old City. Others face
New City
★ CREDIT CARDS: American Express,
Diners Club, Mastercharge, Eurocard
and Visa
★ OWNING COMPANY: Sheraton Hotels
(management)
★ GENERAL MANAGER: David Golsin
★ DISTANCE TO SHOPS: walking distance
★ DISTANCE FROM AIRPORT: 40 km

Jerusalem, a city that no one who is a real traveller can afford to miss, has never been
very lucky with its hotels – I always had the feeling that had it not been for Jerusalem
itself I could well have stayed away. Now things are improving and one of the reasons
is the King Solomon Sheraton. Though it is not quite as grand and as sophisticated as its
Tel Aviv sister, this hotel is going to be a winner. For one thing, its terrace overlooks the
Old City – surely one of the greatest sights in the world. For another, the hotel works,
silently and without fuss, i.e. you don't have to call the plumber all the time and the
staff are finding their feet without too much trouble. The architecture takes a bit of
getting used to until one realizes that in this climate there is a very good reason for it.
Inside, the decor is better than one would expect from the outside – reasonably
subdued, in quite good taste and without too many frills. The lobby is cool and elegant
and the rooms are amazingly quiet and very well furnished in an international style.
The food – always a tricky subject when a hotel first opens – is getting better all the
time. My guess is that the King Solomon Sheraton is going to turn out to be a godsend in
what is essentially a hotel desert.

Tel Aviv

TEL AVIV SHERATON, 115 Hayarkon Street, Tel Aviv 63573

★ TELEPHONE: (03) 286222
★ CABLES: Sheraco Tel Aviv
★ TELEX: 342269
★ IN OPERATION: 7 years
★ RESERVATIONS: Sheraton International
Reservations Offices
★ ROOMS: 365
★ SUITES: 21
★ RESTAURANTS: 4 – Kum Kum Restaurant,
Twelve Tribes Grill Room, Genesis
(vegetarian), Lobbylounge (snacks). All
restaurants kosher
★ BARS: 2
★ DISCOTHEQUE: yes – and pianist in
Lobbylounge
★ SHOPS: 6 – ladies fashions, jewellery,
gift shop, art gallery, duty free shop,
beauty parlour
★ CONFERENCE ROOMS: 3 (12 to 180)
★ BANQUETING ROOMS: 3 (100 to 200)

★ STANDARD BEDROOM SIZE: 24 m²
★ PRIVATE BALCONIES: all rooms
★ SWIMMING POOL: new large outdoor
pool
★ RECREATIONAL ACTIVITIES: swimming,
boating at Tel Aviv Marina
★ GARDENS: no
★ NO. OF STAFF: 420
★ ROOM SERVICE: around the clock
★ ORIENTATION: sea and Jaffa, sea and
marina, sea and city from all double
rooms
★ CREDIT CARDS: all major credit cards
★ OWNING COMPANY: Hotel Cosmopolitan
(1974) Ltd (owning company), Sheraton
management
★ GENERAL MANAGER: Per Kjellstrom
★ DISTANCE TO BEACH: on beach front
★ DISTANCE TO SHOPS: walking distance
★ DISTANCE FROM AIRPORT: 25 km

Without any doubt this is one of the best two or three hotels in the whole of the Middle East. In that strip between the blue Mediterranean and the more mundane delights of Dizengoff, the Tel Aviv Sheraton is the only hotel worth living in – a well-conceived, well-run place where functionalism and good taste marry to live happily ever after. Of course, it's modern, but in the best sense of the word. A great lobby, spacious rooms all beautifully furnished with a care for small details which is a delight to see. Decor is beautifully muted – nothing jars here because the usual Israeli concrete exuberance has been kept at bay. Service is efficient and discreet and the food so far above what it is in the rest of the country that it is remembered with pleasure. In the Twelve Tribes Grill, it is international, stately and served with a good sense of showmanship. What is most surprising, however, is that the usually humble coffee shop, here called Kum Kum, is a very acceptable restaurant in its own right. That's rare. The staff are charming – most of them are students working their way through college (a great idea) and they are all intelligent, multi-lingual and good company. One of the two or three best hotels in the Middle East? It's certainly the best in Israel.

ITALY

Asolo

HOTEL VILLA CIPRIANI, Via Canova, 298, Asolo (Treviso)

★ TELEPHONE: 0423-52166
★ CABLES: Villacipriani, Asolo
★ TELEX: 411060 CIPRAS I
★ IN OPERATION: since 1962
★ RESERVATIONS: Ciga Hotels, Inc, worldwide/Relais et Chateaux, Europe
★ ROOMS: 31 doubles 1 single
★ SUITES: 4
★ RESTAURANTS: 2 – Verandah Restaurant with interconnecting dining room
★ BARS: 1
★ DISCOTHEQUE: no
★ SHOPS: none – but some small showcases
★ CONFERENCE ROOMS: 1 (15 to 20)
★ BANQUETING ROOMS: 1 (100)
★ STANDARD BEDROOM SIZE: 17–18 m^2
★ PRIVATE BALCONIES: yes – 2 rooms with private terraces and other rooms with direct access to the garden
★ SWIMMING POOL: no
★ RECREATIONAL ACTIVITIES: tennis and an 18-hole golf course 30 km away

★ GARDENS: yes
★ NO. OF STAFF: 38
★ ROOM SERVICE: around the clock
★ ORIENTATION: the entrance facade faces north-east, the garden facade faces south-east and the rest of the building faces hills and mountains
★ FURTHER DEVELOPMENTS: enlargement of present garage and parking space, new conference room for 60/80 persons, 6/8 additional rooms and it is hoped a swimming pool in the valley
★ CREDIT CARDS: American Express, Diners Club, Bankamericard, Visa, Eurocard and Master Charge
★ OWNING COMPANY: Cigahotels – Italian Grand Hotel Co
★ GENERAL MANAGER: Sandro Matassini
★ DISTANCE TO SHOPS: walking distance
★ DISTANCE FROM AIRPORT: 60 km (Venice)

The canal-bound Venetians always had an eye on *les plaisirs champêtres* – escaping from time to time to some improbably beautiful Renaissance villa on the Brenta. This hotel is one such and who could wish for better? In this little town, once the home of Eleonora Duse and Robert Browning, is the charming, sixteenth-century villa looking over the green hills. It is a rather difficult place to describe because one really has to be there to absorb the atmosphere of gentle timelessness. One eats al fresco most of the time – the Cipriani cuisine is excellent. The rooms are smallish but beautifully furnished and very comfortable, with flowered balconies everywhere. Public rooms are aristocratically well proportioned and the staff are quite charming and helpful. It is the next best thing to having your own villa within hailing distance of both Venice and glorious Vicenza.

Bellagio

GRAND HOTEL VILLA SERBELLONI, Via Roma 1, I-22021 Bellagio

★ TELEPHONE: (031) 950216
★ CABLES: Serbotel
★ TELEX: 380330 Sernot I
★ IN OPERATION: since 1873
★ RESERVATIONS: direct
★ ROOMS: 68 doubles 12 singles
★ SUITES: 7
★ RESTAURANTS: 1 – plus breakfast room and lakeside terrace
★ BARS: 2
★ DISCOTHEQUE: dancing and orchestra every night in the main hall
★ SHOPS: 2 – ladies' hairdresser and boutique
★ CONFERENCE ROOMS: 4 (30 to 300)
★ BANQUETING ROOMS: 4 (25 to 300)
★ STANDARD BEDROOM SIZE: 25 m²

★ PRIVATE BALCONIES: yes – some rooms
★ SWIMMING POOL: yes – fresh water, heated, 10 × 20 m
★ RECREATIONAL ACTIVITIES: tennis and golf at Grandola, 20 minutes away by car
★ GARDENS: yes – park directly on lakeside
★ NO. OF STAFF: 100
★ ROOM SERVICE: around the clock
★ ORIENTATION: west
★ CREDIT CARDS: Visa Amexco
★ OWNING COMPANY: R. Bucher
★ GENERAL MANAGER: R. Bucher
★ DISTANCE TO BEACH: directly
★ DISTANCE TO SHOPS: directly
★ DISTANCE FROM AIRPORT: 70 km (Linate-Milano) and Malpensa

Anyone who has read previous editions of this guide will know that the editorial presence has a weakness for great staircases. Frescoed ceilings have much the same effect and those are two reasons why I would go back to Villa Serbelloni as often as I can. I did so recently and found that absence did make one's heart grow fonder. This place has style, beauty, urbanity and that grand hotel feeling which cannot easily be manufactured. There, below, is Lake Como, spreading like a tablecloth amidst the rather formal hills. Villa Serbelloni has been here a long time – sixteenth century with here and there a few eighteenth century touches. Rooms are large, airy and high ceilinged, with gilt, marble and curlicued Italian furniture of the period. Linen is fresh and sweet smelling and bathrooms are convention-sized. The family who own Serbelloni know everything there is to know about the hotel business – they are also charming and likeable. The food can often be great and is mostly good. It reaches perfection when consumed on that divine terrace over the lake. There can be few more romantic settings. If it is Como you wish to see, Villa Serbelloni is certainly the right address.

Capri

GRAND HOTEL QUISISANA, Via Camerelle No. 2, 80073 Capri

★ TELEPHONE: 081-8370788
★ CABLES: Quisisana Capri
★ TELEX: 710520
★ IN OPERATION: since 1900
★ RESERVATIONS: Robert F. Warner, Inc, London and New York
★ ROOMS: 100 doubles 15 singles
★ SUITES: 27
★ RESTAURANTS: 2 – Colombaia Restaurant and Quisi Restaurant
★ BARS: 2
★ DISCOTHEQUE: piano bar
★ SHOPS: none
★ CONFERENCE ROOMS: 5 (10 to 600)
★ BANQUETING ROOMS: 3 (15 to 400)
★ STANDARD BEDROOM SIZE: 30 m²

★ PRIVATE BALCONIES: yes – all rooms that face the sea
★ SWIMMING POOL: yes – fresh water, 150 m²
★ RECREATIONAL ACTIVITIES: 3 tennis courts, sauna and massage
★ GARDENS: yes – large park
★ NO. OF STAFF: 150
★ ROOM SERVICE: 07.00–24.00
★ ORIENTATION: most rooms face south to gardens and the sea
★ FURTHER DEVELOPMENTS: proposals to build a new swimming pool and extend the Colombaia Restaurant
★ CREDIT CARDS: Diners Club, Amexco and Eurocard

★ OWNING COMPANY: Hotelverwaltung
   M.G.S.
★ GENERAL MANAGER: Dante Cattaruzza
★ DISTANCE TO BEACH: 1 km

★ DISTANCE TO SHOPS: walking distance
★ DISTANCE FROM AIRPORT: Naples airport
   40 minutes by hydrofoil

Capri in the high summer is a curious, polyglot mixture of heaven and hell. In the so-called off season (which is most of the year) it goes back to being one of the most sensationally beautiful small islands in the world. But, winter or summer, the Quisisana reigns supreme as it has done since the first year of the century – a great lady of a hotel, distinguished and beautifully cared for. It sees little passing flotsam (too expensive for that) and for those who care for hotel excellence, and Capri too, it is a reward indeed. Cool marble halls, splendid carpets and hangings, furniture that has stood the test of time and the bedrooms, quite large for the most part, are supremely comfortable. Many have their own balconies and breakfast on one's terrace with Capri all around is an overwhelming experience. The food is *con amore* and the service is enchantingly discreet. Improvements by the intelligent management in recent years have much enhanced this lovely grand hotel.

Candeli

HOTEL VILLA LA MASSA, 50010 Candeli-Firenze

★ TELEPHONE: 055-630051
★ CABLES: Villamassa
★ TELEX: 573555
★ IN OPERATION: 34 years
★ RESERVATIONS: direct
★ ROOMS: 33 doubles 4 singles
★ SUITES: 6
★ RESTAURANTS: 3 – including La Cave
   Restaurant (not operating in July and
   August)
★ BARS: 2
★ DISCOTHEQUE: yes – also piano in the
   restaurant and piano bar from 22.00 to
   02.00
★ SHOPS: none
★ CONFERENCE ROOMS: 3 (20 to 90)
★ BANQUETING ROOMS: 2 (up to 190)

★ STANDARD BEDROOM SIZE: 16 m^2
★ PRIVATE BALCONIES: only a few
★ SWIMMING POOL: yes – fresh water,
   60 m^2
★ RECREATIONAL ACTIVITIES: golf and
   tennis nearby
★ GARDENS: yes
★ NO. OF STAFF: 40
★ ROOM SERVICE: 07.00–02.00
★ ORIENTATION: south
★ FURTHER DEVELOPMENTS: a tennis club
★ CREDIT CARDS: American Express, Visa
   and Diners Club
★ OWNING COMPANY: I.R.A. S.p.A.
★ GENERAL MANAGER: C. Manetti
★ DISTANCE TO SHOPS: 5 km
★ DISTANCE FROM AIRPORT: 100 km

A divinely beautiful and tranquil Tuscan villa a short walk from the centre of noisy Florence, La Massa is a place in a thousand – mellow, faded yellow walls and greeny blue shutters facing a well-treed garden of sylvan repose. On the other side of the house, the dining terrace lines the bank of the Arno – a view that makes most meals into seven-hour marathons of sensual delight. Inside, the rather stark white of the walls is relieved by magnificent splashes of colour in furnishings and furniture and lovely carpets reign over red tiled floors. The rooms, admittedly rather on the small side, are perfection itself – very, very pretty indeed in a chintzy way and lovingly tended and everything shines with cleanliness and care. Even in the rooms, flowers are changed every morning and in the utter peace of this splendid place one can really reflect on the splendours of the nearby city without having one's eardrums assaulted by the Lambrettas. A real oasis of peace. Food, which used to be La Massa's weak point, is now very much better thanks to the addition of an extra kitchen. Highly recommended.

Cernobbio

GRAND HOTEL VILLA D'ESTE, Via Regina 40, 22010 Cernobbio, Lake Como

★ TELEPHONE: 511471-512471
★ CABLES: Villaeste Cernobbio
★ TELEX: 380025 Vilest I
★ RESERVATIONS: The Leading Hotels of the World
★ ROOMS: 114 doubles 39 singles
★ SUITES: 27
★ RESTAURANTS: 2
★ BARS: 4
★ DISCOTHEQUE: yes – and nightclub
★ SHOPS: 4 – jewellery, boutique, hairdresser and silk textiles
★ CONFERENCE ROOMS: 8 (10 to 250)
★ BANQUETING ROOMS: 4 (45 to 280)
★ STANDARD BEDROOM SIZE: 25 m^2
★ PRIVATE BALCONIES: yes – most rooms
★ SWIMMING POOL: yes – fresh water (two outdoor and one indoor)

★ RECREATIONAL ACTIVITIES: 8 tennis courts, 1 squash court, sauna, gym, 18-hole golf course 20 minutes away and water skiing, sailing and boating
★ GARDENS: yes
★ NO. OF STAFF: 200
★ ROOM SERVICE: 07.00–23.00
★ ORIENTATION: main facade and annexe on lake, other sides face the gardens
★ CREDIT CARDS: American Express and Visa
★ OWNING COMPANY: Villa D'Este S.p.A.
★ GENERAL MANAGER: Mario Arrigo
★ DISTANCE TO SHOPS: 5 km (Como)
★ DISTANCE FROM AIRPORT: 45 km

A sixteenth-century cardinal built the place since he liked to have his heaven here on earth. It is not known whether he made it to the ultimate address but the palazzo he left behind on the shore of Italy's most beautiful lake became home to emperors, kings and princes until a century ago when it opened its doors to us mere mortals. All one needs is money – and taste – because that is something the world-famous Villa d'Este has and requires from visitors. It is superbly palatial, colonnaded and porticoed, tapestried and marbled with a mellowness that only time can bring. It's the same with the ten-acre gardens – they were laid out in the eighteenth century, with a few monumental follies here and there and they have been growing more beautiful ever since. Villa d'Este is a way of life I wish I had the opportunity to get used to. Rooms, especially in the main building, are baronially handsome and service goes with it – quiet, unobtrusive and efficient. In the summer one dines out in the gardens and whether in or out the food is delicious. When you stay at Villa d'Este and the day trippers' boats come gliding on the lake, you just turn your eyes the other way.

Fiesole

VILLA SAN MICHELE, Via Doccia, 50014 Fiesole, Florence

★ TELEPHONE: 59451/2
★ CABLES: San Michele Fiesole
★ TELEX: 570643
★ IN OPERATION: 32 years
★ RESERVATIONS: direct
★ ROOMS: 28 doubles 2 singles
★ SUITES: 2
★ RESTAURANTS: 2
★ BARS: 2
★ DISCOTHEQUE: piano bar
★ SHOPS: none
★ CONFERENCE ROOMS: 1 (40)
★ BANQUETING ROOMS: 1 (60)
★ STANDARD BEDROOM SIZE: 24 m^2
★ PRIVATE BALCONIES: no – but general terrace

★ SWIMMING POOL: no
★ GARDENS: yes – private park overlooking the whole of Florence
★ NO. OF STAFF: 50
★ ROOM SERVICE: 07.00–24.00
★ ORIENTATION: south
★ FURTHER DEVELOPMENTS: a swimming pool
★ CREDIT CARDS: American Express
★ OWNING COMPANY: Cipriani S.p.A.
★ GENERAL MANAGER: Francesco Forlano
★ DISTANCE TO SHOPS: minutes by car
★ DISTANCE FROM AIRPORT: 7 km

A hotel whose facade (and possibly more) was designed by Michelangelo gives me the cultural sensation equal to a bedroom in the Winter Palace. If this were the only reason to stay at the Villa San Michele, it would be reason enough – but it is not. Here is a gracious and perfectly beautiful country hotel overlooking Florence and well away from the noise, looking over terraced gardens and managing to produce a feeling of wellbeing which is beyond compare. A former Franciscan monastery, it still has its own chapel and the cells transformed into magnificent bedrooms. Now the hotel has been acquired by one of the most distinguished hotel companies in Italy, no doubt San Michele will be even better than it was which, frankly, would be difficult. The place is done up with impeccable taste and every piece of furniture is just right for that spot. Out there, on the long arched terrace, Italian light-fantastic cuisine blends wonderfully with the panorama. It's Florence at its best – without the hellish and raucous Vespas.

Florence

HOTEL VILLA MEDICI, Via Il Prato, 42, Firenze

★ TELEPHONE: 261 331
★ CABLES: Mediciotel
★ TELEX: 570179
★ IN OPERATION: 22 years
★ RESERVATIONS: The Leading Hotels of the World, worldwide/Steigenberger Reservation Service, worldwide/Utell International, New York, London, Sydney, Madrid
★ ROOMS: 107
★ SUITES: 10
★ RESTAURANTS: 4
★ BARS: 1 – Lorenzo
★ DISCOTHEQUE: piano bar
★ SHOPS: 1 – leather shop
★ CONFERENCE ROOMS: 4 – 32 m² (20); 70 m² (30); 72 m² (60); 83 m² (90)

★ BANQUETING ROOMS: 1 (100)
★ STANDARD BEDROOM SIZE: 25 m²
★ PRIVATE BALCONIES: 45% have balconies
★ SWIMMING POOL: yes – fresh water
★ GARDENS: yes
★ NO. OF STAFF: 100
★ ROOM SERVICE: 06.00–01.00
★ ORIENTATION: rooms overlook convent, swimming pool and city
★ CREDIT CARDS: American Express, Diners Club, Master Charge, Eurocard
★ OWNING COMPANY: S.I.N.A.
★ GENERAL MANAGER: Manlio Giardi
★ DISTANCE TO SHOPS: 1 km
★ DISTANCE FROM AIRPORT: 80 km (Pisa)

I know one Italian gentleman who always goes to the same hotel in London because he likes the breakfast and I also know one American lady who patronizes another hotel in Rome because 'I like the bathrobes. . . .' For myself, I would go back to the Villa Medici just to climb to the top floor restaurant, order a really fine Italian dinner, sit back and look at Florence in all its beauty – it's probably the best place to do so. I do not care overmuch for the lobby (indifferent) or the bar area (a bit obvious) but the bedrooms are extremely good and pleasantly furnished and have doors giving onto a splendid private terrace. Some public rooms in the older part of the hotel are superb and so are the gardens. Service is quiet, refined and obliging and altogether it is a very worthy hotel for this splendid city.

HOTEL EXCELSIOR, Piazza Ognissanti, 3, Florence

★ TELEPHONE: 264201
★ CABLES: Italexotel
★ TELEX: 570022 Excefi I
★ IN OPERATION: since 1958
★ RESERVATIONS: CIGAHOTELS International Hotel Representatives Ltd (Italian Grand Hotels Company)

★ ROOMS: 148 doubles 59 singles
★ SUITES: 10
★ RESTAURANTS: 1 – Il Cestello
★ BARS: 2 – Donatello bar and cocktail lounge
★ DISCOTHEQUE: no – but piano music in the bar

★ SHOPS: none – only show windows
★ CONFERENCE ROOMS: 5 (up to 510)
★ BANQUETING ROOMS: 5 (up to 510)
★ STANDARD BEDROOM SIZE: 15/16 m^2
★ PRIVATE BALCONIES: yes
★ SWIMMING POOL: no
★ RECREATIONAL ACTIVITIES: golf nearby
★ GARDENS: no
★ NO. OF STAFF: 210
★ ROOM SERVICE: around the clock

★ ORIENTATION: rooms overlook the river, Piazza Ognissanti and Borgognissanti
★ CREDIT CARDS: all major credit cards
★ OWNING COMPANY: Cigahotels Centro Nord, S.p.A.
★ GENERAL MANAGER: Massimo Rosati
★ DISTANCE TO SHOPS: within shopping centre
★ DISTANCE FROM AIRPORT: 80 km (Pisa); 6 km (Peretola)

Following the last edition, many readers wrote to ask why, among several hotels in Tuscany, there was not a single one in Florence itself. Uttering polite noises I explained that it is very difficult to sleep in this fantastically beautiful city simply because of the noise of traffic and people. However, on a more recent visit to the grand old Excelsior, always a very good hotel, I discovered that it had been completely refurbished, including insulation and air-conditioning, which means that now we can sleep happily right on the bank of the Arno. This grand city hotel, with more than a little *bella figura*, has now been restored to its former glories – a magnificent lobby, beautifully furnished with period furniture and a better than average Italian welcome. I particularly liked the Donatello Bar, not one of those gaudy affairs with shiny mosaic but a place where you can sit in comfort and enjoy your drink while looking around. The newly decorated rooms are handsomely done up, with very comfortable beds and enough wardrobe space for a duchess. Service is much better than it was a few years ago and the food has also improved. A walk away are the Ponte Vecchio and the Piazza della Signoria.

Milan

EXCELSIOR HOTEL GALLIA, Piazza Duca d'Aosta 9, 20124 Milan

★ TELEPHONE: 02-6277
★ CABLES: no
★ TELEX: 311160
★ IN OPERATION: since 1932
★ RESERVATIONS: The Leading Hotels of the World, worldwide
★ ROOMS: 248
★ SUITES: 15
★ RESTAURANTS: Gallia's Restaurant – Italian cuisine
★ BARS: 1
★ DISCOTHEQUE: pianist in bar
★ SHOPS: none
★ CONFERENCE ROOMS: 7 (14 to 250)
★ BANQUETING ROOMS: 4 (50 to 300)
★ STANDARD BEDROOM SIZE: 30 m^2
★ PRIVATE BALCONIES: some rooms have balconies

★ SWIMMING POOL: no
★ RECREATIONAL ACTIVITIES: golf, tennis and swimming nearby
★ GARDENS: no
★ NO. OF STAFF: 172
★ ROOM SERVICE: 07.00–23.00
★ ORIENTATION: east and west
★ CREDIT CARDS: Eurocard, Mastercharge and Access
★ OWNING COMPANY: Excelsior Hotel Gallia S.p.A.
★ GENERAL MANAGER: Aldo Vagnozzi
★ DISTANCE TO SHOPS: hotel located in centre of Milan
★ DISTANCE FROM AIRPORT: 8 km

For a city with so much creative talent, Milan is unfortunate in its hotels – very surprising indeed and I have not yet managed to find out why this should be so. Over the years, there have been many entry changes in this book and after much deliberation, we have now settled on the Excelsior Gallia – not because it is so far ahead of the others but simply because, when it comes down to it, it has the best tradition of personal service in a city where people tend to be on the brusque side. In this hotel, this is not the case: the staff are very well trained, cheerful and friendly and they are never fazed by any odd request. Breakfasts are served promptly and table service is fine. The restaurant boasts Italian cuisine but I wish it could be a little more Italian. I cannot say that I would fall in love with the new lobby decor but the rooms, which are fairly large, are adequate if slightly impersonal. The plumbing fortunately works. But on the whole it is the human element that counts.

Montecatini Terme

GRAND HOTEL & LA PACE, Corso Roma 12, 51016 Montecatini Terme

★ TELEPHONE: (0572) 75801
★ CABLES: Paceotel
★ TELEX: 570004 Paceot
★ IN OPERATION: since 1870
★ RESERVATIONS: The Leading Hotels of the World
★ ROOMS: 96 doubles 60 singles
★ SUITES: 14
★ RESTAURANTS: 3
★ BARS: 2
★ DISCOTHEQUE: no – piano bar
★ SHOPS: none
★ CONFERENCE ROOMS: 5 (10 to 220)
★ BANQUETING ROOMS: 2 (150 and 500)
★ STANDARD BEDROOM SIZE: 20 m^2
★ PRIVATE BALCONIES: yes
★ SWIMMING POOL: yes – fresh water, 30 m

★ RECREATIONAL ACTIVITIES: Health Spa with sauna, solarium, massage, underwater massage, tennis; also horse riding and golf nearby
★ GARDENS: yes
★ NO. OF STAFF: 96
★ ROOM SERVICE: 07.00–22.00
★ ORIENTATION: south
★ CREDIT CARDS: American Express
★ OWNING COMPANY: privately owned
★ GENERAL MANAGER: Gino Degli Innocenti
★ DISTANCE TO BEACH: 60 km
★ DISTANCE TO SHOPS: walking distance
★ DISTANCE FROM AIRPORT: 50 km (Pisa)

One of the oddities about writing this book is that unless readers send in comments, one never quite knows who goes where. One German lady from Stuttgart left me in no doubt. She went to the celebrated 'La Pace' and wrote me four pages about it: 'Splendid . . . an amazing place . . . one of the most beautiful hotels I have ever visited . . . one feels like royalty in disguise'. Naturally I am glad she liked this grand old lady of all Italian spa hotels since I have always had a special reverence for it.

The vast public rooms are palatial and so are the furnishings. Everywhere one finds vistas of marble columns, great sweeps of delightfully natural grassland, mysterious nymphs beckoning into the glades – but there is nothing mysterious about the service which seems to glide along on marbled floors, loaded with silverware and tempting morsels. The food in the Versailles-sized restaurant could even tempt me to go to 'La Pace' to take the waters – it would almost be worth it. Rooms are good though some tend to be smaller than one would hope in such a huge building but on the whole they are extremely comfortable and practical.

Though the hotel can be very convivial in the international sense, I have always felt that this was the kind of place I would like to go for a personal 'retreat' like the anchorites of old. One could enjoy solitude and not suffer too much.

Positano

HOTEL LE SIRENUSE, Via C. Colombo, 30, Positano (Salerno)

★ TELEPHONE: 089-875066
★ CABLES: Sirenuse Positano
★ TELEX: 770066 Sirhtl I
★ IN OPERATION: since 1951
★ RESERVATIONS: Utell International, New

York, London/American International, New York
★ ROOMS: 58 doubles 2 singles some with jacuzzi
★ SUITES: 8

★ RESTAURANTS: 1
★ BARS: 2
★ DISCOTHEQUE: no
★ SHOPS: none
★ CONFERENCE ROOMS: 1 (up to 50)
★ BANQUETING ROOMS: 1 (up to 150)
★ STANDARD BEDROOM SIZE: 25 m²
★ PRIVATE BALCONIES: yes
★ SWIMMING POOL: yes – heated, fresh water, 20 × 6 m
★ GARDENS: no
★ NO. OF STAFF: 55

★ ROOM SERVICE: 07.00–23.00
★ ORIENTATION: rooms facing the sea
★ CREDIT CARDS: Amexco, Diners Club and Visa
★ OWNING COMPANY: Marchese Aldo Sersale
★ GENERAL MANAGER: L. Bozza
★ DISTANCE TO BEACH: 100 m
★ DISTANCE TO SHOPS: 100 m
★ DISTANCE FROM AIRPORT: 65 km (Napoli Capodichino)

The president of a multi-national corporation sent this cable from Le Sirenuse: 'Thank you for simply making my holiday and restoring my faith in the Italian way of life.' It's good to get it right sometimes and he was most welcome. Right in the middle of the Positano hillside, constructed from several of the colour-washed cubist houses that perch like the audience in an amphitheatre, Le Sirenuse is the creation of a very intelligent, very aristocratic lady who, in the course of time, acquired five houses with floors on seven different levels, added labyrinthine marble passages, furnished bedrooms the way she would have liked for herself, added a gaggle of terraces, a truly panoramic swimming pool and filled every corner with just the right bibelots. The result is that you get all the best of Positano without any of the aggro and only people like you share the place – it attracts a very good class of customer. Like most hotels in Italy, Le Sirenuse has had its problems with staff but all is now well, including the deliciously simple Italian fare, and if you want to see the overwhelming beauty of the Amalfi coast, this is the place to go, but not in July or August – October is the month I prefer here.

Rome

HOTEL EXCELSIOR, Via Vittorio Veneto 125, 00187 Rome

★ TELEPHONE: 4708
★ CABLES: Excelsior Roma
★ TELEX: Excelsior 610232
★ RESERVATIONS: Cigahotels
★ ROOMS: 415
★ SUITES: 37
★ RESTAURANTS: 2
★ BARS: 2
★ DISCOTHEQUE: no
★ SHOPS: 5
★ CONFERENCE ROOMS: 5 (40 to 600)
★ BANQUETING ROOMS: 6 (20 to 400)
★ STANDARD BEDROOM SIZE: 32 m²
★ PRIVATE BALCONIES: yes

★ SWIMMING POOL: no
★ GARDENS: no
★ NO. OF STAFF: 350
★ ROOM SERVICE: around the clock
★ ORIENTATION: main facade faces Via Veneto
★ CREDIT CARDS: American Express, Diners Club, Bankamericard, Carte Blanche and Eurocard
★ OWNING COMPANY: Cigahotels
★ GENERAL MANAGER: Mario Miconi
★ DISTANCE TO SHOPS: walking distance
★ DISTANCE FROM AIRPORT: 30 km

I have always felt that if one wants to see 'La vita all'Italiana', the best place to do so in comfort is the lobby of the Excelsior. All the chivalry and gallantry of the larger-than-life monde and demi-monde are here – film starlets, movie moghuls, richer than rich industrialists, hungry writers and those legions of beautiful but penniless people who are sure that something is going to turn up today – extras in a permanent Orson Welles–Humphrey Bogart film. Yet the fact is that the Excelsior is also one of the great hotels of the world, one which knows everything, has seen everything and is no longer capable of being in the least surprised. It has a kind of worldly-wise ambience which is quite remarkable with all the expected grandness of a grand hotel – size in public rooms, lovely period furniture, vast bathrooms and service omnipresent. The food is unexpectedly good in such circumstances and one is always surprised at how good the Excelsior remains under pressure that could easily make it very bad.

LE GRAND HOTEL, Via V. E. Orlando, 3, 00185 Rome

★ TELEPHONE: 06/4709
★ CABLES: Granotel Roma
★ TELEX: 610210 Granro I
★ IN OPERATION: since 1894
★ RESERVATIONS: Cigahotels
★ ROOMS: 117 doubles 22 singles
★ SUITES: 36
★ RESTAURANTS: 2 – Le Rallye and Le Pavilion
★ BARS: 2
★ DISCOTHEQUE: no
★ SHOPS: none
★ CONFERENCE ROOMS: 12 (10 to 600)
★ BANQUETING ROOMS: 12 (10 to 300)
★ STANDARD BEDROOM SIZE: 20 m²

★ PRIVATE BALCONIES: yes – some rooms
★ SWIMMING POOL: no
★ RECREATIONAL ACTIVITIES: sauna and massage
★ GARDENS: no
★ NO. OF STAFF: 218
★ ROOM SERVICE: around the clock
★ ORIENTATION: south
★ CREDIT CARDS: Amexco, Bankamericard, Eurocard, Carte Blanche and Visa
★ OWNING COMPANY: Cigahotels
★ GENERAL MANAGER: Nadio Benedetti
★ DISTANCE TO SHOPS: walking distance
★ DISTANCE FROM AIRPORT: 30 km

If you already have an apartment in Manhattan, a studio on the Ile St. Louis and your own Greek island, there is only one thing missing from your life – a suite at the Grand in Rome, one of the world's truly grand, grand hotels. Its fin de siècle magnificence had the right parentage – Ritz and Escoffier opened it together and it has certainly not deteriorated since. Let others have the movie starlets-à-gogo. The Grand has itself, the greatest possible attraction. It is a sumptuous place – all marble and tapestries and gilt, magnificent mirrors and flattering chandeliers. The decor of the main restaurant (scenes from the Comedia dell'Arte) is one of the two or three finest in any hotel eating place known to me. What is more, the food goes with it – splendidly delicate and even Romans agree that its pasta dishes are faultless. The staff – most of them seem to have matured with the hotel – are the last word in jovial courtesy – Italian style – they know everything, including how to get an audience with the Pope.
Not all rooms are alike – they just share a high standard. The best ones and the suites, of course, will ensure that you never want to leave – so much solid, good-taste comfort is hard to come by these days. The beds are superb, the wardrobes huge and in my bathroom there were three kinds of soap and a little note to say that if I did not like any of them I should ask for others. Perhaps what matters most at the Grand is that if you stay there, even the most superior Roman will recognize your existence.

HASSLER VILLA MEDICI, Trinita dei Monti 66, 00187 Rome

★ TELEPHONE: 678.2651/679.2651
★ CABLES: Hasslerotel
★ TELEX: 610208
★ IN OPERATION: since 1944
★ RESERVATIONS: The Leading Hotels of the World
★ ROOMS: 98
★ SUITES: 10
★ RESTAURANTS: 2 – roof restaurant and garden open air restaurant during the summer
★ BARS: 1

★ DISCOTHEQUE: no – but pianist in the bar
★ SHOPS: none
★ CONFERENCE ROOMS: 2 (25 to 60)
★ BANQUETING ROOMS: 2 (25 to 60)
★ STANDARD BEDROOM SIZE: variable
★ PRIVATE BALCONIES: yes – some rooms
★ SWIMMING POOL: no
★ GARDENS: yes
★ NO. OF STAFF: 150
★ ROOM SERVICE: 06.00–23.30
★ ORIENTATION: front faces Spanish Steps, near the Pincio Gardens

★ CREDIT CARDS: no

★ OWNING COMPANY: Hotel Hassler S.p.A.

★ GENERAL MANAGER: Mr Roberto E. Wirth

★ DISTANCE TO SHOPS: immediate

★ DISTANCE FROM AIRPORT: 35 km

Down below are the Spanish Steps. Next door is Trinita dei Monti and within a credit card's throw are all those tempting shops of the Via Sistina and the Via Condotti. If this makes the Hassler sound like a vulgar tourist's one-night-stand, go in and think again. This is one of the most elegant, most private, most refined of all the smaller hotels in European capitals – a place of exquisite taste, smooth, silent service and quality in every single detail. The word plastic is never mentioned at the Hassler. Neither is the word 'group' since this is a hotel for individuals lucky enough to be able to afford it and even luckier in being able to get in at all. The colour schemes are particularly good and here and there are antiques that must be worth a few million, million lira. The rooms are so discreet, so quiet (and in Rome too) and so beautifully organized that you immediately feel at home – if this is the kind of home you have. At the top is a sensationally beautiful restaurant where one spends as much time looking at the view as one does inspecting one's food. The Hassler is for People with an upper-case P.

Sardinia

HOTEL CALA DI VOLPE, 1-07020 Porto Cervo, Costa Smeralda

★ TELEPHONE: 0789 96083

★ CABLES: Calavolpe Portocervo

★ TELEX: 790274

★ IN OPERATION: 21 years

★ RESERVATIONS: The Leading Hotels of the World

★ ROOMS: 125

★ RESTAURANTS: 1 – plus a poolside barbecue

★ BARS: 3

★ DISCOTHEQUE: yes

★ SHOPS: 5 – boutiques, drugstore and hairdressers

★ CONFERENCE ROOMS: none

★ BANQUETING ROOMS: none

★ STANDARD BEDROOM SIZE: 20/30 m^2

★ PRIVATE BALCONIES: yes

★ SWIMMING POOL: yes – salt water

★ RECREATIONAL ACTIVITIES: boating, water skiing, underwater fishing, tennis and golf close by; private harbour for pleasure boats

★ GARDENS: yes

★ NO. OF STAFF: 185

★ ROOM SERVICE: around the clock

★ ORIENTATION: mainly south

★ CREDIT CARDS: American Express, Diners Club, Master Charge, Visa and Eurocard

★ OWNING COMPANY: Costa Smeralda Corporation

★ GENERAL MANAGER: G. Daina

★ DISTANCE TO BEACH: walking distance

★ DISTANCE TO SHOPS: walking distance

★ DISTANCE FROM AIRPORT: 30 km (Olbia)

Architect Jacques Couelle is celebrated the world over as the master of 'the perfect imperfect' and he spent years designing Cala di Volpe for his then client, the Aga Khan, and, although I personally dislike the present being made to look like the past, I must admit that this hotel succeeds where others of the kind would fail miserably. The reason isn't only money – just good taste aplenty with not a single offending note, not a single overstatement in this serpentine cluster of buildings hugging a heavenly peninsula. Rooms are deceptively simple and highly luxurious when you look into the details and the apparent rusticity of the decor comes off with a gentle flourish. Service is impeccable and the food very distinguished indeed and all around you is the incredible Costa Smeralda. What makes Casa di Volpe in the long run is its guests – their lifestyle, their clothes, their personality adds to the hotel picture.

HOTEL PITRIZZA, Liscia di Vacca, 07020 Porto Cervo-Costa Smeralda

★ TELEPHONE: (0789) 92000
★ CABLES: Hotel Pitrizza
★ TELEX: Pitrizza 790037
★ IN OPERATION: since 1964
★ RESERVATIONS: direct and travel agents
★ ROOMS: 22 doubles 6 singles
★ SUITES: 1 (1 double, 1 single, sitting room, bathroom)
★ RESTAURANTS: 1 – and barbecue
★ DISCOTHEQUE: none – but piano bar
★ SHOPS: none
★ CONFERENCE ROOMS: none
★ BANQUETING ROOMS: none
★ STANDARD BEDROOM SIZE: 26 m^2
★ PRIVATE BALCONIES: yes – most of the rooms
★ SWIMMING POOL: yes – salt water, 150 m^2
★ RECREATIONAL ACTIVITIES: tennis club

and golf club nearby; windsurfing, scuba diving, swimming, boat hire
★ GARDENS: yes – 4 acres
★ NO. OF STAFF: 53
★ ROOM SERVICE: around the clock
★ ORIENTATION: clubhouse faces north-east but each villa has a different orientation
★ CREDIT CARDS: American Express, Diners Club and Eurocard
★ OWNING COMPANY: Costa Smeralda Hotels
★ GENERAL MANAGER: Gianfranco Ghione
★ DISTANCE TO BEACH: on the beach
★ DISTANCE TO SHOPS: 4 km to Porto Cervo Village
★ DISTANCE FROM AIRPORT: 30 km Olbia/Costa Smeralda. Private bus service to and from airport

Rusticity only becomes an art form when it is carried out with real respect for nature. Pitrizza is like that – one of the nicest, most informal and yet most elegant hotels I know in the Mediterranean. The Costa Smeralda has a lot of this, of course, but for me the small Pitrizza is the best – a place where one lives simply but gorgeously, comfortably and yet without any of the trappings that appear necessary elsewhere. Rooms are in small private villas, scattered over the rocks overlooking a divine beach. Any one of them will please you, with its own, ultra-private terrace, spacious rooms and decor that is deceptively simple. The Pitrizza is a club-like hotel whose members or habitués appear to know each other without in the least wishing for artificial conviviality. As a resort hotel this one must be one of the most superior for a very long way in all directions.

Siena

CERTOSA DI MAGGIANO, Strada di Certosa No. 82, Siena

★ TELEPHONE: 0577/288180 42083
★ CABLES: Certosotel
★ TELEX: 574221
★ IN OPERATION: since 1975
★ RESERVATIONS: direct/Relais et Chateaux, Paris
★ ROOMS: 5
★ SUITES: 9
★ RESTAURANTS: 1 – also buffet by the swimming pool in the high season
★ BARS: 1 – also one at the swimming pool from April to September
★ DISCOTHEQUE: no – but music in the library
★ SHOPS: none
★ CONFERENCE ROOMS: none
★ BANQUETING ROOMS: none
★ STANDARD BEDROOM SIZE: 28 m^2
★ PRIVATE BALCONIES: yes
★ SWIMMING POOL: yes – fresh water, heated, 12 × 6 m

★ NO. OF STAFF: 20
★ RECREATIONAL ACTIVITIES: tennis and game of draughts in the garden on the ground
★ GARDENS: yes – a large park and promenades in an olive tree garden
★ ROOM SERVICE: 08.00–23.00
★ ORIENTATION: main facade overlooks the country
★ FURTHER DEVELOPMENTS: a further six rooms to be developed
★ CREDIT CARDS: American Express, Diners Club, Bankamericard and Visa
★ OWNING COMPANY: I.T.A.R. S.p.A.
★ GENERAL MANAGER: Anna Grossi Recordati
★ DISTANCE TO BEACH: 60 km
★ DISTANCE TO SHOPS: 1.5 km
★ DISTANCE FROM AIRPORT: 120 km (Pisa)

Whoever uses the word 'Siena' has uttered a noble word – one of two or three favourite Italian cities – I hardly need an excuse to go back and sit on that superlative Piazza del Campo and find the way back to those centuries when people had time to stop, think, create beauty and live with it. And, as is so often the case in Italy, I know just the right place to rest my head. Certosa di Maggiano is a delightful thirteenth-century Carthusian monastery, complete with arched cloister around a divinely proportioned square, ancient gardens with ancient olive trees and so few guests that one feels like being in a friend's house. Both bedrooms and public rooms are extremely tastefully furnished with very good pieces and floors shining with the patina of ages.

The flowers are always fresh and the books lining the library walls look as if they are occasionally read and there are splendid tapestries and paintings everywhere. The lady manager obviously loves the place and so do I because it is just right for Siena which is just a short walk away. The food, while not great, is very acceptable but what counts above all is the atmosphere of the place – calm, civilized and good-mannered.

Taormina

MAZZÁRO SEA PALACE, 98030 Taormina, Sicily

- ★ TELEPHONE: 0942/24004
- ★ CABLES: Palace
- ★ TELEX: 980041 Maseap
- ★ IN OPERATION: since 1972
- ★ RESERVATIONS: The Leading Hotels of the World, New York and London/Italhotels, Torino/Steigenberger Reservation Service, Frankfurt
- ★ ROOMS: 63 doubles 14 singles
- ★ SUITES: 4
- ★ RESTAURANTS: 2 – Bougainvillea and Terrace Restaurant
- ★ BARS: 2 (Piano Bar)
- ★ DISCOTHEQUE: no – but live entertainment
- ★ SHOPS: 1
- ★ CONFERENCE ROOMS: 2 (30 to 300)
- ★ BANQUETING ROOMS: 1 (up to 300)
- ★ STANDARD BEDROOM SIZE: 30 m^2
- ★ PRIVATE BALCONIES: yes
- ★ SWIMMING POOL: yes – salt water, heated, 120 m^2
- ★ RECREATIONAL ACTIVITIES: water sports and tennis available at the Sporting Club in Taormina
- ★ GARDENS: yes
- ★ NO. OF STAFF: 75
- ★ ROOM SERVICE: 07.00–24.00
- ★ ORIENTATION: all rooms overlook the sea
- ★ CREDIT CARDS: American Express, Diners Club and Bankamericard
- ★ OWNING COMPANY: Tirrena Hotels

★ MANAGER: Giovanni Cacopardo
★ DISTANCE TO BEACH: on the beach
★ DISTANCE TO SHOPS: 2 km
★ DISTANCE FROM AIRPORT: 50 km

I have had one or two comments from people who don't like this hotel. Too modern, they say. I, on the contrary, feel that if a hotel is going to be modern, this is the way it should be – the best style, the best design. It is certainly no shy violet, hugging the sands of Taormina beach. You can't miss it, but for the rest it is to my mind an exceedingly good and thoughtfully planned beach hotel. Rooms are very large by continental standards; public rooms are vast and cool and one can glide in and out effortlessly and the private terraces – rare in this part of the world – are large enough to swing a tiger in yet one is never overlooked. What appeals to me most of all, after the cheap-and-nasty beach furniture one sees everywhere these days, is that the Mazzaro variety is handsome, practical and always very clean. Food tends to be somewhat international but who cares in this case? Lovely, mellow Taormina is just up the road and its trattorie are legion. The Mazzaro could be the place for some sun-soaking. But don't go there in July or August.

SAN DOMENICO PALACE HOTEL, Piazza S. Domenico, 5, 98039 Taormina

★ TELEPHONE: 0942-23701
★ CABLES: Sandomenico
★ TELEX: 980013 DOMHOT
★ IN OPERATION: 100 years
★ RESERVATIONS: Utell International
★ ROOMS: 88 doubles 31 singles
★ SUITES: 10
★ RESTAURANTS: 2
★ BARS: 2
★ DISCOTHEQUE: no – but piano in the bar and restaurant every night and a Sicilian mandolin orchestra on Fridays and Sundays
★ SHOPS: none
★ CONFERENCE ROOMS: 3 (30, 100 and 450)
★ BANQUETING ROOMS: 1 (350)
★ STANDARD BEDROOM SIZE: 25 m^2
★ PRIVATE BALCONIES: yes
★ SWIMMING POOL: yes – fresh water, 14 × 5 m
★ RECREATIONAL ACTIVITIES: tennis and water skiing
★ GARDENS: yes
★ NO. OF STAFF: 100
★ ROOM SERVICE: 07.00–23.00
★ ORIENTATION: south and facing Mount Etna

★ CREDIT CARDS: Bankamericard, American Express, Diners Club and Eurocard

★ OWNING COMPANY: Atahotels S.p.A.

★ GENERAL MANAGER: Harald Glogner

★ DISTANCE TO BEACH: 4 km

★ DISTANCE TO SHOPS: 60 m

★ DISTANCE FROM AIRPORT: 50 km

Looking out to Taormina's Greek theatre and the distant profile of Mount Etna, the gardens of this hotel, overflowing with bloom and lovely trees dotted with formally rustic seats and ravishing pines of classical statuary, one looks down to a very large and handsome swimming pool. San Domenico started life as a Dominican monastery in the fourteenth century and the monastic austerity has been tempered with some of the later Renaissance exuberance which prosperity and a falling off of devotion brought in its train. The furnishings are quite beautiful, especially the antiques along the interior cloister. Sicily has always resisted conquerors, and even as rulers, this method has chiefly been the Mafia or its style. Here you will not be kidnapped or shot because you are too important to molest – they will only take you if they know your disposable assets to the last shilling. Sicily has ever been rough on its enemies and kind to its friends.

Venice

HOTEL CIPRIANI, Giudecca 10, 30123 Venice

★ TELEPHONE: (041) 70-77-44

★ CABLES: Hotel Cipriani-Venezia

★ TELEX: 410162 CIPRVE I

★ IN OPERATION: since 1958

★ RESERVATIONS: The Leading Hotels of the World/Fairways & Swinford Travel Ltd, London

★ ROOMS: 90 doubles 4 singles

★ SUITES: 18

★ RESTAURANTS: 2 – Cipriani and Il Gabbiano

★ BARS: 2

★ DISCOTHEQUE: no – but piano bar

★ SHOPS: 2

★ CONFERENCE ROOMS: 4 (50 to 120)

★ BANQUETING ROOMS: 4 (50 to 250)

★ STANDARD BEDROOM SIZE: 30 m^2

★ PRIVATE BALCONIES: yes

★ SWIMMING POOL: yes – salt water, 192 m^2

★ RECREATIONAL ACTIVITIES: new green-set tennis on premises; golf on the Lido; own private yacht harbour – 10 berths; sauna, solarium, steam cabinet, whirlpool baths

★ GARDENS: yes

★ NO. OF STAFF: 160

★ ROOM SERVICE: around the clock

★ ORIENTATION: rooms overlook water and gardens

★ CREDIT CARDS: American Express

★ OWNING COMPANY: Hotel Cipriani S.p.A.

★ GENERAL MANAGER: N. Rusconi

★ DISTANCE TO BEACH: 20 minutes by boat

★ DISTANCE TO SHOPS: 4 minutes by boat

★ DISTANCE FROM AIRPORT: 10 km

For all those who love Venice but hate its crowds, there is only one address: Cipriani's. Here, on Giudecca, a mere few minutes from the heart of this immortal city, is a haven of peace and tranquillity run with omnipresent discretion by one of the great hoteliers of this world. Cipriani's is chic – perhaps the only word for it – but chic with a kind of easy-going grand manner: *bella figura* if you like. The rooms and suites are all different, light and pleasant and some of them have their own terrace-garden right on the pool which, incidentally, is the only hotel pool in Venice. There is a gentleness about Cipriani which soon gets you. The famous gardens are so tenderly cared for that one would swear that's the way things grow, i.e., flowers blooming overnight. Dining out of doors in the soft, velvety Venetian night is one of the rarest pleasures of life. On re-examination, I still believe that the cuisine is the finest of any hotel in Venice and, happily, the world is full of ex-Cipriani chefs who made it here first. The perfect place in which to relax elegantly.

HOTEL GRITTI PALACE, Canal Grande 30100, Venice

★ TELEPHONE: 26044
★ CABLES: Palace Venice
★ TELEX: 410125 Gritti
★ IN OPERATION: since 1948
★ RESERVATIONS: Cigahotels
★ ROOMS: 74 doubles 17 singles
★ SUITES: 11
★ RESTAURANTS: 2
★ BARS: 1
★ DISCOTHEQUE: no
★ SHOPS: none
★ CONFERENCE ROOMS: 4 (15 to 150)
★ BANQUETING ROOMS: 4 (15 to 90)
★ STANDARD BEDROOM SIZE: 25 m^2

★ PRIVATE BALCONIES: yes – some rooms
★ SWIMMING POOL: no
★ GARDENS: no
★ NO. OF STAFF: 110
★ ROOM SERVICE: around the clock
★ ORIENTATION: overlooks Grand Canal
★ CREDIT CARDS: American Express, Diners Club, Bankamericard and Eurocard
★ OWNING COMPANY: Cigahotels
★ GENERAL MANAGER: Nico Passante
★ DISTANCE TO BEACH: 2 km
★ DISTANCE TO SHOPS: 5 minutes
★ DISTANCE FROM AIRPORT: 10 km

What can one say about the Gritti that has not been said a thousand times before? The best loved hotel in the world? The most beautiful? The most original? The most intimate? All adjectival extravaganzas would be justified by this gem of a palace on the Grand Canal and when you enter the world-famous Grill Room to look at the portrait of the old Doge whose home this was, you know that you have arrived, if not socially, then in a unique place. The Gritti is like a casket of jewels – perfection, artistry, great and never-failing good taste: the kind of place where one looks in vain for the almost inevitable faux pas. This is the kind of hotel hospitality that cannot be manufactured but only evolved over the years by a company, a management and a staff who really do care for beauty and quality. If you can have a canal-facing room, or better still, one of the corner ones, you will surely feel as I do that nothing can match it. What is more, the Gritti is not just a beautiful antique. It works smoothly and with a kind of gallant cheerfulness that is remarkable. It seems that everybody instinctively knows what you want. I always end my Venice visit with dinner on the Grand Canal terrace – just to remind myself that heaven exists, here on earth, if you know the right address.

Venice Lido

EXCELSIOR HOTEL, Lungomare Marconi, 40, Lido Venice

★ TELEPHONE: 760201
★ CABLES: Excelido
★ TELEX: 410023 Exceve
★ RESERVATIONS: Cigahotels
★ ROOMS: 252
★ SUITES: 18
★ RESTAURANTS: 3
★ BARS: 3
★ DISCOTHEQUE: Le Maschere (night club)
★ SHOPS: 9
★ CONFERENCE ROOMS: 9 (5 to 650)
★ BANQUETING ROOMS: 5 (500 to 1500)
★ STANDARD BEDROOM SIZE: 40 m^2
★ PRIVATE BALCONIES: yes

★ SWIMMING POOL: yes – fresh water
★ GARDENS: yes
★ NO. OF STAFF: 265
★ ROOM SERVICE: around the clock
★ ORIENTATION: rooms face Adriatic Sea and Lagoon
★ CREDIT CARDS: American Express, Diners Club, Eurocard, Bankamericard, Carte Blanche and Access
★ OWNING COMPANY: Cigahotels
★ GENERAL MANAGER: Ugo Balaudo
★ DISTANCE TO BEACH: walking distance
★ DISTANCE FROM AIRPORT: 15 km

One of the finest grand hotels in all Italy, of the water-side hotels, the Excelsior lives the way it and its guests want and produces a feeling of wellbeing which is unique in such surroundings. The Excelsior has *bella figura*, that odd blend of showbiz, society and good taste that lifts it straight out of the ordinary. To be seen there is the most important thing of all to the Venetians and to be seen with the right companion is even more important because this is the cynosure of the up-market paparazzi. The new strand, with its well ordered army of cabanas, could only have been produced in Italy – you can be by the sea without spoiling your shoes. The Excelsior is chic, resplendent, very beautifully furnished and serviced by people who know what service is. I even like the modernized rooms where real designers have had a say. At night, dining on that divine terrace is one of the great moments of one's stay in Venice.

Verona
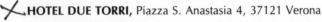
HOTEL DUE TORRI, Piazza S. Anastasia 4, 37121 Verona

- ★ TELEPHONE: 045-595 044
- ★ CABLES: no
- ★ TELEX: 480524
- ★ IN OPERATION: since 1958
- ★ RESERVATIONS: The Leading Hotels of the World, worldwide
- ★ ROOMS: 100
- ★ SUITES: 13
- ★ RESTAURANTS: 2
- ★ BARS: 2
- ★ DISCOTHEQUE: live music in piano bar
- ★ SHOPS: no
- ★ CONFERENCE ROOMS: 4 (32 to 250)
- ★ BANQUETING ROOMS: 2 (60 to 200)
- ★ STANDARD BEDROOM SIZE: 24 m²
- ★ PRIVATE BALCONIES: no

- ★ SWIMMING POOL: no
- ★ RECREATIONAL ACTIVITIES: golf, riding and tennis nearby
- ★ GARDENS: no
- ★ NO. OF STAFF: 90
- ★ ROOM SERVICE: around the clock
- ★ ORIENTATION: west
- ★ CREDIT CARDS: Diners Club, American Express, Visa and Eurocard
- ★ OWNING COMPANY: Dr Enrico Waldner (proprietor)
- ★ GENERAL MANAGER: Raimondo Giavarini
- ★ DISTANCE TO SHOPS: hotel located in centre of Verona
- ★ DISTANCE FROM AIRPORT: 170 km (Milan); 150 km (Venice)

Apart from Venice and Florence, Italy's great art cities are not well off for good hotels. One gets the feeling that locals are saying, 'If you wish to see this or that masterpiece, who cares where you stay. . .'. Verona is an exception with the Due Torri, though it too has had its ups and downs over the years. Now it seems to be back on course – a very plush and comfortable hotel, not too big and with excellent service. You won't have to rough it after all in Romeo and Juliet's home pad. Certainly not in the food line – at the Due Torri this is now one of the best features – solid, traditional Italian food. Rooms are on the whole good and, miracles of miracles for Italy, the air-conditioning works in those hot, sticky summers and you will be glad of it when you return from sightseeing. Furnishings are period, a trifle mixed up perhaps, but good, unobjectionable stuff. And despite the tourist flood, the staff have managed to remain nice.

IVORY COAST
Abidjan
HOTEL IVOIRE INTER-CONTINENTAL, 08 B.P. 1 Abidjan 08

- ★ TELEPHONE: (225) 44-10-45
- ★ CABLES: Inhotelcor Abidjan
- ★ TELEX: 23555 IHC HOT CI
- ★ IN OPERATION: since 1963
- ★ RESERVATIONS: Inter-Continental Hotels Corporation
- ★ ROOMS: 750
- ★ SUITES: 45
- ★ RESTAURANTS: 5
- ★ BARS: 3
- ★ DISCOTHEQUE: yes – and a piano bar

- ★ SHOPS: 14
- ★ CONFERENCE ROOMS: 14 (30 to 2000) Business centre equipped with telefax and library, offering professional secretariat and translation services; 24-hour Reuters world news and stock exchange plus two films each day on video in each room
- ★ BANQUETING ROOMS: 9 (15 to 1200)
- ★ STANDARD BEDROOM SIZE: 25 m²
- ★ PRIVATE BALCONIES: yes

★ SWIMMING POOL: yes – 2, fresh water, 312 m²
★ RECREATIONAL ACTIVITIES: tennis, 18-hole golf course, driving range, bowling alley, ice skating rink, health club with gymnasium, sauna and massage
★ GARDENS: yes
★ NO. OF STAFF: 750
★ ROOM SERVICE: around the clock
★ ORIENTATION: the back faces the residential Cocody area and the front faces the lagoon and the commercial area
★ CREDIT CARDS: Amexco, Diners Club, Carte Blanche, Master Charge, Visa, Bankamericard and Eurocard
★ OWNING COMPANY: Société du Palace de Cocody
★ GENERAL MANAGER: Tom J. Krooswijk
★ DISTANCE TO BEACH: 24 km
★ DISTANCE TO SHOPS: 10 minutes by car
★ DISTANCE FROM AIRPORT: 20 km

This is the best city hotel in black Africa. Having had the pleasure of revisiting the Ivoire, I am in no doubt at all about it. Though Abidjan – the Paris of West Africa – is not exactly the bush, running this kind of enterprise, very big and busy, cannot be easy but I have nothing but praise for management and staff. There is a huge, quite attractive tower block and a more sober, sideways one next door facing a gigantic pool and the famous lagoon. There, conference rooms, saunas, cinema, casino and, name it, the Ivoire has got it. Also some very attractive gardens, well laid out and well kept. American parentage and French influence have combined to produce a kind of hotel that is very rare in the African continent – everything works, laundry, service, messages, shopping, bars and restaurants. The choice of food is vast and attractive – I like the open-air Pavilion restaurant and also the spectacular Toit d'Abidjan. One is impressed by the expertise from the top-class general manager down to the room boy.

JAPAN
Hakone
FUJIYA HOTEL, 359 Miyanoshita, Hakone

★ TELEPHONE: (0460) 2-2211
★ CABLES: Fujiyahotel
★ TELEX: 3892-718
★ RESERVATIONS: direct
★ ROOMS: 150
★ SUITES: 8
★ RESTAURANTS: 3
★ BARS: 1
★ DISCOTHEQUE: no
★ SHOPS: 1
★ CONFERENCE ROOMS: 5 (8 to 260)
★ BANQUETING ROOMS: 3 (30 to 250)
★ STANDARD BEDROOM SIZE: 40 m²
★ PRIVATE BALCONIES: no
★ SWIMMING POOL: yes – 2, indoors and outdoors
★ GARDENS: yes
★ NO. OF STAFF: 200
★ ROOM SERVICE: 10.00–22.00
★ ORIENTATION: mainly east
★ CREDIT CARDS: American Express, Diners Club and Master Charge
★ OWNING COMPANY: Fujiya Hotel Co
★ GENERAL MANAGER: Susumu Saito
★ DISTANCE FROM AIRPORT: 160 km (Narita)

If, apart from the big cities, I had to pick one hotel in Japan, the Fujiya would be it. It's a kind of Japanese Victorian folly, if you can imagine the combination – odd, personal, full of curious corners and recesses and vast bedrooms filled, or should one say, dotted with charmingly useless eastern-western furniture. The staff simply never stop bowing from morning to night and wear a perpetual Japanese show of teeth. But here it is really the gardens that are impressive in the best traditional manner – gorgeous trees, both oversized and undersized, miniature lawns, cascades and pools, cherry blossom and a score of those little Japanese bridges and interesting stones that are complemented by running water. The whole place is truly enchanting, and lies in the middle of the Hakone National Park. Tokyo and its suicidal taxi-drivers look even worse from here.

Kyoto

MIYAKO HOTEL, Sanjo Keage, Kyoto, 605

★ TELEPHONE: (075) 771-7111
★ CABLES: Miyako Kyoto
★ TELEX: 5422-132 Miyako J
★ IN OPERATION: since 1893
★ RESERVATIONS: affiliated with Western International Hotels/Robert F. Warner, New York/John A. Tetley Co, Inc, Los Angeles
★ ROOMS: 422 doubles 21 singles
★ SUITES: 10
★ RESTAURANTS: 7
★ BARS: 1
★ DISCOTHEQUE: live music nightly
★ SHOPS: 27
★ CONFERENCE ROOMS: 15 (40 to 900)
★ BANQUETING ROOMS: 15 (20 to 750)

★ STANDARD BEDROOM SIZE: 33 m^2
★ PRIVATE BALCONIES: yes
★ SWIMMING POOL: yes – 4, fresh water
★ GARDENS: yes
★ NO. OF STAFF: 540
★ ROOM SERVICE: 07.15–23.00
★ ORIENTATION: some rooms face the street, others face gardens and hills
★ CREDIT CARDS: American Express, Diners Club, Carte Blanche, Bankamericard and Master Charge
★ OWNING COMPANY: Westin Hotels Inc
★ GENERAL MANAGER: R. Harada
★ DISTANCE TO SHOPS: 5 minutes by car
★ DISTANCE FROM AIRPORT: 50 km

Kyoto is rather like the Tower of London or Stratford-upon-Avon – the tourist is led there as to an abyss, and the clever travellers stay at the Miyako which is even better because here one can have the new Japan (rather like everywhere else) or the old Japan (quite unique and unlike anywhere else). The new wing is certainly equipped with enough gadgets to take off into space but you will find the Japanese wing, with its authentic Japanese rooms – sliding windows opening up on vast banks of azaleas and a superb 16-acre Japanese garden – a far more rewarding place to stay. If I had to pick on two things that are special to the Miyako, I would bestow the accolade on the extraordinary cleanliness of the place and the cheerful and omnipresent service, complete with so many bows and salutations that one feels embarrassed. One has a vast variety of choices of things to eat but, of course, the best is the Japanese cuisine.

Osaka

THE PLAZA, 2-49, Oyodo-Minami 2-chome, Oyodo-ku, Osaka 531

★ TELEPHONE: (06) 453-1111
★ CABLES: Plazahotel Osaka
★ TELEX: 524-5557 Plaosa J
★ IN OPERATION: 15 years
★ RESERVATIONS: The Leading Hotels in the World
★ ROOMS: 534
★ SUITES: 16
★ RESTAURANTS: 6 – Rendez-vous Grill, Belvedere, Hanagiri, Sui-En, Yodo and The Plaza Pantry
★ BARS: 3 bars, 1 cocktail lounge
★ DISCOTHEQUE: live music in Vista Lounge and Belvedere Restaurant
★ SHOPS: 18 – including watches and clocks, electrical goods, china, furniture, clothes, books, beauty salon, barber, food and chemist

★ CONFERENCE ROOMS: 20
★ BANQUETING ROOMS: 20
★ STANDARD BEDROOM SIZE: 33 m^2
★ PRIVATE BALCONIES: no
★ SWIMMING POOL: yes – fresh water
★ RECREATIONAL ACTIVITIES: Japanese tea ceremony room
★ GARDENS: yes
★ NO. OF STAFF: 700
★ ROOM SERVICE: around the clock
★ ORIENTATION: rooms face north and south
★ CREDIT CARDS: all major credit cards
★ OWNING COMPANY: Asahi Broadcasting Corporation
★ GENERAL MANAGER: Hiroshi Ohno
★ DISTANCE TO SHOPS: 1 km
★ DISTANCE FROM AIRPORT: 13 km

On my first visit to the Plaza, I recall a charming young Japanese lady coming forward as I checked in, bowing and saying: 'Mr Lecler, you have a French name and a British passport. Would you please prefer to be addressed in French or in English?' Well, well.

I immediately wondered what other highlights lay in store. Quite a few – the biggest lobby I have ever seen, a delicious stone garden such as only Japanese can create, a gorgeous swimming pool (right in the middle of Osaka . . .), clean, good-looking furniture, a Japanese orchestra whose members can play Mendelssohn as if born to it and one of the finest European restaurants in the Far East where most of the dishes were created by Paul Bocuse and Louis Outhier and a wedding ceremony room which even at my advanced age I would have been tempted to use had it not meant risking a jail sentence.

In Japan, nowadays the country of the perfectionist, the Plaza is known as the hotel with everything and I for one could certainly not find anything missing in this splendid example of hotelmanship. One can no longer joke about Japanese hotels. One develops respect and admiration.

ROYAL HOTEL, 3-68, Nakanoshima 5-chome, Kita-Ku, Osaka

★ TELEPHONE: (06) 448-1121
★ CABLES: Royalhotel, Osaka
★ TELEX: J63350 Royalhtl
★ IN OPERATION: 49 years
★ RESERVATIONS: Steigenberger Reservation Service/Japan Airlines/Japan Travel Bureau International Inc
★ ROOMS: 835 doubles 600 singles
★ SUITES: 65
★ RESTAURANTS: 17
★ BARS: 4
★ DISCOTHEQUE: live music and dancing nightly in Sky Lounge and musical entertainment in the Cellar Bar
★ SHOPS: 60
★ CONFERENCE ROOMS: 30 (10 to 1500)
★ BANQUETING ROOMS: 30 (25 to 3000)

★ STANDARD BEDROOM SIZE: 30 m^2
★ PRIVATE BALCONIES: no
★ SWIMMING POOL: yes – fresh water, heated, indoor 25 m
★ RECREATIONAL ACTIVITIES: sauna, gym and health club; cultural school in hotel
★ GARDENS: yes
★ NO. OF STAFF: 1100
★ ROOM SERVICE: 06.00–02.00
★ ORIENTATION: faces all directions
★ CREDIT CARDS: American Express, Diners Club, Carte Blanche, Bankamericard and Master Charge
★ OWNING COMPANY: The Royal Hotel Ltd
★ GENERAL MANAGER: Minoru Watanabe
★ DISTANCE TO SHOPS: 10 minutes by car
★ DISTANCE FROM AIRPORT: 16 km

One of the most surprising hotels in the world. Certainly one of the biggest – 1600 rooms, 58 banqueting rooms, 17 restaurants and half a hundred shops. On my first visit to the Royal I wondered how could people run a hotel this size? Well, the Japanese can and do with a style all of their own. In one corner I even discovered some pottery by Bernard Leach next to the Japanese counterpart. The gardens are an absolute poem – a twenty-four syllable haiku perhaps – created by someone with more than the usual Japanese green finger. I approached the French restaurant with trepidation only to find that the onion soup was as good as in Montmartre. There are five Japanese restaurants and one of those marvellous beef places one finds only in Japan. Of the public rooms I much preferred the Japanese lounge, with its marvellous panels, to the main lobby – about the size of the Place de la Concorde. What was a revelation was the personalized service in such an enormous caravanserai – even the floor staff greeted us by name, missing all the 'r's, of course. When modernity is like this, tempered with good taste, I have no objection.

HOTEL OKURA, 10-4 Toranomon, 2-chome, Minato-ku, Tokyo 105

★ TELEPHONE: (03) 582-0111
★ CABLES: Hotelokura
★ TELEX: J 22790 Tokyo 242-2014
★ IN OPERATION: since 1962
★ RESERVATIONS: The Leading Hotels of the World, worldwide/Hotel Okura

Europe Office, Amsterdam/Robert F. Warner, London, New York/John A. Tetley Co, Inc, Los Angeles/Utell International (UK) Ltd, Sydney, Melbourne/Muriel Fleger International, Toronto

★ ROOMS: 980
★ SUITES: 68
★ RESTAURANTS: 8
★ BARS: 4
★ DISCOTHEQUE: no – but piano in French restaurant and music in bar
★ SHOPS: 41
★ CONFERENCE ROOMS: 36 (up to 3000)
★ BANQUETING ROOMS: 36 (up to 3000)
★ STANDARD BEDROOM SIZE: 32 m^2
★ PRIVATE BALCONIES: yes – all rooms on fifth floor (main building)
★ SWIMMING POOL: yes – 2 fresh water
★ RECREATIONAL ACTIVITIES: health club and gymnasium, steam bath, Japanese massage, platform tennis and spa

★ GARDENS: yes – Japanese garden
★ NO. OF STAFF: 1600
★ ROOM SERVICE: 06.00–01.00
★ ORIENTATION: rooms face various directions
★ CREDIT CARDS: Access, American Express, Bankamericard, Barclaycard/Visa, American Torch Club, Chargex, Diners Club, Carte Blanche, Eurocard and Master Card
★ OPERATING COMPANY: Okura
★ GENERAL MANAGER: T. Goto
★ DISTANCE TO SHOPS: central
★ DISTANCE FROM AIRPORT: 60 km

One thing I will never forget about the Okura is the first waiter I spoke to in the French restaurant. He spoke English with a French accent, had been trained in France and learnt English in Japan. When I switched over to French he was absolutely delighted and served my meal with total Gallic aplomb. Another thing I like about this very large hotel is that it is one of the quietest in Tokyo (only Rio is noisier). Modern as can be, the Okura manages to be all things to all travellers – there are eleven types of rooms (Japanese too) and in each case the decor fits in beautifully. It is convenient, well equipped and superbly managed and works with an efficiency which is by now a legend. The doorman keeps a little pad handy and, when you ask for a taxi (each one is driven by a younger kamikaze pilot), he notes where you want to go and hands it to the driver. There is the tea ceremony too if you insist. Plus fresh flowers everywhere, very beautiful Japanese paintings and though you cannot dial the Kremlin on the telephone yet, it surely won't be long.

✓IMPERIAL HOTEL, 1-1-1, Uchisaiwai-cho, Chiyoda-ku, Tokyo 100

★ TELEPHONE: 03-504-1111
★ CABLES: Impho Tokyo
★ TELEX: 222-2346 IMPHOJ
★ IN OPERATION: since 1890
★ RESERVATIONS: Steigenberger Reservation Service/Japan Travel Bureau International Inc/Japan Airlines/ Preferred Hotels Association/Utell International
★ ROOMS: 1135
★ SUITES: 76
★ RESTAURANTS: 6 – Fontainebleau, Prunier, Rainbow Room, Coffee House 'Cycles', Les Saisons and La Brasserie
★ BARS: 4
★ DISCOTHEQUE: no – but live music in the Rainbow Room
★ SHOPS: shopping arcade
★ CONFERENCE ROOMS: 27 (30 to 3000)
★ BANQUETING ROOMS: 27 (30 to 3000)

★ STANDARD BEDROOM SIZE: 37 m^2
★ PRIVATE BALCONIES: no
★ SWIMMING POOL: yes – and sauna and massage
★ GARDENS: yes
★ NO. OF STAFF: 1500
★ ROOM SERVICE: 07.00–01.00
★ ORIENTATION: overlooking the Imperial Palace grounds and Hibiya Park
★ CREDIT CARDS: Diners Club, American Express, Master Charge, Bankamericard, Carte Blanche and Eurocard
★ OWNING COMPANY: Imperial Hotel Ltd
★ GENERAL MANAGER: Ichiro Inumaru
★ DISTANCE TO BEACH: 2 km
★ DISTANCE TO SHOPS: 5 minutes
★ DISTANCE FROM AIRPORT: 65 km (Narita); 10 km (Haneda)

The Emperor of Japan lives next door and, although one can't see him, one is obviously close to the fount of power. When I first knew it, the Imperial used to be as reassuringly old-fashioned as I suspect the palace itself must be, but not any more. Like most things in Japan it's the last word in size and appearance. One banqueting room is a mere 28,000 square feet and in the enormous marble lobby you need a little Honda to get to the reception desk ninety feet away. Yet it all works very smoothly, with lots of little bows and nowhere does it offend because Japanese architects are far too well educated – cultured – for that. The rooms are large, very simply and unostentatiously modern and the suites are big enough for a board meeting. What surprised me despite all this is that the service is delightfully personalized, quiet and efficient. There are six restaurants and you can gorge yourself on tempura or on French cuisine.

JORDAN

Amman

JORDAN INTER-CONTINENTAL, P.O. Box 35014/15, Jabal Amman

★ TELEPHONE: 41361	★ PRIVATE BALCONIES: yes – 250
★ CABLES: Inhotelcor/Amman	★ SWIMMING POOL: yes – fresh water
★ TELEX: 21207/21267	★ GARDENS: yes
★ IN OPERATION: 20 years	★ NO. OF STAFF: 423
★ RESERVATIONS: Inter-Continental Hotels Corporation	★ ROOM SERVICE: around the clock
★ ROOMS: 400	★ ORIENTATION: rooms face south, north, east and west
★ SUITES: 18	★ CREDIT CARDS: all major credit cards
★ RESTAURANTS: 2	★ OWNING COMPANY: Jordan Hotels & Tourism Co Ltd, operated by Inter-Continental Hotels Corporation
★ BARS: 1	
★ DISCOTHEQUE: yes	
★ SHOPS: 8	★ GENERAL MANAGER: Antonius Muellertt Gerbrand
★ CONFERENCE ROOMS: 3 (60 to 250)	
★ BANQUETING ROOMS: 3 (60 to 250)	★ DISTANCE TO SHOPS: 500 m
★ STANDARD BEDROOM SIZE: 24 m^2	★ DISTANCE FROM AIRPORT: 30 km

This hotel began life as a fairly undistinguished chain hotel in a small capital city that badly needed reasonable hotel accommodation. Then, year after year, the Jordan Inter-Continental improved and so markedly that at the last visit I concluded that it was now one of the best hotels in the Middle East. The utter niceness of the Jordanian or Bedouin personality has something to do with it – the staff can't do enough for you. Management has become more involved, more personal and far more quality conscious. The hotel is spacious, well designed and decorated with pleasant local touches but does not go out of its way to impress. It is very clean, beautifully maintained. The rooms are a good size, the bathrooms work and room service is quick and efficient – everything you want is done without a murmur. A splendid buffet is available every day for lunch and in the evening I found the food in the top floor restaurant to be well above the average for the area and served with real expertise. The hotel is a good centre too – rose-red Petra is three hours away by road and in 45 minutes you can fly to the sub-tropical shores of Aqaba.

KENYA

Lamu

PEPONI HOTEL, P.O. Box 24, Lamu

★ TELEPHONE: Lamu 29	★ ROOMS: 21
★ CABLES: Peponi Lamu	★ SUITES: 1
★ TELEX: no	★ RESTAURANTS: 1
★ IN OPERATION: 17 years	★ BARS: 1
★ RESERVATIONS: direct	★ DISCOTHEQUE: no

★ SHOPS: 1 – selling local jewellery, beach wear and toiletries
★ CONFERENCE ROOMS: none
★ BANQUETING ROOMS: 1 (up to 20)
★ STANDARD BEDROOM SIZE: 21 m^2
★ PRIVATE BALCONIES: yes
★ SWIMMING POOL: no
★ RECREATIONAL ACTIVITIES: deep sea fishing, water skiing, windsurfing, dhaow sailing, goggling, spear fishing and limited diving

★ GARDENS: yes – coconut and date palms and bougainvillaea in abundance
★ NO. OF STAFF: 45
★ ROOM SERVICE: 07.00–22.00
★ ORIENTATION: east
★ CREDIT CARDS: American Express
★ OWNING COMPANY: private
★ GENERAL MANAGER: Mrs Wera Korschen
★ DISTANCE TO BEACH: walking distance
★ DISTANCE TO SHOPS: 3 km
★ DISTANCE FROM AIRPORT: 5 km

When, in the last edition but one, I first listed this hotel, I did so with trepidation. I love it, but would others? The first reader's letter to reach me made it plain that I had taken leave of my senses. Then by and by, other letters came: 'Unique', 'Absolutely divine', 'We will never forget Peponi's . . .'. One lady from Sweden wrote: 'Thank you for convincing me that there were still places like this in the world . . .'. I am so glad.

Of course Peponi's is not like the Paris Ritz or the Pierre in New York. For one thing, it is way out there on a crazy, time-forgotten place, an old Swahili port in the very North of Kenya and still a stopping place for those marvellous Arab dhows and with houses – and their huge Zanzibari doors – going back a thousand years. Peponi's is simple, fresh, natural. From its terrace you can see your own beach, all eight miles of it, with scarcely anyone in sight and you can go sailing up and down the fascinating channels of a coastline hardly mapped properly. Then you can come back to an eight-pound lobster for dinner. Yes, there are still places like Peponi's in this world.

Masai Mara

MARA SERENA LODGE, P.O. Box 48690, Nairobi

★ TELEPHONE: Radiocall 3757
★ CABLES: Serena Nairobi
★ TELEX: 22878 Nairobi
★ IN OPERATION: 10 years
★ RESERVATIONS: Serena Lodges & Hotels, P.O. Box 48690, Nairobi
★ ROOMS: 78
★ SUITES: none
★ RESTAURANTS: 1
★ BARS: 1
★ DISCOTHEQUE: no
★ SHOPS: 1 – gift shop
★ CONFERENCE ROOMS: none
★ BANQUETING ROOMS: none
★ STANDARD BEDROOM SIZE: 19 m^2

★ PRIVATE BALCONIES: no
★ SWIMMING POOL: yes – fresh water
★ RECREATIONAL ACTIVITIES: Masai dancing
★ GARDENS: yes
★ NO. OF STAFF: 100
★ ROOM SERVICE: 08.00–22.00
★ ORIENTATION: rooms face game reserve
★ CREDIT CARDS: Diners Club, American Express, Barclaycard Visa
★ OWNING COMPANY: Safari Lodge Properties of Kenya Ltd
★ GENERAL MANAGER: Mr Francis Machariah
★ DISTANCE FROM AIRPORT: own airstrip

Kenya was fortunate in the aristocratic settler from Britain who invented this hotel (and its companion on the coast). He took the local mud-hut architecture and adapted it to make it safe for aristocrats who wanted to hunt in comfort. The result is one of the best of Kenya's modern game lodges. This being Masai country, the architecture is that of a Masai 'manyatta' or village – rough texture hut-like buildings for rooms, all huddled together in the traditional manner. Decor is simple but good and comfort standards as high as are both service and food. Above all, it is the situation that impresses – on a bluff high over one of the finest game reserves – 700 square miles of larger-than-life Africa, with Masai warriors, lots of lion, hippo and other wild creatures. Highly recommended.

Mombasa

SERENA BEACH HOTEL, P.O. Box 90352, Mombasa

★ TELEPHONE: 45721/2/3/4
★ CABLES: Serena Mombasa
★ TELEX: 21220 Mombasa
★ IN OPERATION: 9 years
★ RESERVATIONS: direct
★ ROOMS: 120
★ SUITES: 2
★ RESTAURANTS: 2
★ BARS: 3
★ DISCOTHEQUE: yes
★ SHOPS: 2 – boutique and handicrafts/curios
★ CONFERENCE ROOMS: none
★ BANQUETING ROOMS: none
★ STANDARD BEDROOM SIZE: 22 m^2
★ PRIVATE BALCONIES: yes
★ SWIMMING POOL: yes – fresh water
★ RECREATIONAL ACTIVITIES: tennis, volleyball, boating and windsurfing school
★ GARDENS: yes
★ NO. OF STAFF: 205
★ ROOM SERVICE: around the clock
★ ORIENTATION: most rooms have a sea view
★ FURTHER DEVELOPMENTS: squash courts, water-sports centre and fitness centre
★ CREDIT CARDS: Diners Club and American Express
★ OWNING COMPANY: Safari Lodge Properties of Kenya Ltd
★ GENERAL MANAGER: Mr Mahmud Janmohamed
★ DISTANCE TO BEACH: 40 m
★ DISTANCE TO SHOPS: 20 km
★ DISTANCE FROM AIRPORT: 30 km

All East African beach hotels should look like Serena Beach – with a few variations, of course. The fact that they do not, reflects on the unique quality of the hotel and its architects. Serena Beach is an idealized version of a Swahili village – with little streets winding in and out of clusters of charming cottages, with walls and doors just as they used to be in Zanzibar. Everywhere there are masses of mangrove wood beams, fine carpets, old chests and colourful hangings in the Arab manner. The rooms are simple, cool and attractive which is what one wants in this climate and the beach, Shanzu, is one of the finest tropical beaches anywhere.

The hotel has a central village square, with little shops, an almost permanent market, a coffeemaker and such like. The staff are one huge Maclean-smile from ear to ear and the food they serve is fresh, tasty and attractive – enormous lobsters, firm vegetables and masses of fruit.

Nairobi

NORFOLK HOTEL, P.O. Box 40064, Nairobi

★ TELEPHONE: 335422
★ CABLES: Norfolk
★ TELEX: 22559
★ IN OPERATION: 78 years
★ RESERVATIONS: The Leading Hotels of the World, worldwide/Horis Reservations Systems/United Touring Overseas, London
★ ROOMS: 120
★ SUITES/COTTAGES: 10 suites 8 cottages
★ RESTAURANTS: 3 – Delamere Terrace, Delamere Restaurant, Ibis Grill
★ BARS: 3 plus a mini-bar in each bedroom
★ DISCOTHEQUE: no
★ SHOPS: 2
★ CONFERENCE/BANQUETING/ROOMS: 4 rooms (5 to 500)
★ PRIVATE BALCONIES: many have, some do not
★ SWIMMING POOL: yes – fresh water, heated, bar and meal facilities
★ RECREATIONAL ACTIVITIES: golf and horse riding nearby
★ GARDENS: central courtyard only: shaded, two aviaries housing various species of African birds
★ NO. OF STAFF: 340 approximately
★ ROOM SERVICE: around the clock
★ ORIENTATION: overlooks University Way and the Kenya National Theatre
★ CREDIT CARDS: American Express, Diners Club, Barclaycard, Eurocard and Access

★ OWNING COMPANY: Kulia Investments Ltd

★ GENERAL MANAGER: Richard Kimenyi

★ DISTANCE TO SHOPS: 10 minutes walking, 2 minutes taxi

★ DISTANCE FROM AIRPORT: 16 km

It is hard to say which came first – the Norfolk Hotel or the city of Nairobi and when, some time back, a devastating fire gutted the old place, many habitual Africa hands were seen to shake their heads sadly. No, things would never be the same again. Yet, happily, they are – or almost. Miracles happened and the Norfolk rose again and, just as in the past, you might expect to see Hemingway's or Robert Ruark's ghosts come striding out of the famous bar, and the Lord Delamere Terrace is still the meeting place for anyone who is anyone in this fast-changing African capital. Let's face it – perhaps it was all for the best since some of the old Norfolk did need a change. But it has all been kept much along the same lines: the interior gardens, the state of big game information over the desk, the smiling faces of staff people who've been there for years. The food remains as good as it always was, plentiful and healthy, service and items like plumbing and communications are naturally much improved, the rooms are a good size and still simply and intelligently furnished. I for one would never dream of abandoning the Norfolk legend.

Nanyuki

MOUNT KENYA SAFARI CLUB, P.O. Box 35, Nanyuki, Kenya

★ TELEPHONE: 33.32.32 Reservations Nanyuki Club 2241

★ CABLES: Satcluo

★ TELEX: 22016 Reservations 28120

★ IN OPERATION: 24 years

★ RESERVATIONS: Inter-Continental Hotels, worldwide

★ ROOMS: 30

★ RESTAURANTS: 2

★ BARS: 2

★ DISCOTHEQUE: yes – and live music

★ SHOPS: 3

★ CONFERENCE ROOMS: 3 (40 to 115)

★ BANQUETING ROOMS: 3 (up to 100)

★ STANDARD BEDROOM SIZE: 28 m^2

★ PRIVATE BALCONIES: yes – some rooms

★ SWIMMING POOL: yes – fresh water, heated, 20 × 6 m

★ RECREATIONAL ACTIVITIES: horse riding, golf, tennis, sauna, pond and river fishing, bowling and putting green

★ NO. OF STAFF: 230

★ ROOM SERVICE: 07.00–23.00

★ ORIENTATION: 7000 ft high facing Mount Kenya

★ CREDIT CARDS: American Express, Diners Club, Visa and Master Charge

★ OWNING COMPANY: Mt Kenya Safari Club Ltd, operated by Inter-Continental Hotels Corporation

★ GENERAL MANAGER: Gerald Etter

★ DISTANCE TO SHOPS: 125 miles

★ DISTANCE FROM AIRPORT: 225 km from international airport and 20 km from domestic airport

'Oh my Hemingway and my Blixen long ago.' This is one of the most beautiful and most amusing hotels in the whole of Africa – strictly for rich and well-tended bwanas and their ladies. A few rather elderly white hunters are still to be found in the long bar and some of the trophies on the walls look as though they could jump off and savage you at any moment. The Mount Kenya Safari Club is a place apart – lush, plush, romantic and quite unique. The noises of the African night, the haughty, snowy profile of Mount Kenya and the thrilling grandeur of the country cannot fail to excite you. You can have claret with your dinner, watch the exotic birds strutting on the manicured lawns, enjoy a logfire in your room (which bears no resemblance to a safari tent) or just read the guest book which in itself is a source of endless gossip. Founded by, among others, William Holden, it is now expertly run by one of the world's great hotel chains. The Mount Kenya Safari Club is to Africa as Cartier is to Bond Street.

Samburu

SAMBURU GAME LODGE, P.O. Box 47557, Nairobi

★ TELEPHONE: Radiocall 2051
★ CABLES: Blocotels, Nairobi
★ TELEX: 22146 Blocotels
★ IN OPERATION: since 1961
★ RESERVATIONS: United Touring International, London/Sergat France, Paris/Sergat Italia, Rome/United Touring International, Germany/Alford Leisure Enterprises, Inc, New York
★ ROOMS: 60 doubles 9 singles
★ SUITES: none
★ RESTAURANTS: 1
★ BARS: 2 – one Crocodile Bar affording close view of river and crocodiles
★ DISCOTHEQUE: no
★ SHOPS: 1
★ CONFERENCE ROOMS: none
★ BANQUETING ROOMS: none
★ STANDARD BEDROOM SIZE: 25 m²

★ PRIVATE BALCONIES: yes
★ SWIMMING POOL: yes – fresh water, 50 × 20 ft
★ RECREATIONAL ACTIVITIES: viewing drives in safari vehicles, bird-watching walks and badminton
★ GARDENS: yes – large river frontage on Uaso Nyiro River
★ NO. OF STAFF: 123
★ ROOM SERVICE: 06.00–21.00
★ ORIENTATION: all rooms face south overlooking the river
★ CREDIT CARDS: American Express, Barclaycard and Diners Club
★ OWNING COMPANY: Block Hotels Ltd
★ GENERAL MANAGER: G. A. Crossland
★ DISTANCE FROM AIRPORT: 350 km (Nairobi)

In a country where the natives are not too restless, the Samburu Game Lodge is evidence that life in Kenya is at least throbbing; the crocodiles lying in wait in the river just below the bar, the elephants across the water and the dancing at the nearby villages (a non-tourist pas-de-deux) are just what the missionary ordered. One of the best game lodges, the traveller who comes here gets a real feel of Africa. His cottage is African-style, thatched and simple but comfortable and clean. His food, despite the remoteness, is among the best Kenya can offer – the game is, of course, excellent – and that goes a long way. Despite the unending stream of tourists day after day, the staff still greet you as if you were Stanley or Livingstone. These days the 'safari' has been devalued as much as many currencies – but not at Samburu. Everything here is larger than life and contains all the elements you had expected from your African adventure. This is Hemingway Africa as she should be. What a pity Karen Blixen cannot write any more about her beloved Kenya or the district of Karen named after her.

Tsavo National Park

TAITA HILLS LODGE, c/o Hilton International Nairobi, P.O. Box 30624, Nairobi

★ TELEPHONE: Radio Call 2011
★ CABLES: Hiltels Nairobi
★ TELEX: 22252
★ IN OPERATION: 12 years
★ RESERVATIONS: Hilton Reservation Service
★ ROOMS: 60
★ SUITES: 2
★ RESTAURANTS: 1
★ BARS: 2
★ DISCOTHEQUE: yes
★ SHOPS: 1
★ CONFERENCE ROOMS: 2 (up to 110)
★ BANQUETING ROOMS: 2 (up to 110)
★ STANDARD BEDROOM SIZE: 16 m²

★ PRIVATE BALCONIES: yes
★ SWIMMING POOL: yes – fresh water
★ RECREATIONAL ACTIVITIES: tennis, mini-golf, camel riding, darts, game-viewing safaris, boat rides on Lake Jipe, traditional dancers, lectures and film shows
★ GARDENS: yes
★ NO. OF STAFF: 80
★ ROOM SERVICE: 07.00–23.00
★ ORIENTATION: rooms overlook the Taita Hills
★ CREDIT CARDS: Diners Club, American Express, Carte Blanche, Master Charge and Hilton Hotels Corp

★ GENERAL MANAGER: Mr Brian Burrows
★ DISTANCE FROM AIRPORT: own airstrip

★ OWNING COMPANY: Hilton International Co

I must confess that neither nature nor circumstance meant me to be a boy scout. So, much as I love the tented camps I must also admit that after a day's game viewing – and you'd be surprised how tiring and dusty it is – it is pleasant to come back to a hotel like Taita Hills – clean, modern, efficient and not at all unpleasant to look at. It is a good-looking wood and stone building which goes well with its wild surroundings. Rooms are practical and beautifully equipped for a few days' stay and the bathrooms work like a dream. In such a place I do not even dislike the rather synthetised African decor – at least it does not offend. Taita Hills is what is called a base camp. From there you go anywhere in the vast Tsavo Game Park and only a few miles away is Taita's little sister, Salt Lick Lodge, with its thatched roundavels on stilts and its walkways. The elephants, by the way, are just down below you. Food and drink in both places are excellent.

KOREA
Seoul
SEOUL HILTON INTERNATIONAL, CPO Box 7692, Seoul, Korea

★ TELEPHONE: 753 7788/753 3788
★ CABLES: HILTELS SEOUL
★ TELEX: 26695
★ IN OPERATION: since October 1983
★ RESERVATIONS: any Hilton International Hotel or through Hilton Reservation Service Offices, worldwide
★ ROOMS: 643
★ SUITES: 69
★ RESTAURANTS: 7
★ BARS: 3
★ DISCOTHEQUE: Rain Forest disco operated by Juliana's of London
★ SHOPS: arcade of 18 shops
★ CONFERENCE ROOMS: 7 (60 to 360)
★ BANQUETING ROOMS: 7 (40 to 250)
★ STANDARD BEDROOM SIZE: 33.15 m^2
★ PRIVATE BALCONIES: no

★ SWIMMING POOL: indoor, heated, fresh water, 90.3 m^2
★ RECREATIONAL ACTIVITIES: athletics club with gym and sauna
★ GARDENS: no
★ NO. OF STAFF: 899
★ ROOM SERVICE: around the clock
★ ORIENTATION: rooms face west (over city) or east (over Mount Namsan)
★ CREDIT CARDS: all major credit cards
★ OWNING COMPANY: Dongwoo Development Co Ltd and operated by Hilton International
★ GENERAL MANAGER: James A. Smith
★ DISTANCE TO SHOPS: hotel located in city centre
★ DISTANCE FROM AIRPORT: 15 km (Kimpo International)

Like most Far Eastern cities, Seoul has grown so fast, and its hotels with it, that for quite a few years one found it hard to make a choice between the mediocre and the not-so-bad. Now there is no doubt – the best has got to be the new Hilton: a very large hotel into which the world-famous chain has poured all its expertise. Inevitably, it looks a little slab-like and faces the city centre on one side and the Namsan Hill on the other. Bedrooms are quite large and airy, furnished in a quiet and unshowy fashion – I am so glad to see that writing desks are back in favour in the world's best hotels. About time too. The company which more or less gave the world decent bathrooms has done its best here too – large, functional and attractive. Food goes from the simple, fresh and quick to the grand style, and you can have it Japanese, Chinese, European or American; to work off excesses there is a fully equipped gymnasium. If you wish to hold a conference, they'll translate your fine words into eight languages at the touch of a button. If you must go to Seoul, this is the only place to patronize.

LIECHTENSTEIN

Vaduz

PARK HOTEL SONNENHOF, 9490 Vaduz, Fürstentum Liechtenstein

★ TELEPHONE: (075) 2 11 92
★ CABLES: Sonnenhofhotel
★ TELEX: 77 78 1
★ IN OPERATION: since 1962
★ RESERVATIONS: direct or Relais de Campagne/Chateaux Hotels
★ ROOMS: 21
★ SUITES: 12
★ RESTAURANTS: 1
★ BARS: none
★ DISCOTHEQUE: no
★ SHOPS: none
★ CONFERENCE ROOMS: one (15 to 20)
★ BANQUETING ROOMS: none
★ STANDARD BEDROOM SIZE: 22 m^2

★ PRIVATE BALCONIES: yes
★ SWIMMING POOL: yes – fresh water
★ RECREATIONAL ACTIVITIES: hiking, riding, sauna, golf (24 km away)
★ GARDENS: yes
★ NO. OF STAFF: 18
★ ROOM SERVICE: 07.00–23.00
★ ORIENTATION: faces the Rhine valley
★ CREDIT CARDS: Visa, Master Charge, Eurocard, American Express
★ OWNING COMPANY: private
★ GENERAL MANAGER/OWNER: Emil Real
★ DISTANCE TO SHOPS: 1 km
★ DISTANCE FROM AIRPORT: 120 km (Zurich)

One has to go to one of Europe's smallest countries to discover one of the continent's finest hotels. In terms of quality, personalized management, food and above all general appointments, the Sonnenhof is an admirable hotel. Set on a wooded slope just outside Vaduz, the Sonnenhof's rooms, and particularly suites, are among the finest I have ever stayed in; beautifully fitted, with handsome lighting and unusually fine real wood fittings – everything made to measure and certainly designed by people who know the best. Everything works to perfection, silently and efficiently. There is a refrigerator-bar, good sitting space, wardrobes and bathrooms. The hotel is well furnished with local antiques and charming rustic wooden pieces, the flowers are forever fresh and the whole place is spotless. The food simply cannot be matched in this part of the world – even the table d'hôte is excellent, light and beautifully served by a bevy of smiling, dirndl-skirted girls. It is a family-run hotel and one must give the highest possible praise to an enterprise that is a model of a small, new, family-run and owned venture.

MACAU

MACAU EXCELSIOR, P.O. Box 3016, Avenida da Amizade, Macau

★ TELEPHONE: 567 888
★ CABLES: Excelsior
★ TELEX: 88588 MACEX OM
★ IN OPERATION: since 1984
★ RESERVATIONS: Mandarin International Hotels, London, New York, Chicago, Los Angeles, Vancouver, Tokyo, Hong Kong, Singapore, Sydney/The Leading Hotels of the World
★ ROOMS: 438
★ SUITES: 2 presidential suites, 20 1-bedroom suites, 10 2-bedroom suites
★ RESTAURANTS: 5
★ BARS: 3
★ DISCOTHEQUE: no – but live music or pianist
★ SHOPS: 15 – handicrafts, boutique,

pharmacy, jeweller, florist, cake shop etc
★ CONFERENCE ROOMS: 5 (130–252 m^2)
★ BANQUETING ROOMS: 6 (50 to 300)
★ STANDARD BEDROOM SIZE: 26 m^2
★ PRIVATE BALCONIES: 32 suites have balconies
★ SWIMMING POOL: yes – fresh water, 10 × 20 m
★ RECREATIONAL ACTIVITIES: squash courts (2), tennis courts (2), sauna, health club, table tennis
★ GARDENS: no
★ NO. OF STAFF: 550
★ ROOM SERVICE: around the clock
★ ORIENTATION: rooms overlook China Sea or park

★ CREDIT CARDS: American Express, Visa, Master Card, Diners Club
★ OWNING COMPANY: Hong Kong Land Company Ltd (operated by Mandarin International Hotels Ltd)
★ GENERAL MANAGER: Eric Andre Waldburger
★ DISTANCE TO BEACH: 20 minutes' drive
★ DISTANCE TO SHOPS: 1.5 km
★ DISTANCE FROM AIRPORT: nearest airport is Hong Kong (Macau to Hong Kong by jetfoil, 55 minutes)

People used to go to Macau as if they were going slumming – a bit of sleazy life, a whiff of that pungent Chinese-Portuguese mixture and, of course, gambling. But where on earth did one stay? One did not, and the traveller's visit was limited by the jetfoil's departure for Hong Kong. Not so any more. Now, you can actually go to Macau, enjoy it and stay there since the illustrious Mandarin Company decided to build the Macau Excelsior. Some hotel. One look at the grand staircase off the lobby assures you that you are on your way to the Celestial Empire. There is a Chinese restaurant to end all Chinese restaurants and the Grill Room is almost as good as its Hong Kong twin – which is giving it high praise indeed. The main bar is resplendent with Lusitanian goodies and, from any bedroom, look out and you face the China Sea in all its splendour. What is perhaps remarkable is that right from its opening date, this hotel showed off its parentage brilliantly – unmatched service, quiet comfort and food that is worth the trip. No, one no longer goes to Macau just for the day.

MALAYSIA

Kuala Lumpur

KUALA LUMPUR HILTON, P.O. Box 577, Jalan Sultan Ismail, Kuala Lumpur

★ TELEPHONE: 422122/422222
★ CABLES: Hiltels
★ TELEX: MA 30495
★ IN OPERATION: since November 1972
★ RESERVATIONS: Hilton Reservation Service
★ ROOMS: 190 doubles 404 singles
★ SUITES: 84
★ RESTAURANTS: 6
★ BARS: 7
★ DISCOTHEQUE: yes – Tin Mine
★ CONFERENCE ROOMS: 10 (10 to 1350)
★ BANQUETING ROOMS: 10 (10 to 1100)
★ SHOPS: 82 – shopping arcade offering a large variety of souvenir items, antiques, jewellery, hairdressing salon, doctor's clinic and airline offices
★ STANDARD BEDROOM SIZE: 20 m^2
★ PRIVATE BALCONIES: yes
★ SWIMMING POOL: yes – fresh water
★ RECREATIONAL ACTIVITIES: tennis, squash, saunas and indoor games; golf, horse riding and bowling nearby
★ GARDENS: yes
★ NO. OF STAFF: 1015
★ ROOM SERVICE: around the clock
★ ORIENTATION: rooms overlook racecourse, hills and city clock
★ CREDIT CARDS: American Express, Diners Club, Visa, Carte Blanche, Eurocard and Air Canada
★ OWNING COMPANY: Pernas International Hotels and Properties
★ GENERAL MANAGER: Manfred Stoecklein
★ DISTANCE TO SHOPS: 500 m
★ DISTANCE FROM AIRPORT: 22 km

One of the great mysteries of one's travelling life is that Malaysia, a superbly beautiful and varied country, has so few really good hotels and that is why, by default, the KL Hilton shines, which, in a way, is doing it an injustice. Here, the famous chain has done its best to introduce some interesting and very pleasant touches of individuality. Every balcony for instance – and there are hundreds of them – has its own bougainvillaea bush which is automatically water-sprinkled. In the bars and restaurants the Malaysian batiks are authentic. Happily, there is pleasing colour and good service – a smile comes naturally to those delightful people. The rest is what one would expect – Hilton functional, very well organized and dependable.

Penang

RASA SAYANG HOTEL, Batu Feringgi, Penang, Malaysia

★ TELEPHONE: 811 811
★ CABLES: Rasayang
★ TELEX: 40065
★ IN OPERATION: 10 years
★ RESERVATIONS: Shangri-La International, London, Los Angeles, Tokyo, Hong Kong, Singapore, Australia and Malaysia
★ ROOMS: 320
★ SUITES: 13
★ RESTAURANTS: 3
★ BARS: 3
★ DISCOTHEQUE: yes
★ SHOPS: 13 – antiques, jewellery, souvenirs, drugstore, beauty and barber shop, pottery, cameras, batik materials and clothes
★ CONFERENCE ROOMS: 17 (17–435 m²)
★ BANQUETING ROOMS: 5 (20 to 400)
★ STANDARD BEDROOM SIZE: 27 m²
★ PRIVATE BALCONIES: in superior rooms only

★ SWIMMING POOL: yes – 2, fresh water
★ RECREATIONAL ACTIVITIES: water skiing, boating, swimming, sailing, squash and tennis, putting green, volleyball, table tennis, jungle hikes, health club with gym, foam bath, sauna, O-Furo
★ GARDENS: yes
★ NO. OF STAFF: 570
★ ROOM SERVICE: around the clock
★ CREDIT CARDS: Access, Barclaycard, Diners Club, Master Charge, American Express, Carte Blanche, Eurocard, Petrocard
★ OWNING COMPANY: Rasa Sayang Beach Hotels (PG) Sdn Bhd
★ GENERAL MANAGER: Mr Al Wymann
★ DISTANCE TO BEACH: in front of hotel
★ DISTANCE TO SHOPS: 17 km to city
★ DISTANCE FROM AIRPORT: 31 km (Bayan Lepas)

In a country where small is always beautiful, Rasa Sayang is possibly the exception: it is big and beautiful and probably the best resort hotel in Malaysia. Coming from the same stable as Singapore's world famous Shangri La, it has to match up to expectations but, of course, it is a resort hotel and as such is more relaxed, more loose-limbed. There is an overall good sense of decor without too much razzmatazz and we particularly liked the fact that plastic is almost never seen – one sits on real cane chairs in the gardens and the terraces. The suites are especially gorgeous, being extremely well conceived and decorated. Rooms are a good size, bathrooms are fine and the public rooms are more elegant than one has a right to expect in a resort hotel. In front of it all is Penang Island's superb Batu Feringgi beach, all fine white sand and very long. As a resort pad Rasa Sayang must of course conform to the basic parameters when it comes to things like food, but on the whole it is perfectly acceptable – especially in the grillroom and the Japanese restaurant.

Trengganu

TANJONG JARA BEACH HOTEL, Kuala Dungun, Trengganu

★ TELEPHONE: (096) 841 801
★ CABLES: Pemresort
★ TELEX: 51449 JARA MA
★ IN OPERATION: since 1980
★ RESERVATIONS: direct or Pempena Consult, 17th Floor, Wisma MPI, Jalan Raja Chulan, P.O. Box 328, Kuala Lumpur
★ ROOMS: 84 doubles
★ SUITES: 6
★ RESTAURANTS: 1
★ BARS: 2
★ DISCOTHEQUE: yes

★ SHOPS: shopping arcade
★ CONFERENCE ROOMS: 2
★ STANDARD BEDROOM SIZE: 46 m²
★ PRIVATE BALCONIES: yes
★ SWIMMING POOL: yes – fresh water
★ RECREATIONAL ACTIVITIES: water skiing, windsurfing, sailing, snorkelling, fishing, tennis, squash, scuba diving
★ GARDENS: yes – 77 acres
★ NO. OF STAFF: 220
★ ROOM SERVICE: 07.00–23.00
★ ORIENTATION: all rooms have a sea view

★ CREDIT CARDS: American Express, Visa, Carte Blanche, Diners Club

★ OWNING COMPANY: T.D.C. (Tourist Development Corporation)

★ GENERAL MANAGER: vacant

★ DISTANCE TO BEACH: on the beach

★ DISTANCE TO SHOPS: 8 km

★ DISTANCE FROM AIRPORT: 55 km (Kuala Trengganu); 160 km (Kuantan)

For years, in common with all travellers who love beautiful but little-known places, I have been waiting for a really good hotel on that divine East Coast of Malaysia. Now I have found it. Tanjong Jara is everything I could have wished for: a magnificent beach, totally unpolluted and seemingly without end, a hotel designed with imagination and good taste and people so charming that they can't do enough for you. The hotel is a cluster of attractive cottages built of rare timber of which this country has so much and some of them are actually built on stilts on the water. The lush gardens bloom everlastingly, there is no noise and no hustle and you can just be yourself on one of the world's truly most beautiful coastlines. There is a very good swimming pool (as if one needed it here . . .) and furnishings and decor are exotic enough to please the most demanding. Food is fresh: fish was brought ashore this morning and as for fruit, the staff just go along picking it off the trees for your breakfast tray. All around is Malay Malaysia (as against the Chinese community on the West Coast) — gentle people living in marvellously picturesque fishing villages built on stilts. The people welcome you as an honoured guest, with ceremony plus a hint of fun to come. A few miles to the north is the celebrated Beach of Passionate Love. Do go to Tanjong Jara.

MALDIVES

BIYADOO ISLAND RESORT, Malé, Republic of Maldives

★ TELEPHONE: 3516

★ CABLES: no

★ TELEX: 77003 TAJMF

★ IN OPERATION: since December 1982

★ RESERVATIONS: Utell International, worldwide

★ ROOMS: 96

★ SUITES: none

★ RESTAURANTS: 1

★ BARS: 2

★ DISCOTHEQUE: sometimes

★ SHOPS: 2

★ CONFERENCE ROOMS: both restaurant and bar can be used as a conference room (127 m² or 233 m²)

★ BANQUETING ROOMS: none

★ STANDARD BEDROOM SIZE: 15 m²

★ PRIVATE BALCONIES: all rooms have balcony or terrace

★ SWIMMING POOL: no

★ RECREATIONAL ACTIVITIES: volleyball, table tennis, darts, cards, excursions, water sports

★ GARDENS: landscaped tropical vegetation

★ NO. OF STAFF: 100

★ ROOM SERVICE: no

★ ORIENTATION: rooms are in six blocks around the island and a few metres from the beach

★ CREDIT CARDS: American Express

★ OWNING COMPANY: Taj International Hotels

★ GENERAL MANAGER: Mr John Rambhunjan

★ DISTANCE TO BEACH: walking distance

★ DISTANCE TO SHOPS: 25 km (Malé)

★ DISTANCE FROM AIRPORT: 25 km (Halule

The Maldives are tiny coral dots spread about the Indian Ocean and certainly some of the newest escape spots. When I first went there, years and years ago, I had an overnight trip from Colombo on a leaky boat. Now, you can fly there in an hour. Nothing but the pale blue sea, the blinding white beach and the green of the coconut palms. On Biyadoo, India's Taj group have built this resort hotel with their usual dash of inspiration — there is nobody else on the island but you, your fellow guests and the hotel staff. Days are one long laze (there is nothing to do except swim, snorkel and sunbathe). Sunsets are among the greatest spectacles in the natural world. Rooms are airy and fairly basic but comfortable. Bathrooms work, with the first hot water ever felt on the islands . . . and you can have air-conditioning if you want it, but who does

One just leaves everything open. On the next island, Villi Varu, there is another mini-Taj resort and you can go and visit. By the way, at Biyadoo, if you wish to catch your own fish for lunch, the management graciously gives you a skillet and a charcoal brazier. Well, well.

MALTA

Gozo

HOTEL TA'CENC, Sannat, Gozo

- ★ TELEPHONE: 556819/556830/551520
- ★ CABLES: Tacencotal
- ★ TELEX: 479 Refinz MW
- ★ IN OPERATION: 12 years
- ★ RESERVATIONS: Gozo Holidays, King's Langley, England/Moteltour, Milano, Italy/Holiday Maker, Zurich/Airtours International, Frankfurt
- ★ ROOMS: 38
- ★ SUITES: 12
- ★ RESTAURANTS: 2 including 1 on terrace in summer
- ★ BARS: 2 including 1 on beach
- ★ DISCOTHEQUE: yes
- ★ SHOPS: 2 – boutique and bookshop
- ★ CONFERENCE ROOMS: 1 (up to 80)
- ★ BANQUETING ROOMS: 1 (up to 80)
- ★ STANDARD BEDROOM SIZE: 25–30 m^2
- ★ PRIVATE BALCONIES: yes
- ★ SWIMMING POOL: yes – fresh water, 300 m^2
- ★ RECREATIONAL ACTIVITIES: 2 floodlit tennis courts, table tennis and billiards
- ★ GARDENS: yes
- ★ NO. OF STAFF: 96
- ★ ROOM SERVICE: 07.00–24.00
- ★ ORIENTATION: rooms face sea and gardens
- ★ CREDIT CARDS: American Express, Diners Club and Barclaycard
- ★ OWNING COMPANY: Hotel Operators Ltd
- ★ GENERAL MANAGER: Mr P. de Muro
- ★ DISTANCE TO BEACH: 8 minutes by car (free minibus service)
- ★ DISTANCE TO SHOPS: 10 minutes by car
- ★ DISTANCE FROM AIRPORT: 90 minutes by car and ferry

Intelligent and sophisticated simplicity – that's the keynote here and I believe Ta'Cenc to be one of the most interesting holiday hotels in the Mediterranean. Many of my readers agree. On this gorgeous, cliffy island of Gozo, Ta'Cenc is a cluster of buildings the colour of champagne, spread around a very large and beautifully clean swimming pool. There is a main building and lots of cottages where rooms are large and airy, kept scrupulously clean and furnished with simple but comfortable furniture, modern in character but good quality. The beds are particularly good and so is the storage space and bathrooms work like a dream. Most of the activity is outside – gardens, terraces, poolside and one al fresco restaurant where the food, basically Italian in character, is attractive. Service is cheerful and the staff quickly adapt to the wishes of individual guests. The sea is two miles away. You won't find hordes of cheap package tourists here.

MEXICO

Acapulco

PIERRE MARQUES PRINCESS HOTEL & CLUB DE GOLF, Playa Revolcadero, P.O. Box 474, Acapulco, Gro, Mexico CP 39300

- ★ TELEPHONE: 4 20 00
- ★ CABLES: Piermar
- ★ TELEX: 16826 Pierme
- ★ IN OPERATION: 27 years
- ★ RESERVATIONS: Princess Hotels International Inc, San Francisco
- ★ ROOMS: 332
- ★ SUITES: 6
- ★ RESTAURANTS: 2 (7 at the sister hotel next door)
- ★ BARS: 2 (5 at the sister hotel next door)

★ DISCOTHEQUE: live music (discotheque at hotel next door)
★ SHOPS: 3 – hairdresser, travel agency, tobacco shop/pharmacy
★ CONFERENCE ROOMS: facilities for 40 to 450
★ BANQUETING ROOMS: facilities for 40 to 450
★ STANDARD BEDROOM SIZE: 28 m^2
★ PRIVATE BALCONIES: yes – all rooms
★ SWIMMING POOL: yes – 3, fresh water (more pools at sister hotel next door)
★ RECREATIONAL ACTIVITIES: tennis, golf; arrangements can be made for riding, deep-sea fishing, sailing, water skiing, snorkelling, scuba diving

★ GARDENS: yes
★ NO. OF STAFF: 545 (winter), 360 (summer)
★ ROOM SERVICE: 07.00–23.00
★ ORIENTATION: 90% of the rooms face the sea
★ CREDIT CARDS: American Express, Diners Club, Master Charge, Visa, Carte Blanche, Carnet
★ OWNING COMPANY: Princess Hotels International
★ GENERAL MANAGER: Jorge Munuzuri
★ DISTANCE TO BEACH: hotel is located on the beach
★ DISTANCE TO SHOPS: 9 km
★ DISTANCE FROM AIRPORT: 5 km

I first visited this hotel close on twenty years ago and always had a soft spot for it. Then as time went on, I began hating Acapulco and all that it stands for – so that was that. Obviously, some people feel differently and I have had many letters asking why I did not list a hotel in this much-vaunted resort. So I went back and I am afraid I still don't like Acapulco but if you must go there then by all means stay at the Pierre Marques – 240 acres on Revolcadero Beach, two golf courses and every conceivable leisure pursuit attended to. The decor, overwhelmingly 'gringo', is nevertheless fairly muted when compared with its neighbours. Rooms are good, clean and well furnished and the public rooms are not overdone. There is a magnificent swimming pool right next to the Pacific Ocean and enough terraces to house conventions (which, alas, they sometimes do). Another good thing about the Pierre Marques is that it is far enough from Acapulco to ignore the latter.

Puerto Vallarta

HOTEL GARZA BLANCA, P.O. Box 58, Puerto Vallarta, Jalisco

★ TELEPHONE: 2-10-23 & 2-10-83
★ CABLES: no
★ TELEX: 06518
★ IN OPERATION: 16 years
★ RESERVATIONS: John A. Tetley Co, Los Angeles/Robert F. Warner or direct
★ ROOMS: none
★ SUITES: 40 and 31 villas
★ RESTAURANTS: 1
★ BARS: 1
★ DISCOTHEQUE: live music
★ SHOPS: 2
★ CONFERENCE ROOMS: none
★ BANQUETING ROOMS: none
★ STANDARD BEDROOM SIZE: 32 m^2
★ PRIVATE BALCONIES: yes
★ SWIMMING POOL: yes – 1 main pool 23 × 6 m, and 40 private pools, fresh water

★ RECREATIONAL ACTIVITIES: water skiing, scuba diving, fishing, tennis and city and jungle tours
★ GARDENS: yes
★ NO. OF STAFF: 110
★ ROOM SERVICE: 07.45–23.30
★ ORIENTATION: all rooms face the Pacific
★ FURTHER DEVELOPMENTS: plans to build 44 suites and 27 villas
★ CREDIT CARDS: Master Charge, American Express and Visa
★ OWNING COMPANY: Garza Blanca, S.A.
★ GENERAL MANAGER: Salvador E. Fernandez, C.P.
★ DISTANCE TO BEACH: walking distance
★ DISTANCE TO SHOPS: 7.5 km
★ DISTANCE FROM AIRPORT: 15 km

Since 'The Night of the Iguana' everybody wanted to see the odd-looking place where they made the film and whereas Acapulco was getting overrun, Puerto Vallarta became *the* place, which it still is. Alas, it too suffers from the Acapulco disease except for Garza Blanca which I think is a super small holiday hotel on this legendary coast. The small white beach is quite gorgeous and if you want to be very close to it, choose one of the beachside suites. But if you want to be on your own, cross the road and climb up the hillside to one of the ineptly called chalet suites – a little Mexican house all to yourself in its own tiny garden and its own tiny swimming pool – quite divine and very private. There is a sunken, tiled bathtub and a very pleasant sitting room. The hotel is small so everybody congregates on that quite lovely dining terrace, made famous by Ava Gardner, for meals and the food ranges from the acceptable to the very good. Mercifully, the dreadful tourists known in the film never come here – Richard Burton must have scared them off.

San Juan del Rio

HOTEL GALINDO, P.O. Box 16, San Juan del Rio, Queretaro, Mexico

★ TELEPHONE: (91-467) 20050
★ CABLES: no
★ TELEX: 12804
★ IN OPERATION: 12 years
★ RESERVATIONS: direct
★ ROOMS: 157
★ SUITES: 9
★ RESTAURANTS: 3 – Florentino, Bosque and Garden Restaurant
★ BARS: Lobby bar
★ DISCOTHEQUE: no
★ SHOPS: tobacconist
★ CONFERENCE ROOMS: grand ballroom – 110 m^2
★ BANQUETING ROOMS: 13 (35 to 854)
★ STANDARD BEDROOM SIZE: 26 m^2
★ PRIVATE BALCONIES: 18 rooms have private terraces

★ SWIMMING POOL: yes – fresh water
★ RECREATIONAL ACTIVITIES: tennis courts, horse riding, putting green, 18-hole championship golf course a few minutes away
★ GARDENS: yes
★ NO. OF STAFF: 175
★ ROOM SERVICE: 07.00–22.00
★ ORIENTATION: all directions – some facing interior courtyards
★ CREDIT CARDS: American Express, Carte Blanche, Diners Club, Master Charge and Visa
★ OWNING COMPANY: Corporation
★ GENERAL MANAGER: Pasquale Del Prete
★ DISTANCE TO SHOPS: 10 km
★ DISTANCE FROM AIRPORT: 90 minutes' drive from Mexico City

One of the rarest things in my type of work is discovering a good hotel totally by accident and this is what happened in the case of Galindo. Touring around the Bajio – Mexico's colonial heartland where (poor fellow) Emperor Maximilian met his end, I came across this magnificent old hacienda turned into a hotel, had a look around, loved it and stayed. I have never regretted it, since this is without doubt one of the finest country hotels in this magnificent country. Legend has it that it was Hernan Cortes himself who built Galindo for his Indian wife – possibly hard to prove – but it looks as if it was that genuine: a beautiful, mellow and lovingly kept hacienda with great processions of interior courtyards filled with flowers and fountains, superb public rooms, especially the main restaurant which looks great and serves delicious food, and yes, even the original chapel of the estate. Bedrooms are period of course, beautifully serviced and since the hotel has been taken over by a reliable worldwide company the formerly *mañana* attitude has gone – for good one hopes. In feeling and atmosphere, Galindo is so far from raucous Mexico City that it is worth the trip just to see the difference.

MONACO

Monte Carlo

HOTEL HERMITAGE, Square Beaumarchais

★ TELEPHONE: 56 67 31
★ CABLES: Hermit Monte Carlo
★ TELEX: 479 432

★ IN OPERATION: 87 years
★ RESERVATIONS: S.B.M Paris, London, New York, Germany and Scandinavia

* ROOMS: 211
* SUITES: 11
* RESTAURANTS: 1
* BARS: 1
* DISCOTHEQUE: no
* SHOPS: none
* CONFERENCE ROOMS: 2 (50 to 80)
* BANQUETING ROOMS: 3 (30 to 250)
* STANDARD BEDROOM SIZE: 25 m²
* PRIVATE BALCONIES: yes – most rooms
* SWIMMING POOL: yes – salt water, 25 × 15 m
* GARDENS: no

* NO. OF STAFF: 175
* ROOM SERVICE: 07.00–24.00
* ORIENTATION: south
* CREDIT CARDS: American Express, Diners Club, Master Charge and Eurocard
* OWNING COMPANY: Société des Bains de Mer
* GENERAL MANAGER: Mr J. Rauline
* DISTANCE TO BEACH: walking distance
* DISTANCE TO SHOPS: walking distance
* DISTANCE FROM AIRPORT: 24 km

An architect could not have built a hotel like this: it must have been a pastry chef. A Viennese pastry chef at that, perhaps in partnership with a Bohemian painter from the court of mad King Ludwig of Bavaria. The Hermitage is the only hotel I know where they have to put security guards on the washrooms, lest people should come in with hammer and chisel and steal the washbasins. Here, in a hotel that is less famous and less cosmopolitan than its stablemate, are endless vistas of vast corridors with painted ceilings, bouquets of cherubs climbing up every wall and ceilings literally dripping with rococo plaster and crystal candelabras. A monument to the scandalous good times of the Edwardian era. Women clients love the Hermitage because, like candlelight, it is intensely flattering. Rooms and suites are like aristocratic lovenests, the kind that go with Dom Perignon, red roses and a telephone off the hook. Service is unlikely to disturb you – it only comes when called – and when you walk into the Belle Epoque Restaurant, you know instinctively that the Prince of Wales must have sat upstage, by the second column on the left.

HOTEL DE PARIS, Place du Casino

* TELEPHONE: (93) 50 80 80
* CABLES: Parisotel
* TELEX: 469925 Parihotcarlo
* IN OPERATION: since 1866
* RESERVATIONS: direct
* ROOMS: 260 doubles 10 singles
* SUITES: 30
* RESTAURANTS: 2
* BARS: 2
* DISCOTHEQUE: live music and piano in bar
* SHOPS: 7
* CONFERENCE ROOMS: 2 (up to 30)
* BANQUETING ROOMS: 2 (100 to 400)
* STANDARD BEDROOM SIZE: 25 m²
* PRIVATE BALCONIES: yes
* SWIMMING POOL: yes – salt water, 25 × 15 m

* RECREATIONAL ACTIVITIES: saunas with tennis and squash at the Monte Carlo Country Club and also 18-hole golf course
* GARDENS: yes
* NO. OF STAFF: 400
* ROOM SERVICE: around the clock
* ORIENTATION: rooms face the sea, gardens and shopping street
* CREDIT CARDS: American Express, Diners Club, Visa, Master Charge, Access and Eurocard
* OWNING COMPANY: Société des Bains de Mer
* GENERAL MANAGER: Mr K. H. Vanis
* DISTANCE TO BEACH: 1 km
* DISTANCE TO SHOPS: walking distance
* DISTANCE FROM AIRPORT: 24 km

This hotel (well over a century of it) is for plutocrats, oilcrats, aristocrats and any other crats and is about as reticent as King Kong. Yet, what it does to keep the show on the road is carried out with such consummate panache, such skilled showmanship that can be forgiven anything. If you dine on that terrace at night (admission is about as tough as the Royal Enclosure at Ascot), nibble at your langouste and sip your Dom Perignon, you are part of the show. Ordinary mortals pass by, drop one or two comments about your plate (or your jewels) and go on and if you can sit there unblushingly, the Hotel de Paris is for you. And, of course, one should add – as if this were necessary – that this is a very great hotel indeed, with a guest list longer and more illustrious than most royal palaces.

Everything here is larger than life – the sugar-icing architecture, the nymphs climbing up every column, the chandeliers dripping with light. Rooms range from the fairly plain to the outlandishly lush – it's the kind of hotel where the concierge is worth any highly paid secretary, he'll make your appointments for you if you wish. The best suites are on the harbour side, so that you can see what the Greek tycoons are doing on their floating battleships. The Empire Restaurant has not changed a bit since the days of Nick the Greek and the fin d'everything demi mondaines – it is overpoweringly superb.

MOROCCO

Fès

HOTEL PALAIS JAMAI, Bab-el-Guissa, Fès

- ★ TELEPHONE: 343-31, 32, 33 and -24746
- ★ CABLES: Hotransat
- ★ TELEX: 519-74
- ★ IN OPERATION: since 1920
- ★ RESERVATIONS: direct/The Leading Hotels of the World
- ★ ROOMS: 115
- ★ SUITES: 20
- ★ RESTAURANTS: 2
- ★ BARS: 1
- ★ DISCOTHEQUE: yes
- ★ SHOPS: 2
- ★ CONFERENCE ROOMS: 1 (up to 80)
- ★ BANQUETING ROOMS: 1 (150)
- ★ STANDARD BEDROOM SIZE: 28 m^2
- ★ PRIVATE BALCONIES: yes
- ★ SWIMMING POOL: yes – heated
- ★ GARDENS: yes
- ★ NO. OF STAFF: 200
- ★ ROOM SERVICE: around the clock
- ★ ORIENTATION: facing old city and the mountain
- ★ CREDIT CARDS: American Express, Diners Club, Visa and Blue Card
- ★ OWNING COMPANY: O.N.C.F., Rabat
- ★ GENERAL MANAGER: J. F. Piques
- ★ DISTANCE TO SHOPS: 200 m
- ★ DISTANCE FROM AIRPORT: 15 km

Once it was the Grand Vizier's palace in this most beautiful of all Moroccan cities and his own room is still there for one to see. Now, as a traveller, you are the Grand Vizier and may all your dreams be peopled with veiled ladies scurrying about carrying trays of sweet whatnots. Of course, the Palais Jamai, like most things in this world, has changed – not always for the better and I don't care much for the overstuffed chairs in the otherwise lovely sitting room with its mosaic walls. Rooms have got smaller too – inevitably – but on the whole this is still one of the shining hotel stars of Morocco, with extremely good service, sensationally good Moroccan food served in the right setting and those little touches of extravagance which please so much. The gardens have hardly been touched by the new planners – the birds sing, the fountains fount and the lush trees give pleasant shade. Right there, opposite the white medina where thousands of craftsmen still work on silver, gold, leather and textiles, you are in a very special world.

Marrakech

HOTEL LA MAMOUNIA, Avenue Bab Jdid, Marrakech

- ★ TELEPHONE: 323-81
- ★ CABLES: Mamounia Marrakech
- ★ TELEX: 730-18
- ★ IN OPERATION: since 1920
- ★ RESERVATIONS: The Leading Hotels of the World
- ★ ROOMS: 168
- ★ SUITES: 22
- ★ RESTAURANTS: 4
- ★ BARS: 2
- ★ DISCOTHEQUE: yes
- ★ SHOPS: yes

★ CONFERENCE ROOMS: none
★ BANQUETING ROOMS: none
★ STANDARD BEDROOM SIZE: 30 m^2
★ PRIVATE BALCONIES: yes
★ SWIMMING POOL: yes – fresh water, heated in winter
★ RECREATIONAL ACTIVITIES: golf, riding and skiing close by
★ GARDENS: yes – 17 acres of secluded gardens, olive and orange groves

★ NO. OF STAFF: 400
★ ROOM SERVICE: around the clock
★ ORIENTATION: south and west
★ CREDIT CARDS: American Express, Diners Club, Visa and Master Charge
★ OWNING COMPANY: O.N.C.F.
★ GENERAL MANAGER: Peter H. Spaeth
★ DISTANCE TO SHOPS: 2 km
★ DISTANCE FROM AIRPORT: 5 km

As the liveried Moorish servant shows you into the tiled and latticed, colonnaded court that serves for a foyer in La Mamounia you step decisively into an illustration of the 1001 Arabian Nights. Your next contact with reality will come when you pay the bill on leaving. This was Winston Churchill's favourite haunt and from his balcony he painted the Atlas sunset time and again. As you sit there dreaming, looking over the fantastic red ramparts of Marrakech or down into those lush gardens, one gets a view of Islamic culture free of Ayahtollahs. Like all great hotels, La Mamounia has modernized itself – I don't care much for the main restaurant or the bar but fell in love – again – with the sensational Bhaja Moroccan Restaurant where the food is out of this world. I, who do not like poolside barbecues on principle, was frankly amazed at the quality of the food dispensed out there in the noonday shade. Then there are those miles of glittering tiled Moorish corridors, the carved ceilings and above all the divine gardens.

Rabat

HILTON INTERNATIONAL RABAT, P.B. 450 R.P. Souissi, Rabat

★ TELEPHONE: 721-51/722-42/723-43
★ CABLES: Hiltels
★ TELEX: 31913-32026
★ IN OPERATION: since 1967
★ RESERVATIONS: Hilton Reservation Service
★ ROOMS: 215 doubles 31 studios
★ SUITES: 9
★ RESTAURANTS: 4 – Chellah Grill, Bab Es Sama, coffee shop and pool restaurant
★ BARS: 2
★ DISCOTHEQUE: live music – Moroccan orchestra, belly dancer, tea dancer and guitarist
★ SHOPS: 10 – barbers, beauty parlour, library, minerals, bank, car rental, handicraft shop, ladies' kaftan dress shop, travel agency and art gallery
★ CONFERENCE ROOMS: 6 (up to 700)
★ BANQUETING ROOMS: 6 (up to 700)

★ STANDARD BEDROOM SIZE: 24 m^2
★ PRIVATE BALCONIES: yes
★ SWIMMING POOL: yes – fresh water, 25 × 20 m and a children's pool
★ RECREATIONAL ACTIVITIES: tennis, sauna, 3-hole golf course and driving range
★ GARDENS: yes
★ NO. OF STAFF: 300
★ ROOM SERVICE: around the clock
★ ORIENTATION: west and east
★ CREDIT CARDS: American Express, Diners Club, Visa, Master Charge, Carte Blanche, Carte Bleue and Hilton Credit Card
★ OPERATING COMPANY: Hilton International Co
★ GENERAL MANAGER: Peter Mueller
★ DISTANCE TO BEACH: 8 km
★ DISTANCE TO SHOPS: 2 km
★ DISTANCE FROM AIRPORT: 13 km

As far as Hiltons go I tend to prefer the smaller ones to the bigger ones since they seem to offer the Hilton-best without the Hilton-grandiose. Rabat is one of these and it is also probably the quietest of them all, standing some way out of the city. You can actually doze by the swimming pool without any rude awakenings from musak or motor cars. It is a well-behaved hotel – charming staff, good service and the decor is much less manufactured than usual in this group. Colours are fresh and there are some nice handicrafts around as well as some of the loveliest carpets in North Africa. Rooms are Hiltonish – a good size and very functional and room service is particularly fast and discreet. I found the Moroccan food to be somewhat toned down for transatlantic digestive tracts but the French variety was perfectly acceptable.

Taroudant

LA GAZELLE D'OR, P.O. Box 60, Taroudant

- ★ TELEPHONE: (085) 20-39/20-48
- ★ CABLES: Gazelor Taroudant
- ★ TELEX: 81902
- ★ IN OPERATION: since 1960
- ★ RESERVATIONS: direct
- ★ ROOMS: 21
- ★ RESTAURANTS: 1 main restaurant and terrace by pool for snack lunches
- ★ BARS: 1
- ★ DISCOTHEQUE: yes
- ★ SHOPS: none
- ★ CONFERENCE ROOMS: none
- ★ BANQUETING ROOMS: none
- ★ STANDARD BEDROOM SIZE: 24 m^2
- ★ PRIVATE BALCONIES: all the rooms have terraces
- ★ SWIMMING POOL: yes – fresh water, Olympic size
- ★ RECREATIONAL ACTIVITIES: tennis, table tennis and riding (4 horses)
- ★ GARDENS: yes – 20 acres
- ★ NO. OF STAFF: 50
- ★ ROOM SERVICE: 07.00–23.00
- ★ ORIENTATION: all rooms face the gardens and Atlas Mountains
- ★ FURTHER DEVELOPMENTS: Turkish bath. massage facilities, billiard and card room and television and video room
- ★ CREDIT CARDS: American Express, Diners Club and Visa
- ★ OWNING COMPANY: privately owned
- ★ GENERAL MANAGER: R. Tibari
- ★ DISTANCE TO BEACH: 80 km (Agadir Beach)
- ★ DISTANCE TO SHOPS: 1 km (Taroudant); 80 km (Agadir); 250 km (Marrakech)
- ★ DISTANCE FROM AIRPORT: 80 km

Oldtime pashas would probably have designed this place for themselves, had they had Parisian taste, American plumbing and Italian panache. As it is, it's a hotel for the pashas of today – those who know what they want and are prepared to pay for it. Near this delicious little fortified city in the far south of Morocco, La Gazelle d'Or is an oasis of the good life – twenty acres of parkland blooming with orange blossom and Bougainvillaea, pools and whispering waters, desert dancers to entertain you in the evening while you are supping on the finest French and Moroccan food and that's only the beginning. La Gazelle d'Or, conceived years ago by a man of immense taste, offers twenty-one cottages of extreme beauty and comfort – mosaic ceilings, Berber carpets, handmade furniture and beautiful antiques and super silent service which glides along marble floors in Moroccan slippers. You can ride, swim, play tennis and imagine that you are an oil sheikh on holiday by playing at falconry in what is undoubtedly one of the most ravishing and extraordinary countries in the world. There are not many places like this any more – sheer folly – and very few have this hotel's amazing peace and quiet.

NEPAL

Kathmandu

HOTEL SOALTEE OBEROI, Tahachal, Kathmandu, Nepal

- ★ TELEPHONE: 211211
- ★ CABLES: Soaltee or Obhotel, Kathmandu
- ★ TELEX: 2203 NP
- ★ IN OPERATION: since 1969
- ★ RESERVATIONS: Loews Representation International, New York, London,

Tokyo/Oberoi Hotels, India/Stinnes Touristic Representations, Frankfurt/HRI/The Leading Hotels of the World, New York, London, Hong Kong, Tokyo, Singapore and Sydney
- ★ ROOMS: 290

★ SUITES: 25
★ RESTAURANTS: 4 – The Alfresco, Himalchuli, Garden Room and Gurkha Grill
★ BARS: 2 – Rodi Bar and Bamboo Bar
★ SHOPS: 10
★ CONFERENCE ROOMS: 3 (30 to 250)
★ BANQUETING ROOMS: 1 (200)
★ STANDARD BEDROOM SIZE: 20 m^2
★ PRIVATE BALCONIES: no
★ SWIMMING POOL: yes – fresh water, 36 × 27 m
★ RECREATIONAL ACTIVITIES: tennis, golf
★ (nearby), saunas, health club, casino, mini-golf, excursions and treks in the mountains are organized by the hotel
★ GARDENS: yes
★ NO. OF STAFF: 600
★ ROOM SERVICE: around the clock
★ CREDIT CARDS: American Express, Diners Club, Bankamericard and Visa
★ OPERATING COMPANY: Oberoi Hotels
★ GENERAL MANAGER: Herbert G. Sossna
★ DISTANCE TO SHOPS: 2 km
★ DISTANCE FROM AIRPORT: 10 km

Once, Nepal was the home of the flower children and, as I know to my cost, suitable only for the bravest of the middle-aged. One took one's chances with the local hotels. Now that an experienced and versatile company have taken over the Soaltee you can see Nepal without any pain and because Nepal is Nepal – a quite unique country whose Himalayas are better and higher than anyone else's – the result is the best of all possible worlds. The Soaltee is a good hotel of international standards, modern, comfortable, well run and with the occasional touch of the exotic which makes all the difference. Rooms are ample in size, very well furnished with taste and some regard for the long-distance traveller's needs. Bathrooms work too which, all things being unequal, is something of a miracle up here and as for the service, there are two charming, smiling Nepalese boys and girls to every guest which means that your slightest wish is their command – they execute it with rare flourish and much good humour. The food, which rather spoilt my first visits to this distant kingdom, is now extremely palatable. And, if you like that sort of thing, you can play in the only casino for 3000 miles around. For myself I much prefer to see Nepal, places like Pokkhara and Bhatgaon, or trek to some modest base camp.

NETHERLANDS

Amsterdam

AMSTEL HOTEL, 1 Professor Tulpplein, 1018 GX Amsterdam

★ TELEPHONE: (020) 226060
★ CABLES: Amstelotel
★ TELEX: 11004
★ IN OPERATION: since 1866
★ RESERVATIONS: Utell International
★ ROOMS: 111
★ SUITES: 7
★ RESTAURANTS: 1 – La Rive
★ BARS: 1
★ DISCOTHEQUE: no – but live music in the bar and restaurant
★ SHOPS: 1
★ CONFERENCE ROOMS: 7 (4 to 200)
★ BANQUETING ROOMS: 7 (4 to 200)
★ STANDARD BEDROOM SIZE: 25 m^2
★ PRIVATE BALCONIES: no
★ SWIMMING POOL: no
★ GARDENS: yes
★ NO. OF STAFF: 125
★ ROOM SERVICE: around the clock
★ ORIENTATION: facing Amstel River and quiet square
★ CREDIT CARDS: American Express, Visa, Diners Club, Eurocard, Mastercard
★ OWNING COMPANY: Inter-Continental Hotels
★ GENERAL MANAGER: P. J. Vermey
★ DISTANCE TO BEACH: 45 km
★ DISTANCE TO SHOPS: 1.5 km
★ DISTANCE FROM AIRPORT: 20 km

This is the best hotel in Holland. The Amstel is so grand that even the Dutch Royal family use it for their special occasions and, over the last century, so have such diverse people as Gladstone and Paul Kruger, Isadora Duncan and Rachmaninoff, Henry Moore and Winston Churchill. This is not counting the crowned heads and all those cigar-loving Dutch tycoons. The Amstel is *the* social focus of glorious Amsterdam. The main restaurant, La Rive, is one of the most beautiful I have ever been in and the service and food are matchless. There is also a very, but very attractive bar – the kind of public room which is not always the best. Most rooms are large and palatial, very quiet and distinguished – splendid solid furniture – antique and last century – and lovely carpets. The all round expertise embodied in the Amstel is quite fantastic – nothing ever seems to go wrong and the hotel's location, right on the Amstel bank, could not be better.

HOTEL PULITZER, Prinsengracht 315-331, 1016 GZ Amsterdam

★ TELEPHONE: (020) 228333
★ CABLES: pulitzeramsterdam
★ TELEX: 16508 pulam
★ IN OPERATION: 13 years
★ RESERVATIONS: Nicholas Lawson Ltd, London/Utell International, Australia/Robert F. Warner, London, New York/Stinnes, Frankfurt/ MacLaughlan, Toronto
★ ROOMS: 193
★ SUITES: 2 senior 3 junior
★ RESTAURANTS: 2 – Pulitzer's coffee shop, Patio restaurant: De Goudsbloem

★ BARS: 1
★ DISCOTHEQUE: occasionally in bar
★ SHOPS: 1 – gift shop
★ CONFERENCE ROOMS: 4
★ BANQUETING ROOMS: 3 (10 to 180)
★ STANDARD BEDROOM SIZE: 25 m^2
★ PRIVATE BALCONIES: some rooms with private terrace
★ SWIMMING POOL: no
★ RECREATIONAL ACTIVITIES: city sights within easy reach
★ GARDENS: yes
★ NO. OF STAFF: 80

★ ROOM SERVICE: 06.30—23.00
★ ORIENTATION: east and west
★ CREDIT CARDS: Bankamericard, Diners Club, American Express and Eurocard
★ OWNING COMPANY: Golden Tulip Hotels

★ GENERAL MANAGER: Theo Inniger
★ DISTANCE TO BEACH: 20 km
★ DISTANCE TO SHOPS: 500 m
★ DISTANCE FROM AIRPORT: 20 km

Take nineteen lovely gabled seventeenth-century houses along one of those marvellous canals in Amsterdam, touch them up outside to defy time (but not too much) and inside create a hotel of unique quality and you have the Pulitzer, surely one of the world's most unusual hostelries and also one of the most famous. Every one of the Pulitzer's rooms is different – it's a matter of pride and of policy. Some of them have superb old timbers, others mellow old brick walls and yet others have high, gabled ceilings. Bathrooms are bathrooms and they work. The great secret of course is Dutch thoroughness as well as respect for the past – and respect for the individual. Here you are never a number – everybody knows you by name. Nothing is too much trouble and the same goes for the food which is supremely beautiful to look at and good to eat. There is a sweet interior courtyard kept with personal pride and in my own mind there will never be any doubt that this is one of Europe's finest medium-sized hotels – one with a personality you will never forget.

The Hague

HOTEL DES INDES, Lange Voorhout 54-56, The Hague

★ TELEPHONE: 070-469553
★ CABLES: Indes-Haag
★ TELEX: 31196
★ IN OPERATION: since 1881
★ RESERVATIONS: Utell International Ltd, London/Quality Inn, U.S.A./NRC, Amsterdam/Crest Reservation, Europe
★ ROOMS: 67 doubles 10 singles
★ SUITES: 4
★ RESTAURANTS: 1 – serves fresh food in a classical style
★ BARS: 1
★ DISCOTHEQUE: live music for private parties and music in the restaurant
★ SHOPS: souvenirs and papers etc can be bought at the reception desk
★ CONFERENCE ROOMS: 6 (30 to 150)

★ BANQUETING ROOMS: 7 (10 to 250)
★ STANDARD BEDROOM SIZE: 20—40 m^2
★ PRIVATE BALCONIES: yes – 5 rooms
★ SWIMMING POOL: no
★ GARDENS: no
★ NO. OF STAFF: 65
★ ROOM SERVICE: around the clock
★ ORIENTATION: main facade faces south overlooking a beautiful square
★ CREDIT CARDS: American Express, Diners Club, Visa and Eurocard
★ OWNING COMPANY: Crest Hotels
★ GENERAL MANAGER: B. E. N. Felix
★ DISTANCE TO BEACH: 5 km
★ DISTANCE TO SHOPS: 200 m
★ DISTANCE FROM AIRPORT: 40 km

In a previous edition of the guide I confessed, being a light sleeper, that my liking for this particular hotel went back to the night, years ago, when I noticed that after ten p.m., all upstairs staff wore felt-soled shoes. Inevitably I had a letter from an American lady stating that her room-service waiter did not use such footwear. Oops. Research revealed the reason which proved to be that all floors have been renovated and re-carpeted. Despite my kind correspondent I maintain that the Des Indes is still one of the continent's nicest, quietest and most comfortable hotels. The former baronial residence, it has a good pedigree, has been welcoming and charming guests for a century and though it has new owners they are sure to respect tradition. Rooms vary in size and some of them have been quietly modernized, often with very good, calm colour schemes and fine furniture. Public rooms are excellent, especially the main drawing-room with its famous rotunda ceiling and the restaurant where you never hear the tinkle of glassware or cutlery.

Carpet slippers or not, the staff are very quiet indeed, very well trained and obliging. Management is unobstrusive but always on hand. A very fine residence.

NORWAY

Bergen

HOTEL NORGE, Ole Bulls Plass 4, P.O. Box 662, N-5001, Bergen

- ★ TELEPHONE: (475) 32 30 00
- ★ CABLES: Norge
- ★ TELEX: 42 129
- ★ IN OPERATION: since 1885, but was rebuilt in 1964
- ★ RESERVATIONS: KLM – Golden Tulip Hotels B.A. Reservation System
- ★ ROOMS: 129 doubles 90 singles
- ★ SUITES: 6
- ★ SHOPS: 2 – perfumery and souvenirs with bookstand
- ★ RESTAURANTS: 9 – the Grillen, Restaurant Ole Bull, the Corner Pub, the Baldakinen Restaurant, Norge Dancing and the Garden Room Restaurant etc
- ★ BARS: 2 in winter and 3 in summer
- ★ DISCOTHEQUE: yes – Corner Disco Pub, also dancing to the best orchestras in Norge Dancing and the Garden Room Restaurant (summer time only)
- ★ CONFERENCE ROOMS: 6 (50–140)

- ★ BANQUETING ROOMS: 7 (35 to 450)
- ★ STANDARD BEDROOM SIZE: 17 m^2
- ★ PRIVATE BALCONIES: yes – some rooms
- ★ SWIMMING POOL: no
- ★ GARDENS: no
- ★ NO. OF STAFF: 400
- ★ ROOM SERVICE: 07.00–22.00
- ★ ORIENTATION: Ole Bulls Place and the City Park
- ★ CREDIT CARDS: American Express, Diners Club, Eurocard, Access, Master Charge and Visa
- ★ OWNING COMPANY: Hotel Norge – A/S De Forenede Hoteller
- ★ GENERAL MANAGER: Fridtjof Thirslund Berge
- ★ DISTANCE TO BEACH: 1 km
- ★ DISTANCE TO SHOPS: in the shopping centre
- ★ DISTANCE FROM AIRPORT: 20 km

In a dozen years' absence from Bergen it was a pleasure to rediscover this hotel – surely one of the two or three best in Scandinavia. The architecture may be undistinguished but the decor is not, as befits the home of so much fine design. Dining in the Grill one noticed how comfortable the chairs were. Why can't everybody design chairs like these or the ones in the bedrooms and the sparkling lobby and even in the coffee shop. In a busy business city, the Norge is absolutely ideal – fast, efficient, clean and so helpful that it's like having a super secretary following you around. It is very popular locally and 'le tout Bergen' throngs to the nine restaurants and the conference rooms are almost always booked. The rivers and fjords have salmon and there is a fishing fleet in the harbour, so the fish-eater is going to leave the Norge with the sad certainty that meals will not often be so good again.

Oslo

GRAND HOTEL, P.O. Box 9615, Egertorvet 0128, Oslo I

- ★ TELEPHONE: 42 93 90
- ★ CABLES: no
- ★ TELEX: 71683 grand n
- ★ IN OPERATION: since 1874
- ★ RESERVATIONS: Steigenberger Reservation Service, Frankfurt
- ★ ROOMS: 311
- ★ SUITES: 5
- ★ RESTAURANTS: 5 – Fritzner Grill Room, Etoile, Palmen, Bonanza and Grand Café
- ★ BARS: 3 – Limelight Bar, Grand Plaisir Bar and Bonanza Bar
- ★ DISCOTHEQUE: Bonanza

- ★ SHOPS: shopping centre in adjacent building
- ★ CONFERENCE ROOMS: 9 (6 to 350)
- ★ BANQUETING ROOMS: 2 (550)
- ★ STANDARD BEDROOM SIZE: 17–30 m^2
- ★ PRIVATE BALCONIES: yes
- ★ SWIMMING POOL: yes – fresh water, 8 × 12.5 m
- ★ RECREATIONAL ACTIVITIES: sauna, solarium, keep fit facilities
- ★ GARDENS: no
- ★ NO. OF STAFF: 400
- ★ ROOM SERVICE: 07.00–23.00
- ★ ORIENTATION: towards main street

★ CREDIT CARDS: American Express, Visa, Diners Club and Eurocard
★ OWNING COMPANY: A/S Grand Hotel
★ GENERAL MANAGER: Helge Holgersen
★ DISTANCE TO SHOPS: walking distance
★ DISTANCE FROM AIRPORT: 11 km

Always the best hotel in Oslo, Ibsen lived here for a long time and for many decades the guests felt like some of his less-than-exuberant characters. The Grand was grand but sombre. But enterprise (and money) has brought this great dinosaur right down the evolutionary chain with not just a face-lift but a complete rejuvenation, so that today it compares very favourably with first class metropolitan hotels elsewhere. It still has comforting reminders of past glories – the reception for instance and also the enormous wall paintings. But now the rooms have been transformed beyond recognition and the suites are especially spectacular – good design and great comfort. There is a new and quite superb penthouse restaurant where the food, Scandinavian-French-international, is worthy of praise and there is also the delicately-revamped Speilen period restaurant. Service is extremely efficient and, of course, this being Norway, the whole place is as clean as a whistle.

OMAN
Muscat-Muttrah

MUSCAT INTER-CONTINENTAL HOTEL, P.O. Box 7398, Muttrah, Sultanate of Oman

★ TELEPHONE: 600500
★ CABLES: Inhotelcor
★ TELEX: 5491 IHC MCT ON
★ IN OPERATION: since 1977
★ RESERVATIONS: Inter-Continental Hotels
★ ROOMS: 243 doubles 20 cabanas
★ SUITES: 2 royal 2 deluxe 12 standard
★ RESTAURANTS: 3 – Qurm Restaurant, Musandam Coffee Shop, Sohar Snack Bar/Delicatessen
★ BARS: 2 – Al Ghazal Pub, Sur Bar
★ DISCOTHEQUE: yes – in Sur Club
★ SHOPS: 12 – including hairdresser, florist, gift shops, jewellery shops, news-stand, bank, boutique, car rental, handicrafts, carpets, laundry, playschool and business centre
★ CONFERENCE ROOMS: 5 (20 to 700)
★ BANQUETING ROOMS: 5 (15 to 500); for cocktails up to 900
★ STANDARD BEDROOM SIZE: 26 m^2
★ PRIVATE BALCONIES: yes
★ SWIMMING POOL: yes – 327.5 m^2

★ RECREATIONAL ACTIVITIES: 3 floodlit tennis courts, 2 air-conditioned squash courts, 18-hole golf-putting green, windsurfing, jogging trails
★ GARDENS: yes – 36,000 m^2
★ NO. OF STAFF: 400
★ ROOM SERVICE: around the clock
★ ORIENTATION: ocean and mountain views
★ FURTHER DEVELOPMENTS: health club with gym and sauna, 2 additional tennis courts, 6-lane bowling alley, 6 additional shops, library, clipper lounge
★ CREDIT CARDS: American Express, Diners Club, Visa, Carte Blanche, Access, Eurocard, Master Charge
★ OWNING COMPANY: Government of Oman/Operator: Inter-Continental Hotels
★ GENERAL MANAGER: Gerhard R. Schmidt
★ DISTANCE TO BEACH: on the beach
★ DISTANCE TO SHOPS: 10 km
★ DISTANCE FROM AIRPORT: 25 km

From cut-throat pirates and pearl divers to the Inter-Continental in one generation is the story of both the Sultanate of Oman and this hotel. And providing you-know-who does not get there before you, we suggest that you go now to this rather grand and magnificent country and stay at this hotel – like that you can have the best of both worlds. Part of the new generation of American chain hotels, this one is not at all offensive – large, sun-coloured concrete and built around that new-fangled architectural gimmick – the interior atrium, a piece of planning which at least gives you a quiet room – in this case large and airy, furnished with good sound hotel pieces which, if not always beautiful, are at least practical. It always mitigates the fiercer effects of the sun. Beds and bathrooms are particularly good and the service is efficient. All the food is imported but is extremely well handled and prepared by a staff who have been well trained. There are nice gardens and a huge swimming pool. From here you could sail by dhow to that fantastic Musandam Peninsula which guards the Straits of Hormuz – like most out-of-this-world spots it seems destined to become the centre of this world's troubles very soon. Let us hope it overcomes them.

PAPUA NEW GUINEA

KARAWARI LODGE, P.O. Box 371, Mount Hagen, Papua New Guinea

★ TELEPHONE: 52-1438
★ CABLES: no
★ TELEX: 52012 Transng
★ IN OPERATION: 7 years
★ RESERVATIONS: United Touring International Ltd, London, Tokyo, Germany, Paris, Rome/Travel Consultants International, California/Trans Niugini Tours Pty Ltd, Papua New Guinea
★ ROOMS: 20 double
★ SUITES: no
★ RESTAURANTS: 1
★ BARS: 1
★ DISCOTHEQUE: no
★ SHOPS: variety of items sold in Lodge Office
★ CONFERENCE ROOMS: 1 (up to 40)
★ BANQUETING ROOMS: 1 (up to 40)
★ STANDARD BEDROOM SIZE: 22 m²

★ PRIVATE BALCONIES: all rooms
★ SWIMMING POOL: yes – fresh water
★ RECREATIONAL ACTIVITIES: chess, backgammon and cards; good selection of books
★ GARDENS: yes
★ NO. OF STAFF: 20
★ ROOM SERVICE: 07.00–22.00
★ ORIENTATION: rooms overlook Karawari River and Amboin Station or overlook tropical rain forest
★ CREDIT CARDS: American Express and Diners Club
★ OWNING COMPANY: Karawari Lodge Pty Ltd
★ GENERAL MANAGER: N. Bevan
★ DISTANCE TO SHOPS: no shops within 100 miles
★ DISTANCE FROM AIRPORT: private airport 10 minutes away

Once again, readers of this book will think that I have taken leave of my senses. One of the 300 Best Hotels in the World in Papua New Guinea? A joke, surely. I swear it is not and if you don't believe me, go and see for yourself. In this astonishingly beautiful country, at least half of which seems to be vertical and where they keep coming across people who have never seen a Western face, is a mountain top and on its lee is Karawari Lodge, one of the most unusual hotels in the world and the very end of what one might call civilization. Sit on the terrace as the sun goes down and you'll convince yourself that the world was born yesterday. Down below is the wide Karawari River which flows into the now world-famous Sepik – dugout canoes, crocodiles, unknown orchids and the vast enveloping jungle with the occasional village on stilts of charming people who paint their faces and wear a bunch of leaves back and front and, let it not be forgotten, are also great artists at carving (their creations cost a fortune on Fifth Avenue).

Karawari is built just like a Sepik village – the 'haus tamburan', or spirit house, is the main building, made of tropical timber without a single nail and filled with fantastic artifacts. Your cottage is another wooden hut on stilts (no, there are no chandeliers) and after the first raised eyebrow you'll love it, especially when tropical birds wake you up by pecking on your roof. Food is better than one has any right to expect – they even have Australian wine – but what really counts is being here, at the edge of the world – a world untouched and unsullied. Wearing your floppy jungle hat, you get ready for another speedboat excursion into the Stone Age. In twenty-five years of travelling, this is almost certainly the most unusual hotel I have ever visited. Don't miss it.

PHILIPPINES
Manila
THE MANILA HOTEL, P.O. Box 307, Rizal Park, Metro Manila

★ TELEPHONE: 47-00-11

★ CABLES: Manilhotel

★ TELEX: ITT 40537 MHotel PM/ETPI 63496 MHotel PN/RCA 22479 MHC PH

★ IN OPERATION: since 1912

★ RESERVATIONS: Utell International Ltd, New York, Frankfurt, London, Australia and Paris/Cardinal Hotel Booking Service, Hong Kong/John A. Tetley, Los Angeles, Washington/Stinnes Touristic, Germany/OIREP, Italy/Orientours, Bangkok, Belgium, West Germany/Sugi Tours International, Japan/Networld Inc, New York/KLM/Golden Tulip Worldwide Hotels System, Holland/Robert F. Warner, New York/Supereps International, London/Muriel Fleger International, Ontario

★ ROOMS: 506

★ SUITES: 64

★ RESTAURANTS: 7 – Champagne Room, Maynila, Cowrie Grill, Café Ilang-Ilang, Sea Breeze Grill, Roma Ristorante Italiano and Lobby Lounge

★ BARS: 3 – Tap Room, Pool Bar and Champagne Salon

★ DISCOTHEQUE: Après open nightly, except Mondays, and featuring top band alternating with disco music

★ SHOPS: 11 (including duty free shop)

★ CONFERENCE ROOMS: 10 (15 to 100)

★ BANQUETING ROOMS: 4 (150 to 1400)

★ STANDARD BEDROOM SIZE: 40 m^2

★ PRIVATE BALCONIES: 9 suites have balconies

★ SWIMMING POOL: yes – fresh water, 426.53 m^2 plus baby pool, 46.60 m^2

★ RECREATIONAL ACTIVITIES: the Manila Hotel Bay Club which has putting greens, tennis and squash courts, sauna, whirlpool and massage services, men's and ladies' gyms, sporting goods shop, dietetic snack bar

★ GARDENS: yes

★ NO. OF STAFF: 1055

★ ROOM SERVICE: around the clock

★ CREDIT CARDS: American Express, Carte Blanche, Diners Club, Master Charge, Visa, Eurocard, Bank of America and Pacific

★ OWNING COMPANY: GSIS – Government Service Insurance System

★ GENERAL MANAGER: Frans Schutzman

★ DISTANCE TO SHOPS: 1 km

★ DISTANCE FROM AIRPORT: 10 km (Manila International Airport)

Travel broadens the mind. And makes you blink with surprise. When I walked for the first time into the redecorated Manila Hotel, I gained the firm impression that this was the most beautiful hotel in the world. In retrospect I would not go as far as that but this is certainly a hotel of such splendour, such artistry, such magnificence that it must on no account be missed. The great marble lobby has kept its Filipino-Hispanic columns and its marble and is, without any doubt this time, the most impressive hotel lobby i know. The same adjectives can be applied to the Champagne Room with its wrought metalwork, its cane and its crystal trees and I defy any designer to do better – it has had the attention of some Oriental Cecil Beaton. But it was when I inspected the suites, especially the historic MacArthur Suite and the Presidential Suite, that I realized what a genuine treasure-house the Manila is. The story goes that the Philippines First Lady took a personal interest in the doing-up of the hotel – obviously she is on good terms with every museum in the islands because the place simply gleams with the most marvellous antiques, carvings, paintings and furniture – and all this mixed extremely cleverly with a modernity that can't be bettered anywhere. The staff is an army – there are always six white-clad bellboys waiting at attention when you arrive and service everywhere in this vast hotel is super-efficient and smiling. The Dutch gentleman who runs the Manila is one of those people who has been everywhere and done everything, and he has the great good luck – and judgment – to run a hotel that is probably unique in the world.

THE MANILA MANDARIN HOTEL, Makati Avenue, Makati, Metro Manila 3117

- ★ TELEPHONE: 816-3601
- ★ CABLES: Mandahotel Manila
- ★ TELEX: MANDA PN 63756
- ★ IN OPERATION: since 1976
- ★ RESERVATIONS: The Leading Hotels of the World, worldwide
- ★ ROOMS: 468
- ★ SUITES: 20
- ★ RESTAURANTS: 4 – L'Hirondelle, Tivoli, The Marquee Coffee Shop and Clipper Lounge
- ★ BARS: 3
- ★ DISCOTHEQUE: no – but dancing and live music in the bar
- ★ SHOPS: 3 – drugstore, souvenirs and delicatessen
- ★ CONFERENCE ROOMS: 7 (10 to 700)
- ★ BANQUETING ROOMS: 7 (10 to 700)
- ★ STANDARD BEDROOM SIZE: 27 m^2
- ★ PRIVATE BALCONIES: no
- ★ SWIMMING POOL: yes – fresh water
- ★ RECREATIONAL ACTIVITIES: health club with exercise area and sauna and massage
- ★ GARDENS: no
- ★ NO. OF STAFF: 800
- ★ ROOM SERVICE: around the clock
- ★ ORIENTATION: three facades
- ★ CREDIT CARDS: American Express, Visa, Master Charge, Carte Blanche and Diners Club
- ★ OWNING COMPANY: Mandarin International Hotels Ltd
- ★ GENERAL MANAGER: Wolfgang K. Hultner
- ★ DISTANCE TO SHOPS: walking distance
- ★ DISTANCE FROM AIRPORT: 8 km

Having had the pleasure of visiting the Manila Mandarin twice in eight years, I have nothing but praise for a company that opens a new hotel only when it knows it will be the best in the locality. This one is a magnificent, ultra-modern hostelry where one is hard put to find fault. Everything runs smooth as silk and, in this rather noisy city, it is quiet in the extreme. Rooms are large, very well planned and a pleasure to be in and the suites, especially the Mandarin Suite with its own swimming pool, worth booking ahead for. Food and drink are extremely sophisticated and, in the famous L'Hirondelle restaurant, quite stunning in both quality and cadre. The staff, lavishly numerous, are every watchful, ever willing and dedicated to making you feel at least a twenty-one gong tycoon. Without a murmur, they even repaired a suitcase handle mangled by the airline.

PORTUGAL

Bussaco

PALACE HOTEL BUSSACO, 3050 Mealhada

- ★ TELEPHONE: 31-93101
- ★ CABLES: Palace Bussaco
- ★ TELEX: 53049 Bucaco P
- ★ IN OPERATION: since the beginning of the century
- ★ RESERVATIONS: direct
- ★ ROOMS: 80
- ★ SUITES: 4
- ★ RESTAURANTS: 1
- ★ BARS: 1
- ★ DISCOTHEQUE: no
- ★ SHOPS: 1
- ★ CONFERENCE ROOMS: 1 (80)
- ★ BANQUETING ROOMS: 1 (80 to 120)
- ★ STANDARD BEDROOM SIZE: 20 m^2
- ★ PRIVATE BALCONIES: yes – some rooms
- ★ SWIMMING POOL: yes – fresh water, 50 × 20 m
- ★ RECREATIONAL ACTIVITIES: tennis
- ★ GARDENS: yes
- ★ NO. OF STAFF: 60/80
- ★ ROOM SERVICE: around the clock
- ★ ORIENTATION: south, east and north
- ★ CREDIT CARDS: Bankamericard, Diners Club, American Express and Barclaycard/Visa
- ★ OWNING COMPANY: private
- ★ GENERAL MANAGER: Jose R. Santos
- ★ DISTANCE TO SHOPS: 25 km (Coimbra)
- ★ DISTANCE FROM AIRPORT: 100 km (Oporto); 220 km (Lisbon)

This unusual hotel is Portuguese Manueline architecture gone mad – curlicues decorate arches, crazy towers and improbable staircases and carved ceilings. Once, it was the King of Portugal's hunting lodge and now that the kings are all somewhere else, it is the visitor who has the chance to try this extraordinary way of life. All around are great, green, forested hills where, no doubt, His Majesty hunted everything there excluding peasants. The trees are among the largest and finest I have seen in Europe and a short stroll brings royal delight – there is always a fountain, or a pond or some folly at the end of a vista. Inside, the place is very ornate indeed but, happily, the furnishings are in extremely good taste and carpets particularly beautiful. As in all onetime palaces, rooms vary a lot in size and quality – so make sure you are not relegated to the servants' wing. The best are very good indeed even if the bathroom plumbing turns out to be a bit on the noisy side. As always in Portugal, the food is superabundant, so watch your waistline.

Estoril

HOTEL PALACIO, Estoril

- ★ TELEPHONE: 2680400
- ★ CABLES: Palacio
- ★ TELEX: 12757 Plage P
- ★ IN OPERATION: since 1930
- ★ RESERVATIONS: The Leading Hotels of the World
- ★ ROOMS: 190
- ★ SUITES: 27
- ★ RESTAURANTS: 2
- ★ BARS: 2
- ★ DISCOTHEQUE: yes
- ★ SHOPS: none
- ★ CONFERENCE ROOMS: 7 (20 to 450)
- ★ BANQUETING ROOMS: 4 (30 to 350)
- ★ STANDARD BEDROOM SIZE: 30 m^2
- ★ PRIVATE BALCONIES: yes – in most rooms
- ★ SWIMMING POOL: yes – thermal water
- ★ RECREATIONAL ACTIVITIES: golf course nearby belonging to the hotel
- ★ GARDENS: yes
- ★ NO. OF STAFF: 230
- ★ ROOM SERVICE: around the clock
- ★ ORIENTATION: rooms face west and east
- ★ CREDIT CARDS: American Express, Diners Club and Eurocard
- ★ OWNING COMPANY: Estoril-Plage S.A.R.L.
- ★ GENERAL MANAGER: Manuel Henrique Ai Quintas
- ★ DISTANCE TO BEACH: walking distance
- ★ DISTANCE TO SHOPS: 200 m
- ★ DISTANCE FROM AIRPORT: 30 km

One of the things which have changed for the better in Portugal is the Palacio and I suspect that this is due largely to its eminent general manager, one of the best in the business, who has managed to keep the Palacio where it was – at the top. It's a dreamy place, ageless, all regal corridors and superbly beautiful lobbies, a bar that is like a bar – cheerful and convivial – and above all a staff so knowledgeable that they guess instinctively not only your nationality but your tastes and habits. One never has to ask for the same thing twice – it's there – right down to the ceremonial whiter-than-white tablecloth they put on if you order a cup of tea. I like the old, grand rooms, but one must admit that the air-conditioned duplex suites by the swimming pool are also a very good buy. It is a quiet, well brought up, distinguished hotel. Food and drink, a bit of a problem during 'the troubles', are now back to normal and perfectly acceptable.

Evora

POUSADA DOS LOIOS, Largo Conde de Vila Flor, P-7000 Evora

- ★ TELEPHONE: 24051 or 24052
- ★ CABLES: Pousada Evora
- ★ TELEX: 43288
- ★ IN OPERATION: 20 years
- ★ RESERVATIONS: direct or Portuguese National Tourist Offices
- ★ ROOMS: 32
- ★ SUITES: 1
- ★ RESTAURANTS: 1
- ★ BARS: 1
- ★ DISCOTHEQUE: no
- ★ SHOPS: 1

★ CONFERENCE ROOMS: none
★ BANQUETING ROOMS: none
★ STANDARD BEDROOM SIZE: 20–25 m²
★ PRIVATE BALCONIES: 2 terraces
★ SWIMMING POOL: no
★ GARDENS: 1
★ NO. OF STAFF: 49
★ ROOM SERVICE: no
★ ORIENTATION: views over city

★ CREDIT CARDS: Master Card, Visa, American Express and Diners Club
★ OWNING COMPANY: ENATUR-Empresa National de Turismo, E.P.
★ GENERAL MANAGER: Manuel Cardoso
★ DISTANCE TO SHOPS: walking distance
★ DISTANCE FROM AIRPORT: 145 km (Lisbon)

Anyone who cares for the past ought to go to Evora – the loveliest little provincial city in Portugal, with its own Roman temple. There is a charming, Government-owned hotel, the Pousada dos Loios, which is bliss – an original, untouched sixteenth-century convent with cloisters (you dine in one of them), long flagstoned passages, convoluted columns and lots of splendid carvings. Rooms vary but the best are superb – some of them have four-poster beds and everywhere the furniture is a national treasure.

Because Evora is a bit out of the normal tourist beat, not so many people go there which means that the staff are not overwhelmed – they are nice, friendly and helpful and if not brimming over with the joy of life (no Portuguese ever is) they try their best. As everywhere else in this delightfully old-fashioned country, the food is plentiful and perfectly acceptable.

Lisbon

HOTEL RITZ, Rua Rodrigo da Fonseca 88, Lisbon

★ TELEPHONE: 69 20 20
★ CABLES: Ritzotel Lisbon
★ TELEX: 1258 RITZP
★ IN OPERATION: since 1959
★ RESERVATIONS: Inter-Continental Hotels
★ ROOMS: 306
★ SUITES: 20
★ RESTAURANTS: 3
★ BARS: 2
★ DISCOTHEQUE: no
★ SHOPS: 6 in the hotel and 6 in the gallery
★ CONFERENCE ROOMS: 7 (5 to 500)
★ BANQUETING ROOMS: 3 (up to 500)
★ STANDARD BEDROOM SIZE: 32 m²

★ PRIVATE BALCONIES: yes
★ SWIMMING POOL: no
★ GARDENS: yes
★ NO. OF STAFF: 470
★ ROOM SERVICE: around the clock
★ ORIENTATION: overlooking city or Tagus Estuary and park
★ CREDIT CARDS: all major credit cards
★ OWNING COMPANY: Sodim/operated by Inter-Continental
★ GENERAL MANAGER: Mr B. Schutz
★ DISTANCE TO BEACH: 20 km
★ DISTANCE TO SHOPS: 1 km
★ DISTANCE FROM AIRPORT: 12 km

Since it first opened twenty odd years ago I must confess to having had a long love affair with this hotel. Managed by an extremely expert international chain it will now get the publicity it deserves. Everything at the Lisbon Ritz is worth looking at – the carpets (made specially for the hotel), the furnishings, the bathrooms, the service, even the guests. If there is a fault I haven't seen it.

Rooms are vast and the best have that superb view of Lisbon. Every room and everything else has that ageless quality which is the hallmark of a great hotel. The staff are charming. The Portuguese are normally quiet and polite, and remain impassive even if you require them to make running repairs to a garment early on a Sunday morning. Bathrooms are palatial and superbly clean at all times – I know because I once left a 'secret' mark on a towel and on returning, it had been changed. Flowers are fresh, lobbies gleaming after the early morning work and from the lift man to the front office manager everyone greets you as if you were someone really important. The food, once the weak link in this Ritz, has now been improved beyond recognition.

Madeira

REID'S HOTEL, Estrada Monumental, 139, P 9000 Funchal, Madeira

- ★ TELEPHONE: (91) 23 00 1
- ★ CABLES: Reidshotel Funchal
- ★ TELEX: 72 139 Reids P
- ★ IN OPERATION: since 1891, extended in 1937 and 1968
- ★ RESERVATIONS: direct or HRI/The Leading Hotels of the World
- ★ ROOMS: 168
- ★ SUITES: 15
- ★ RESTAURANTS: 2 and 1 grill-room
- ★ BARS: 3
- ★ DISCOTHEQUE: live music and dancing in main bar
- ★ SHOPS: 2
- ★ CONFERENCE ROOMS: 2 (20 to 40)
- ★ BANQUETING ROOMS: 3 (20, 50 and 80)
- ★ STANDARD BEDROOM SIZE: 24 m^2

- ★ PRIVATE BALCONIES: yes
- ★ SWIMMING POOL: 3 – sea water, 2 of which are heated all year round
- ★ GARDENS: yes – 50,000 m^2
- ★ NO. OF STAFF: 350
- ★ ROOM SERVICE: around the clock
- ★ ORIENTATION: most rooms face the sea or the gardens
- ★ CREDIT CARDS: American Express, Visa, Eurocard, Master Charge
- ★ OWNING COMPANY: Island Hotel (Madeira) Ltd
- ★ GENERAL MANAGER: Georges C. A. Hangartner
- ★ DISTANCE TO BEACH: on grounds
- ★ DISTANCE TO SHOPS: 1.5 km
- ★ DISTANCE FROM AIRPORT: 17 km

Tradition being what it is one never knows whether people go to Madeira to stay at Reid's or the other way around. This grand old hotel, created so long ago for the British upper classes who liked their tea (with their milk in the cup first, of course) and also loved gardens, is still home from home for the island race but by now Reid's has become famous all over the world and no wonder. It is charming, beautifully kept, easy on the eye and also the last word when it comes to service and evening entertainment. Rooms are a good size, simple but very comfortable and many have large balconies where you can sit and contemplate this sweet, green and gold island. The staff cover many generations and they are literally everywhere and extremely willing. The food, once rather plain, is now above the average, but what makes Reid's are its gardens – the finest of any hotel on the island. In fact, you can forget all the other Madeira hotels – I wouldn't dream of going anywhere else but to Reid's.

Sintra

HOTEL PALACIO DOS SETEAIS, Rua Barbosa du Bocage, 8–12, Sintra

- ★ TELEPHONE: 923 3200
- ★ CABLES: Seteais
- ★ TELEX: 42410 HOPASE P
- ★ IN OPERATION: since October 1955
- ★ RESERVATIONS: direct
- ★ SUITES: 10 doubles 8 singles
- ★ ROOMS: 1
- ★ RESTAURANTS: 1
- ★ BARS: 1
- ★ DISCOTHEQUE: no – there is a piano for the guests' use
- ★ SHOPS: none
- ★ CONFERENCE ROOMS: none – two lounges can be adapted at certain times of the year
- ★ BANQUETING ROOMS: none – two lounges can be adapted

- ★ STANDARD BEDROOM SIZE: 25 m^2
- ★ PRIVATE BALCONIES: yes
- ★ SWIMMING POOL: no
- ★ GARDENS: yes
- ★ NO. OF STAFF: 60
- ★ ROOM SERVICE: 08.00–23.00
- ★ ORIENTATION: main facade faces south, but there are rooms facing every cardinal point
- ★ CREDIT CARDS: American Express, Diners Club, Master Charge and Visa
- ★ OWNING COMPANY: Hotel Tivoli Ltd
- ★ GENERAL MANAGER: Joaquim Machaz
- ★ DISTANCE TO BEACH: 10–13 km
- ★ DISTANCE TO SHOPS: 1 km
- ★ DISTANCE FROM AIRPORT: 30 km

When the Duke of Wellington was looking for a suitable place to sign an armistice with Napoleon's generals, he was fortunate that the 'Palace of the Seven Sighs' was at hand and there could not have been a more fitting place. I have always loved this grand, graceful place in lovely Sintra. It was built in the eighteenth century by a Dutch architect for a richer-than-rich Portuguese nobleman and only the best would do. Seteais has majesty, good looks, a magnificent park, unique tapestries up and down the monumental staircases and enough 'azulejos' to please any admirer of things Portuguese. When Seteais serves lunch or dinner, it does so – but of course – on the country's own Sèvres, the lovely and delicate Vista Alegre porcelain – an absolute delight. Rooms are vast, some of them so much so that one needs a bicycle to reach the bathroom which, in turn, is part of the gurgling period of European plumbing. Furniture and furnishings are worth a king's ransom and, one would say, so is the staff – two to every guest. The food, which used to be one of this hotel's weakest points (the kitchens are miles away), has now been much improved.

SAUDI ARABIA

Damman

HOTEL DAMMAN OBEROI, I Street, Damman 31422, P.O. Box 5397

- ★ TELEPHONE: 8345555
- ★ CABLES: no
- ★ TELEX: 602071 Obhotel SJ
- ★ IN OPERATION: 3 years
- ★ RESERVATIONS: Loews Reservations Inc, London, New York, Los Angeles, Tokyo, Frankfurt/Oberoi Hotels (I) Pvt Ltd, New York, Sydney, Jakarta
- ★ ROOMS: 308
- ★ SUITES: 40
- ★ RESTAURANTS: 3 – Cantonese, Grillroom, coffee shop
- ★ BARS: none – Saudi Arabia has total prohibition
- ★ DISCOTHEQUE: no – prohibited by law
- ★ SHOPS: 5 – drugstore, men's shop, pastry shop, travel agency, car rental
- ★ CONFERENCE ROOMS: 4 (100 to 1000)
- ★ BANQUETING ROOMS: 4 (50 to 500)

- ★ STANDARD BEDROOM SIZE: 28 m^2
- ★ PRIVATE BALCONIES: no
- ★ SWIMMING POOL: yes – fresh water
- ★ RECREATIONAL ACTIVITIES: sauna/turkish bath, massage, billiards, snooker, card room, tennis courts
- ★ GARDENS: yes
- ★ NO. OF STAFF: 420
- ★ ROOM SERVICE: around the clock
- ★ ORIENTATION: east and west
- ★ CREDIT CARDS: Amex, Diners Club, Visa, Master Charge
- ★ OWNING COMPANY: Civil Works Co/Operated by Oberoi Hotels International
- ★ GENERAL MANAGER: Mr Ratan Tata
- ★ DISTANCE TO SHOPS: 2 km
- ★ DISTANCE FROM AIRPORT: 20 km

Anyone who travels in the Gulf is, by now, used to surprises. The latest one is probably the Damman Oberoi which, since the mad room boom is over in this part of the world, is almost certainly the last hotel of its kind. They won't make them like this any more. It is big and ultra modern but its intelligent designers have had the wit to occasionally produce an understated Arabic face to the world – there are quite a few nice little touches. And of course, anything you can do elsewhere, you can do here too – probably better – like holding a telephone conference with six people from your room or relaxing in one of the best equipped gymnasiums in the hotel business. Rooms are big and plushy and the bathrooms are worth the journey; and the food in the three restaurants is fine – especially the Arabic and Chinese varieties – you won't get bored. Of course it is an Indian-operated hotel as you soon notice when the *durwan* at the door, dressed to kill, gives you a salute that would shatter a parade ground. Service is super-smiling.

SEYCHELLES

BIRD ISLAND LODGE, P.O. Box 404, Seychelles

★ TELEPHONE: 21525
★ CABLES: BIRD SEYCHELLES
★ TELEX: 2334 SZ
★ IN OPERATION: 10 years
★ RESERVATIONS: direct
★ ROOMS: 25 bungalows
★ SUITES: none
★ RESTAURANTS: 1
★ BARS: 1
★ DISCOTHEQUE: no
★ SHOPS: 1 – souvenirs and toiletries
★ CONFERENCE ROOMS: none
★ BANQUETING ROOMS: none
★ STANDARD BEDROOM SIZE: 20 m²
★ PRIVATE BALCONIES: all rooms have verandahs
★ SWIMMING POOL: no

★ RECREATIONAL ACTIVITIES: tennis, billiards, ping pong, beach fishing, game fishing, library and indoor games
★ GARDENS: yes – the whole island is private
★ NO. OF STAFF: 30
★ ROOM SERVICE: morning tea and coffee
★ ORIENTATION: all rooms adjacent to main swimming beach of Bird Island
★ CREDIT CARDS: Diners Club, Visa and American Express
★ OWNING COMPANY: Bird Island Ltd (private company)
★ GENERAL MANAGER: Guy Savy
★ DISTANCE TO BEACH: on the beach
★ DISTANCE TO SHOPS: 1 km

Now that almost every hotel on these superlatively beautiful islands, the Seychelles, has become a package holiday supermarket, there is only one place left to go: Bird Island Lodge. Its slogan is 'Our guests come back every year . . . and three million birds can't be wrong'. The birds of course are the graceful noddies, unique to this part of the world and at home here since Bird Island is basically a nature preserve. It is also a small, divine island, green and richly tropical, surrounded on all sides by the whitest sand beaches one is likely to see anywhere. The sea is pale blue, the sky blue and gold and there is absolutely nothing to do except swim, sunbathe, eat and drink (quite civilized really) and make friends with Esmeralda, believed to be the largest tortoise in the world.

This is a world of small island enchantment, with only a few locally built cottages with terraces and gardens all over and a feeling of peace and isolation which is quite priceless these days. If you wish to escape (from the tax collector, the newspapers or even your wife/husband . . .) Bird Island is the place you are looking for.

SINGAPORE

GOODWOOD PARK HOTEL, 22 Scotts Road, 0922 Singapore

★ TELEPHONE: 7377411
★ CABLES: Goodwood
★ TELEX: RS 24377
★ IN OPERATION: since 1929
★ RESERVATIONS: Steigenberger Reservation Service, worldwide/Southern Pacific Hotel Corporation, worldwide/Utell International, worldwide/Golden Tulip Hotels/KLM Airlines, worldwide
★ ROOMS: 124 doubles 14 singles
★ SUITES: 108
★ RESTAURANTS: 6 – Gordon Grill, Min Jiang Sichuan Restaurant, Garden Seafood Restaurant, L'Espresso, Coffee Lounge and Shima Japanese Restaurant

★ BARS: 1 – Highland bar
★ DISCOTHEQUE: yes
★ SHOPS: 4 – drugstore, gift shop, jewellery and crystal, hairdressing salon
★ CONFERENCE ROOMS: 2 (50 to 300)
★ BANQUETING ROOMS: 2 (140 to 400)
★ STANDARD BEDROOM SIZE: 35 m²
★ PRIVATE BALCONIES: yes – most rooms
★ SWIMMING POOL: yes – 2, fresh water, 22 × 13 m and 22 × 11 m
★ RECREATIONAL ACTIVITIES: health club
★ GARDENS: yes
★ NO. OF STAFF: 450
★ ROOM SERVICE: around the clock
★ ORIENTATION: all directions – the hotel stands on a hill

★ CREDIT CARDS: American Express, Visa, Diners Club, Master Charge, Carte Blanche and Goodwood Group

★ OWNING COMPANY: Goodwood Hotels Corporation

★ GENERAL MANAGER: Mrs Mavis Oei

★ DISTANCE TO SHOPS: directly

★ DISTANCE FROM AIRPORT: 24 km

In the business that concerns us, the most difficult job is not building a new hotel – it is restoring an old one and in this context I have no hesitation in saying that Singapore's Goodwood Park is where everybody should go to take lessons because here enterprise, infinite good taste and superb management have taken an old hulk – circa 1900 – and transformed it into a hostelry of dazzling excellence. Here one sits amidst fourteen acres of some of the most expensive real estate in the world and the grand hotel syndrome plus the Eastern magic turns the whole place into an instant success story. The Goodwood Park is perfection: rooms are vast and suites vaster, especially that superb Brunei Suite and yet nowhere is there any hint of razzle-dazzle. Furniture is handsome and beautifully kept, carpets are splendiferous, decor so delicate and so beautifully blended that you wonder who could have worked such miracles. Even the Coffee Lounge (which anywhere else would surely be the state dining-room) is magnificent. The food goes with it all – splendidly varied, fresh and good-looking and with both Oriental and Western touches. Next door is the East's answer to Fortnum & Mason or Fauchon's – the greatest food shop in this part of the world. The staff, legions of them, are super-efficient, gentle and attentive. One really feels that in a place where Noël Coward stayed and Pavlova danced, one has the best of both worlds. Goodwood Park is an astonishing hotel which deserves every adjective in the book. Don't miss it. Singapore would not be Singapore without it.

SHANGRI-LA HOTEL, Orange Grove Road, Singapore 1025

★ TELEPHONE: 7373644

★ CABLES: Shangrila

★ TELEX: Shangla RS 21505

★ IN OPERATION: 13 years

★ RESERVATIONS: Shangri-La International Regional Sales Offices, London, Los Angeles, Hong Kong, Sydney, Japan, Kuala Lumpur/Utell, worldwide

★ ROOMS: 700

★ SUITES: 50

★ RESTAURANTS: 5 – Golden Peacock, Shang Palace, Nadaman Japanese Restaurant, Coffee Garden and Waterfall Cafe

★ BARS: 3 – including poolside

★ DISCOTHEQUE: Xanadu Discotheque

★ SHOPS: 18 – jewellery, watches, fabrics, ceramics, boutiques, cameras, antiques, drugstore, ladies' and gentlemen's hairdressers

★ CONFERENCE ROOMS: 12 (15 to 1500)

★ BANQUETING ROOMS: 10 (40 to 1100)

★ STANDARD BEDROOM SIZE: 32 m^2 (41.3 m^2 in garden wing)

★ PRIVATE BALCONIES: yes

★ SWIMMING POOL: yes – fresh water

★ RECREATIONAL ACTIVITIES: pitch and putt, tennis, squash, sauna, steambath, hydropool, gymnasium

★ GARDENS: yes

★ NO. OF STAFF: 1250

★ ROOM SERVICE: around the clock

★ ORIENTATION: rooms face either garden or city

★ CREDIT CARDS: American Express, Diners Club, Bankamericard, Master Charge and Carte Blanche

★ OWNING COMPANY: Shangri-La International Hotel Management Pte Ltd

★ GENERAL MANAGER: Randolph Guthrie

★ DISTANCE TO BEACH: 9 km

★ DISTANCE TO SHOPS: 300 m

★ DISTANCE FROM AIRPORT: 20 km

I have known this hotel more or less since it opened but it was only recently after a somewhat longer stay than usual that I began to realize what a truly magnificent living machine it really is – and I say the word machine without any disrespect. Shangri-La is superb, beautifully organized, magnificently designed and serviced, down to the smallest detail, with enthusiasm and knowhow. I believe it to be a tribute to the intelligence and knowhow of this particular chain. Rooms are immaculate and if you are lucky enough to have one of the garden-side ones, my belief is that you won't find better or more practical and elegant anywhere. Balconies open not onto a frenetic city but onto a vista of greenery and peace. On the other side, it opens onto an atrium filled with more than one hundred varieties of tropical plants. Every service in the hotel – a complicated business with this size – works like a charm. People smile, execute immediately and without demur. Even the proverbial coffee-shop (usually the humdrum set-up where a hotel fails) is not only sumptuous but quick at offering tasty food. Those who love the old and mature should not be put off by the rather overpowering lobby or indeed the tomorrow architecture. Shangri-La is a great hotel – one of the best I know.

THE MARCO POLO, Tanglin Road, Singapore, 1024

★ TELEPHONE: 474-7141

★ CABLES: Homarcpolo

★ TELEX: 21476

★ IN OPERATION: 11 years

★ RESERVATIONS: Steigenberger Reservations Service, worldwide/British Airways Assoc Hotels, London/Utell/Golden Tulip, worldwide

★ ROOMS: 574

★ SUITES: 29

★ RESTAURANTS: 5 – The Rotisserie Steakhouse, Brasserie la Rotonde, La Pinata, El Patio and San Marco Restaurant

★ BARS: 3

★ DISCOTHEQUE: yes – and live music in the restaurant

★ SHOPS: shopping arcade – boutiques, objets d'art, ladies' beauty salon, barbershop and drugstore

★ CONFERENCE ROOMS: 4 (50 to 150)

★ BANQUETING ROOMS: 4 (50 to 100)

★ STANDARD BEDROOM SIZE: 28 m^2

★ PRIVATE BALCONIES: no – but 10 terrace rooms have individual sun porches leading to the swimming pool

★ SWIMMING POOL: yes – 2, fresh water, semi-Olympic size and children's pool

★ RECREATIONAL ACTIVITIES: fitness centre with fully equipped gym, sauna, massage and juice bar, a jogging track and also within walking distance of a golf course

★ GARDENS: yes

★ NO. OF STAFF: 770

★ ROOM SERVICE: around the clock

★ ORIENTATION: faces Tanglin and Grange Roads

★ CREDIT CARDS: American Express, Diners Club, Bankamericard and Master Charge

★ OWNING COMPANY: Hong Kong & Kowloon Wharf

★ GENERAL MANAGER: Mr Manfred Timmel

★ DISTANCE TO BEACH: 15 km

★ DISTANCE TO SHOPS: 800 m

★ DISTANCE FROM AIRPORT: 36 km

Apart from the gewgaws in the shops and the Chinese wallpanels in the main restaurant, the Marco Polo appears brand new. Yet, this sister ship of Hong Kong's famed Peninsula was the first purpose-built hotel in the perpetual motion that is Singapore. What counts here is service – absolutely superb, smiling, efficient and never, but never, on a day off. If you are lucky enough (and rich enough) to stay in the Marco Polo Suite you get a lady's maid or valet thrown in. Not that my room needed either – the floor service was so good that I had no time to ask for anything. Rooms and suites are very large, perhaps a little impersonal – modern but highly enjoyable with fabulous views all around. The vast lobby is banked with orchids and other exotica and the welcome is beatific. It's the kind of hotel that offers so many facilities that one is never bored – not even with the food because all the Orient's specialities are here. Marco Polo himself, who brought Chinese noodles back to Italy where they now call them spaghetti, would be astonished at the hotel that bears his name.

SOUTH AFRICA
Cape Town
MOUNT NELSON HOTEL, P.O. Box 2608, Cape Town 8000

★ TELEPHONE: 021-23-1000
★ CABLES: Hostel
★ TELEX: 572-7804
★ IN OPERATION: since 1899
★ RESERVATIONS: Canaries Hotels Ltd, Sussex/Loews Reservations Inc, New York, Montreal and Tokyo/Claude Duteil, Paris/Golden Tulip Reservations, worldwide
★ ROOMS: 99 de luxe twins 18 standard twins 12 single/bath
★ SUITES: 20
★ RESTAURANTS: 3 – the Grill Room, the Garden Room and the Oasis Restaurant
★ SHOPS: 2
★ BARS: 3 – Lord Nelson, Grill Room Cocktail Bar and Poolside Bar
★ DISCOTHEQUE: no – but live music in the Grill Room
★ CONFERENCE ROOMS: 5 (up to 450)
★ BANQUETING ROOMS: 6 (24 to 350)
★ STANDARD BEDROOM SIZE: 30 m^2, but all rooms vary

★ PRIVATE BALCONIES: yes – some rooms
★ SWIMMING POOL: yes – fresh water, heated, 19 × 18.5 m
★ GARDENS: yes
★ NO. OF STAFF: 320
★ ROOM SERVICE: around the clock
★ RECREATIONAL ACTIVITIES: tennis, squash, a new swimming pool; golf, mountain climbing, sailing and deep sea fishing within easy reach
★ ORIENTATION: rooms face Table Mountain and gardens
★ CREDIT CARDS: American Express, Diners Club, Barclaycard, Standard, Access, Master Charge and Eurocard
★ OWNING COMPANY: African Lands and Hotels Ltd
★ GENERAL MANAGER: Mr D. Angus Dodds
★ DISTANCE TO BEACH: 3 km
★ DISTANCE TO SHOPS: 500 m
★ DISTANCE FROM AIRPORT: 20 km

In a stunningly beautiful country where, alas, modern vulgarity is creeping along, this is the only place to stay happily in any of the big cities. Mount Nelson is an institution – a hotel that has got grander and more elegant with the years, shows none of the usual South African moneymania and still offers peace, quiet and great serenity. The rooms vary a lot – many of them are being done up – but the best are shiningly clean and fresh, with pretty wallpapers and furnishings and lots of room to move about. There is no exaggerated luxury anywhere, just good planning and a choice of furniture that many hotels could copy. The staff – most of them have been there a long time – are quite charming and helpful and food and wine are better than the South African average. The crowning point of Mount Nelson, of course, is its situation – amid glorious gardens with flowers the size of soup plates, lots of green arbours and much tranquillity.

Constantia
ALPHEN HOTEL, P.O. Box 35, Constantia 7848, Cape

★ TELEPHONE: 021 74-1011
★ CABLES: Alphen
★ TELEX: 57 26195
★ IN OPERATION: since 1962
★ RESERVATIONS: direct or via Relais et Chateaux, Paris
★ ROOMS: 11 singles 14 twins 4 lux twins
★ SUITES: 1
★ RESTAURANTS: 1
★ BARS: 2
★ DISCOTHEQUE: no
★ SHOPS: none

★ CONFERENCE ROOMS: 2 (15 and 120)
★ BANQUETING ROOMS: 2 (36 and 150)
★ STANDARD BEDROOM SIZE: 25 m^2
★ SWIMMING POOL: yes – fresh water
★ RECREATIONAL ACTIVITIES: tennis, squash and sauna across the road, with golf and horse riding 15 minutes' drive from the hotel
★ GARDENS: yes
★ NO. OF STAFF: 40
★ ROOM SERVICE: 06.00–22.00
★ ORIENTATION: all directions

★ CREDIT CARDS: Diners Club, American Express, Barclaycard and Standard Bank
★ OWNING COMPANY: Constantia Valley Hotels (Pty) Ltd
★ GENERAL MANAGER: L. H. Gould
★ DISTANCE TO BEACH: 10 km
★ DISTANCE TO SHOPS: 3 km
★ DISTANCE FROM AIRPORT: 25 km

South Africa is a long way away but it is worth going there just to stay at the Alphen. I have thought so for many years and those readers who have been there more recently confirm this belief. This is a truly delicious place, a Cape Dutch-cum-Georgian house classified as a national monument, immaculately kept in perfect order, elegantly furnished and a delight to the eye. There is tradition and hospitality. Bedrooms are most attractive, with handsome beds and also good bathrooms. The grounds are magnificent and in this wine country of South Africa, one has a lot to see and, indeed, a lot to drink for this region produces some of the finest wines outside Europe and at the Alphen they go hand in hand with fine, fresh food.

Stellenbosch

LANZERAC RAWDON'S HOTEL, P.O. Box 4, Stellenbosch 7600

★ TELEPHONE: 71132, 71182/3/4
★ CABLES: Lanzerac Stellenbosch
★ TELEX: 57-0395 SA
★ IN OPERATION: 25 years
★ RESERVATIONS: direct
★ ROOMS: 31 doubles 5 singles
★ SUITES: 7
★ RESTAURANTS: 4
★ BARS: 2
★ DISCOTHEQUE: live music on Saturday and Sunday evenings
★ SHOPS: yes – gift shop
★ CONFERENCE ROOMS: none
★ BANQUETING ROOMS: none
★ STANDARD BEDROOM SIZE: 25 m^2
★ PRIVATE BALCONIES: yes – most rooms
★ SWIMMING POOL: yes – fresh water
★ GARDENS: yes
★ NO. OF STAFF: 100
★ ROOM SERVICE: 06.00–24.00
★ ORIENTATION: rooms overlook courtyard and countryside
★ CREDIT CARDS: Standard Card, Barclaycard/Visa, Diners Club
★ OWNING COMPANY: Lanzerac Hotels (Pty) Ltd
★ GENERAL MANAGER: David Rawdon (owner)
★ DISTANCE TO BEACH: 25 km
★ DISTANCE TO SHOPS: 5 km
★ DISTANCE FROM AIRPORT: 30 km

This is by far the prettiest hotel in Southern Africa – gentle, mellow, beautiful and kept in pristine condition. In this historic little town of Stellenbosch, it is, of course, an old Cape Dutch house, complete with gables, standing in acres of gardens whose blooms have won many prizes. It is an old wine estate – vineyards have been tilled on this site for over 200 years – and Lanzerac still makes its own wine – very acceptable wine at that. Many of the rooms have been converted from wine cellars on the original estate and both they and the public rooms are prettily furnished with good antiques but it is no museum – it remains very much an authentic Dutch colonial house. The whole place shines with cleanliness and peace. The rooms run from the comfortable to the very special and the food – fresh and delicately cooked – goes hand in hand with the quality of the wine. Stellenbosch is a beautiful town and this hotel does it justice.

SOUTH AMERICA – BRAZIL

Rio de Janeiro

OURO VERDE HOTEL, 1456 Avenida Atlantica, 22021 Rio de Janeiro

★ TELEPHONE: 542-1887
★ CABLES: Ouverhotel
★ TELEX: 2123848 OVHT BR
★ IN OPERATION: since 1951
★ RESERVATIONS: direct
★ ROOMS: 51 doubles 5 singles

★ SUITES: 5
★ RESTAURANTS: 1
★ BARS: 1
★ DISCOTHEQUE: no
★ SHOPS: none
★ CONFERENCE ROOMS: none
★ BANQUETING ROOMS: none
★ PRIVATE BALCONIES: yes – some rooms
★ STANDARD BEDROOM SIZE: 25 m², plus hall and private bathroom
★ SWIMMING POOL: no

★ GARDENS: no
★ NO. OF STAFF: 140
★ ROOM SERVICE: around the clock
★ ORIENTATION: facing Copacabana beach
★ CREDIT CARDS': American Express
★ OWNING COMPANY: privately owned
★ GENERAL MANAGER: H. G. Brandt
★ DISTANCE TO BEACH: on the beach
★ DISTANCE TO SHOPS: walking distance
★ DISTANCE FROM AIRPORT: 30 km

In this extraordinarily photogenic city, most hotels seem to be sitting on launching pads about ready to take off for outer space which, after all, is where they should be. That's why I like the little Ouro Verde on Copacabana and, apparently, the bankers who read *Fortune* agree with me. Ouro Verde, while modern, is not outrageous – small, rather intimate, very comfortable and serviced with old world excellence which is rare in Brazil. People take your messages as a matter of course and make up your room when you are not in it – which is as it should be. You are never, but never, disturbed and your room – perfectly large enough – is furnished in a way that won't give you nightmares. Bathrooms work and are nicely devoid of plumbing exaggerations and the public rooms are so quiet, in this noisy country, that you can actually converse without shouting. The food is one of Ouro Verde's strongest points – a vast and beautifully equipped kitchen serves the best hotel meals in Rio. The hotel incidentally does not welcome groups.

Salvador

BAHIA OTHON PALACE HOTEL, Avenue Presidente Vargas, 2456 – Salvador, BA

★ TELEPHONE: 247-1044
★ CABLES: Bahiaothon
★ TELEX: 711217
★ RESERVATIONS: Reservothon Rio de Janeiro; Telex: 02123265/Windotel Ltd, London
★ ROOMS: 231
★ SUITES: 37
★ RESTAURANTS: 2
★ BARS: 3
★ DISCOTHEQUE: yes
★ SHOPS: 10
★ CONFERENCE ROOMS: 3 (25 to 800)
★ BANQUETING ROOMS: 6 (20 to 450)
★ STANDARD BEDROOM SIZE: 30 m²

★ PRIVATE BALCONIES: yes
★ SWIMMING POOL: yes – fresh water
★ GARDENS: yes
★ NO. OF STAFF: 350
★ ROOM SERVICE: around the clock
★ ORIENTATION: all rooms have sea view
★ CREDIT CARDS: American Express, Master Charge, Bankamericard and Diners Club
★ OWNING COMPANY: Hotels Othon S.A.
★ GENERAL MANAGER: Guilherme A. Gomes
★ DISTANCE TO BEACH: on the beach
★ DISTANCE TO SHOPS: 10 km
★ DISTANCE FROM AIRPORT: 30 km

In Brazil the glamour is in Rio, the money in Sao Paulo but ask any Brazilian where the heart of the country really beats and he will answer 'in Bahia' – or rather Salvador dos Todos Os Santos to give this incredible city its full name. This is tropical Brazil, chocolate-coloured Brazil, with a great rhythm and fantastic markets. It's also the oldest city in Brazil with fine beaches on both sides and magnificent churches. For a long time it looked as if the hotels were a further arm of Portuguese colonialism. Now there is the Othon and one is glad to see a new Brazilian hotel that really functions properly. Rooms are gay and often amusingly furnished with local pieces. The staff mostly wear local costume which ripples as they move and goes well with the wide smiles. What is most remarkable here is the food. Bahia food is Brazil's finest and in the Lampiao Restaurant you get the full treatment. A very fine hotel in a most unusual city.

SOUTH PACIFIC
Fiji

THE FIJIAN HOTEL, Private Mail Bag, Nadi Airport, Fiji

★ TELEPHONE: 50155

★ CABLES: Resorts, Fiji

★ TELEX: FJ 4241 Fijian

★ IN OPERATION: since September 1967

★ RESERVATIONS: John Tetley Co Inc, U.S.A./Supereps International, London/Utell International, Toronto, Melbourne, Sydney and New York/Shangri-La International

★ ROOMS: 316

★ SUITES: 13 plus 4 beach *burés*

★ RESTAURANTS: 4 – the Golden Cowrie, Ka Levu, Lagoon Terrace and Takali Terrace

★ BARS: 5

★ DISCOTHEQUE: yes – every evening

★ SHOPS: 5

★ CONFERENCE ROOMS: 4 (40 to 350)

★ BANQUETING ROOMS: 4 (24 to 280)

★ STANDARD BEDROOM SIZE: 38 m²

★ PRIVATE BALCONIES: yes

★ GARDENS: yes

★ SWIMMING POOL: yes – fresh water, 2, 15 × 8 m and 24.5 × 10.5 m

★ RECREATIONAL ACTIVITIES: tennis, golfing, bowling, snorkelling, water skiing, scuba diving, horse riding, guided reef walks, sailing, paddle boats, rowing boats, game fishing, reef fishing, para-sailing and coral viewing boat trips

★ NO. OF STAFF: 530

★ ROOM SERVICE: around the clock for drinks, 07.00–23.00 for food

★ ORIENTATION: all rooms face the lagoon or ocean

★ CREDIT CARDS: Diners Club, American Express, Visa, Mastercard and JTB

★ OWNING COMPANY: Fiji Resorts Ltd

★ GENERAL MANAGER: Keaton S. Woods

★ DISTANCE TO BEACH: walking distance

★ DISTANCE TO SHOPS: 12 km

★ DISTANCE FROM AIRPORT: 62.8 km

With mass tourism as it is, many holiday hotels tend to deteriorate in the natural order of things. One exception is the Fijian, the most complete resort in those lovely islands and one of the best in the Pacific. As a hotel, it saw architects and artists long before accountants turned up to make their ugly calculations to match the architecture and turn an ideal into the coldest of cold cash. The buildings, many of them shaped like Fijian *burés* or huts, display lots of good local timber and stone and drape themselves along an incomparable bay with superfine sands and a fringe of coconuts. Gardens are well tended and rooms are unusually large, always with a double bed and a single and bathrooms are very good. This is a rambling hotel, with lots of places to go, good shops and many activities like fishing, snorkelling, coral-watching, golf and tennis. Public rooms are largely al fresco and the food, especially in the Golden Cowrie Restaurant, is an elegant Pacific surprise. You can have peace and quiet too – the hotel is on its own private island, linked to the shore by a causeway. What makes the Fijian are the Fijians – great mountains of manhood who look as if they had turned from cannibals to babysitters in two generations – and those who make up the staff are enormous, cheerful and amusing. Their smiles look like the keys of a piano.

TURTLE ISLAND LODGE, P.O. Box 9317, Nadi International Airport, Turtle Island, Fiji

★ TELEPHONE:(Nadi) 72921

★ CABLES: no

★ TELEX: 5197

★ IN OPERATION: since 1979

★ RESERVATIONS: C.C. Evanson & Co, Washington, U.S.A.

★ ROOMS: 12 (cottage-style on beach)

★ SUITES: 6 (cottage-style on beach)

★ RESTAURANTS: covered dining area and on beach

★ BARS: 2 – 1 on the beach and one inside

★ DISCOTHEQUE: no – but live musical entertainment provided

★ SHOPS: no – but toiletries and books available

★ CONFERENCE ROOMS: none

★ BANQUETING ROOMS: none

★ STANDARD BEDROOM SIZE: 25 m²

★ PRIVATE BALCONIES: all rooms open onto beach

★ SWIMMING POOL: no

★ RECREATIONAL ACTIVITIES: exclusive use of island; sailing, windsurfing, snorkelling, shelling, canoeing, glass bottom paddle boating, fishing, riding, guided hiking tours, village trips and private beach

★ GARDENS: 500 acres

★ NO. OF STAFF: 25

★ ROOM SERVICE: 07.00–23.00

★ ORIENTATION: all rooms on beach overlooking lagoon

★ CREDIT CARDS: American Express

★ OWNING COMPANY: Richard Evanson

★ GENERAL MANAGER: Martin Livingston

★ DISTANCE TO BEACH: on beach

★ DISTANCE TO SHOPS: 25 minutes by seaplane

★ DISTANCE FROM AIRPORT: 75 km

If you like islands and you wonder where paradise is, I have got the address for you – it's Turtle Island Lodge. My own memories of the Yasawas off the coast of Viti Levu go back some twenty years when you went there for a day or two and hoped that people hadn't forgotten the food. Now there is Turtle Island: five hundred acres, with twelve beaches and never more than fifteen other guests besides yourself, the nearest approach you might ever get to an island of your own. You sleep in a typical *buré*, that's a Fijian hut, and these are cooled by the breezes all the way around (plus a ceiling fan). You eat where it sounds nice to eat that day, inside, outside, on the beach, anywhere and what you eat is what the fisherman caught that day – could be lobsters or crabs or fish, chicken, quail or duck. The bar is well stocked and service is smiling (Fijians are the smilingest people on earth . . .).

You don't spend money on Turtle because everything is included. Also, you don't know what you will be doing this or that day (if anything) because everything is spontaneous. There is no noise, no bustle, no dress requirements. Just you and Turtle and its absolutely unique, beautiful white beaches surrounded by lagoons. The whole thing is the dream of an intelligent American who just likes it that way. Incidentally, this is where Hollywood filmed the movie *The Blue Lagoon* a couple of years back. Fortunately, they left. Bula Bula – welcome to you.

French Polynesia

KAINA VILLAGE, B.P. 2460, Papeete, Tahiti, French Polynesia

★ TELEPHONE: 2-75-53 Papeete

★ CABLES: Kaina Tahiti

★ TELEX: 339 FP Sogeclif

★ IN OPERATION: since January 1979

★ RESERVATIONS: direct

★ ROOMS: 16 overwater bungalows

★ SUITES: 2 family suites

★ RESTAURANTS: 1

★ BARS: 1 (overwater)

★ DISCOTHEQUE: yes – twice a week; Polynesian songs and guitars in the evening

★ SHOPS: 1

★ CONFERENCE ROOMS: none

★ BANQUETING ROOMS: none

★ STANDARD BEDROOM SIZE: 24 m²

★ PRIVATE BALCONIES: each overwater bungalow has a terrace

★ SWIMMING POOL: no – but there is the lagoon

★ RECREATIONAL ACTIVITIES: billiard's room, pearl diving demonstration, picnics on beach, reef excursions, snorkelling, scuba diving, windsurfing and deep sea fishing

★ GARDENS: yes

★ NO. OF STAFF: 21

★ ROOM SERVICE: none

★ ORIENTATION: on the lagoon

★ CREDIT CARDS: American Express, Diners Club and Visa

★ OWNING COMPANY: S.A.R.L. Kaina Village

★ GENERAL MANAGER: André Teriimana Chaze

★ DISTANCE TO BEACH: on the lagoon

★ DISTANCE TO SHOPS: Manihi 520 m from Tahiti

★ DISTANCE FROM AIRPORT: 90 minutes by air from Tahiti

Once upon a time, if you went to Tahiti that was the blessed end of the world. Then travel agents discovered Gauguin's island and its immediate neighbours, lady tourists with blue-rinsed hair came along and bang went your dream. Now you have to go further. Where? The Tuamotous. The what? you may ask. Quite – your travel agent isn't likely to know too much about its heavenly archipelago of tiny atolls way out there in the blue Pacific and that is why you should go now, while there is still time. Kaina Village is on Manihi atoll – nothing but tall coconut trees, sandy beaches that look peroxided and a pale blue lagoon with your *faré* or hut on top. Dreamland? It certainly is and it is so far off the beaten track that the Joneses don't go there. Too much trouble. You do what comes naturally – eat, sleep, have a drink under the trees, go fishing or move over to Manihi's famous underwater farm where lustrous black pearls are cultivated. But do believe this, old traveller: the real pearl is Kaina Village and the chance to live a lifestyle that has almost disappeared.

Western Samoa

AGGIE GREY'S HOTEL, P.O. Box 67, Apia, Western Samoa

- ★ TELEPHONE: 22-880
- ★ CABLES: Aggies
- ★ TELEX: Aggies SX 257
- ★ IN OPERATION: 42 years
- ★ RESERVATIONS: direct/Instant Hotels, Australia and New Zealand/Utell International
- ★ ROOMS: 40 doubles 40 twins 22 singles
- ★ SUITES: 5 family rooms and 10 individual bungalows
- ★ RESTAURANTS: 1
- ★ BARS: 2
- ★ DISCOTHEQUE: live music every evening
- ★ SHOPS: 1
- ★ CONFERENCE ROOMS: 1 (50)
- ★ BANQUETING ROOMS: 1 (up to 200)
- ★ STANDARD BEDROOM SIZE: 25 m^2
- ★ PRIVATE BALCONIES: yes

- ★ SWIMMING POOL: yes – fresh water, 25 × 12 m
- ★ RECREATIONAL ACTIVITIES: tennis and golf close by and horse riding by arrangement
- ★ GARDENS: yes
- ★ NO. OF STAFF: 120
- ★ ROOM SERVICE: 08.30–20.30
- ★ ORIENTATION: north-west
- ★ CREDIT CARDS: American Express, Diners Club, Carte Blanche, Visa and Master Charge
- ★ OWNING COMPANY: Aggie Grey's Hotel Ltd
- ★ GENERAL MANAGER: Alan Grey
- ★ DISTANCE TO BEACH: 1 km
- ★ DISTANCE TO SHOPS: walking distance
- ★ DISTANCE FROM AIRPORT: 35 km

This is undoubtedly one of the two funniest, most unconventional hotels I have ever come across in my travels. For a long time, it was 'the pub' for beachcombers, writers and remittance men washed ashore in beautiful Samoa and has figured in books and movies. Then, things being what they are, Aggie Grey's became a 'proper' hotel – more's the pity – but it still retains a natural, unrehearsed atmosphere which enlivens the visit and Aggie is still there herself – a dignified old lady who's seen the world go by. It's largely al fresco, with a bunch of bananas hanging outside your window, huts called *falé* here spread about some gorgeous gardens and a staff of gentle and smiling Polynesians for whom life seems to be one long 'South Pacific'. Service is odd, erratic and absolutely charming and as for food, you take what's coming – it's mostly good though you don't always know what it is. There are evenings of song and dance in the biggest *falé* in the South Pacific, the original beach of 'Return to the Islands' is not far away and the place is alive with memories. At night, the bar hums with tall stories from far away. If I am in these parts, I would not dream of missing Aggie Grey's.

SPAIN

Burgos

HOTEL LANDA PALACE, Carretera Madrid, Km. 236 Burgos, Spain

- ★ TELEPHONE: (947) 206 343/(947) 206 344
- ★ CABLES: Landapalace
- ★ TELEX: no

★ IN OPERATION: since 1964
★ RESERVATIONS: David B. Mitchell & Co Inc, New York/Relais et Chateaux, Paris
★ ROOMS: 39
★ SUITES: 8
★ RESTAURANTS: 2
★ BARS: 1
★ DISCOTHEQUE: no
★ SHOPS: yes – for local crafts
★ CONFERENCE ROOMS: 1 (40)
★ BANQUETING ROOMS: 2 (175)
★ STANDARD BEDROOM SIZE: 20 m^2
★ PRIVATE BALCONIES: 25 rooms
★ SWIMMING POOL: yes

★ RECREATIONAL ACTIVITIES: billiards, ping-pong
★ GARDENS: yes
★ NO. OF STAFF: 80
★ ROOM SERVICE: 08.00–23.00
★ ORIENTATION: east and west
★ CREDIT CARDS: none
★ OWNING COMPANY: Landa Palace S.A.
★ GENERAL MANAGER: Maria Victoria Landa
★ DISTANCE TO BEACH: 142 km
★ DISTANCE TO SHOPS: 2 km
★ DISTANCE FROM AIRPORT: 111 km (Vitoria)

Just outside Burgos (who does not want to see this fabulous city?) is Landa Palace – another one of those quite superb hotels of Spain. It has long been well known to discerning travellers. Alas, I only saw it properly a few months ago and I don't suppose I shall ever forget it. The moment you enter the vast, pillared lobby and look at the furnishings and the pictures, you know that this is going to be great class and nowhere are you disappointed. A great deal of artistry, sober good taste and inventive hotel-keeping have been invested in this mellow period building. Antiques abound and everybody knows what Spanish antiques can be like. There are timbered ceilings, magnificent screens and marbled floors. Almost every bedroom is different and again with a great sense of style. Service is silent and amiable and the food in the lovely vaulted dining room is by far the best of any hotel in the area. Staying here is the way to really feel Spain.

Jaen

PARADOR NACIONAL DEL CASTILLO DE SANTA CATALINA,
Apartado 178, Jaen

★ TELEPHONE: 232287-232288
★ CABLES: Paral
★ TELEX: no
★ IN OPERATION: since 1965
★ RESERVATIONS: direct
★ ROOMS: 37 doubles 6 singles
★ SUITES: no
★ RESTAURANTS: 2
★ BARS: 1
★ DISCOTHEQUE: no
★ SHOPS: none
★ CONFERENCE ROOMS: 1 (26)
★ BANQUETING ROOMS: 2 (100 to 250)
★ STANDARD BEDROOM SIZE: 30 m^2

★ PRIVATE BALCONIES: yes
★ GARDENS: yes
★ NO. OF STAFF: 50
★ ROOM SERVICE: 08.00–24.00
★ ORIENTATION: north-west
★ CREDIT CARDS: Visa, American Express, Diners Club and Eurocard
★ OWNING COMPANY: Ministerio Comercio Y Turismo
★ GENERAL MANAGER: Jose ma Ronda Arauzo
★ DISTANCE TO BEACH: 120 km
★ DISTANCE TO SHOPS: 5 km
★ DISTANCE FROM AIRPORT: 97 km

Presiding over this interesting city whose name only a Spanish tongue can pronounce properly is this excellent parador – one of the most interesting in the Government-run chain. It is an old castle – very Spanish and extremely interesting from the visual point of view – ancient stones, great windows, marvellous views. Rooms are large and slightly monastic in style but there is nothing monkish in the comfort and the decor – the latter ranking very high for being simple and the real thing. The bathrooms work which makes a change in Spain and the staff are quite good, though, as always in paradors, a little distant. Probably they see too many awkward foreigners. Public rooms are quite beautiful, including the magnificent vaulted dining room. The food is not quite so magnificent. If one has one criticism to level at paradors, it is the somewhat institutional character of their cuisine.

Leon
HOTEL SAN MARCOS, Plaza de San Marcos 7, Leon

- ★ TELEPHONE: 23 73 00
- ★ CABLES: Hostal
- ★ TELEX: 89809
- ★ IN OPERATION: 17 years
- ★ RESERVATIONS: Keytel International UK, London/Iberohotel, Frankfurt, Dusseldorf/Marketing Ahead, U.S.A., Canada/Chico Int, Colombia
- ★ ROOMS: 258
- ★ SUITES: 15
- ★ RESTAURANTS: 3
- ★ BARS: 1
- ★ DISCOTHEQUE: no
- ★ SHOPS: none
- ★ CONFERENCE ROOMS: 3 (15 to 600)
- ★ BANQUETING ROOMS: 2 (180 to 500)
- ★ STANDARD BEDROOM SIZE: 24 m^2
- ★ PRIVATE BALCONIES: yes
- ★ SWIMMING POOL: no
- ★ GARDENS: patios
- ★ NO. OF STAFF: 180
- ★ ROOM SERVICE: around the clock
- ★ ORIENTATION: faces main square
- ★ CREDIT CARDS: Diners Club, American Express, Bankamericard, Eurocard and Carte Blanche
- ★ OWNING COMPANY: Empresa Nacional de Turismo, S.A.
- ★ GENERAL MANAGER: Carlos de Luxan
- ★ DISTANCE TO SHOPS: 100 m
- ★ DISTANCE FROM AIRPORT: 100 km

One of the most beautiful hotels in the whole of Europe. Behind that fantastic facade, it is like living in a museum but one that is warm, gentle and forever uplifting. The best of Spain is here – art, history, tradition, all translated into magnificent furniture, priceless carpets and genuine works of art in every corner where you care to look. Even what is new is worth looking at – the best design and the finest materials. Many readers might say: 'That's all very well, but does the plumbing work?' Hand on heart, it does, since the hotel now belongs to a very experienced hotel company.

It still has to do some work on the food, which is vaguely Spanish international, but the rest of the hotel operation is well within our terms of reference. Even the smallest rooms are quite acceptable – handsomely furnished and well maintained.

Madrid
VILLA MAGNA, Paseo de la Castellana, 22, Madrid 28046

- ★ TELEPHONE: 275 12 27
- ★ CABLES: Villamagna
- ★ TELEX: 22914 vima e
- ★ IN OPERATION: since May 1972
- ★ RESERVATIONS: The Leading Hotels of the World
- ★ ROOMS: 174 doubles 16 singles
- ★ SUITES: 10
- ★ RESTAURANTS: 1
- ★ BARS: 1 and 1 piano bar
- ★ DISCOTHEQUE: no
- ★ SHOPS: 6
- ★ CONFERENCE ROOMS: 2 (100 to 250)
- ★ BANQUETING ROOMS: 2 (30 to 250)
- ★ STANDARD BEDROOM SIZE: 34 m^2
- ★ PRIVATE BALCONIES: no
- ★ SWIMMING POOL: no
- ★ RECREATIONAL ACTIVITIES: sauna
- ★ GARDENS: yes
- ★ NO. OF STAFF: 300
- ★ ROOM SERVICE: around the clock
- ★ ORIENTATION: east overlooking Serrano Street and west overlooking Castellana Avenue
- ★ FURTHER DEVELOPMENTS: colour TV
- ★ CREDIT CARDS: American Express and Diners Club
- ★ OWNING COMPANY: Nerja S.A.
- ★ GENERAL MANAGER: Eduardo Martin
- ★ DISTANCE TO SHOPS: a few minutes' walk
- ★ DISTANCE FROM AIRPORT: 15 km

No latter-day returning conquistador could have done better than this. In a large garden right in the centre of Madrid, the Villa Magna is sumptuous, elegant, eye-filling and I cannot think of any hotel chain that would dare operate a hotel like this. Accountants would not like it. This is a grand gesture, Spanish style and there is no imitation. The plants are real, the leather is leather and the acres of marble were not produced overnight. Bedrooms are vast (suites are airfield size) and excellently furnished with good, sound pieces all kept scrupulously spotless. I would very much like to roll one of the carpets up and take it home. Even the lifts are attractive and the public rooms are done up with a style that only top-drawer Spaniards can manage. The staff are multi-lingual, very urbane and helpful. I have often tried hard to find fault with this hotel — so have our readers — and so far we have nothing but praise. Food is elegantly international and served with great decorum. In a capital city that is not now short of good hotels, the Villa Magna is superlative.

Mallorca

HOTEL FORMENTOR, Puerto de Pollensa, Formentor, Mallorca

- ★ TELEPHONE: 531300
- ★ CABLES: Formentorotel
- ★ TELEX: 68523
- ★ IN OPERATION: since 1930
- ★ RESERVATIONS: Hotels of Distinction Ltd, London/Claude L. C. Duteil, France
- ★ ROOMS: 106 doubles 7 singles
- ★ SUITES: 17
- ★ RESTAURANTS: 3 – General Restaurant, Beach Restaurant and Grill Room
- ★ BARS: 2 – one at the beach and one in the hotel
- ★ DISCOTHEQUE: yes
- ★ SHOPS: 1
- ★ CONFERENCE ROOMS: 1 (80 to 150)
- ★ BANQUETING ROOMS: 3 (100, 150 and 300)
- ★ STANDARD BEDROOM SIZE: 27 m^2
- ★ PRIVATE BALCONIES: yes – in 12 rooms and 10 suites
- ★ SWIMMING POOL: yes – 2, fresh water
- ★ RECREATIONAL ACTIVITIES: mini-golf, 5 tennis courts (2 floodlit), riding, water skiing, fishing, boat excursions, cinema etc
- ★ GARDENS: yes
- ★ NO. OF STAFF: 200
- ★ ROOM SERVICE: around the clock
- ★ ORIENTATION: most rooms face the sea, the rest face the mountains
- ★ CREDIT CARDS: American Express, Diners Club, Visa and Eurocard
- ★ OWNING COMPANY: Inmobilaria Formentor, S.A.
- ★ GENERAL MANAGER: Juan Carlos Mascaro
- ★ DISTANCE TO BEACH: 150 m
- ★ DISTANCE TO SHOPS: 9 km
- ★ DISTANCE FROM AIRPORT: 70 km

If you are Mediterranean bound, one of the ways of avoiding tourist pollution (and other kinds too) is to take plenty of travellers' cheques with you, fly to Palma and get your taxi to drive you to this hotel. Once on its peninsula, behind the curtain of pines, you are undoubtedly where you deserve to be – at one of the finest resort hotels in the Mediterranean, one that has been going for a long time, has tradition, good looks and only the 'right' people between its walls. Nothing here is cheap or skimped. Decor is handsome but muted and the whole 'feel' of the place is one of gentle relaxation. Rooms are sizeable and very well equipped as well as extremely well serviced and the public rooms, particularly the magnificent lobby are well worth living in. There are gardens everywhere, lots of private spots, a very good beach, two swimming pools and if you want anything, why, just raise your finger. Everybody who is anybody has been at Formentor, including the King of Spain, and for comfort one could not do better. Since I was there last I have heard a few reports about the food not being what it used to be. But for the time being I don't believe them.

Marbella

HOTEL LOS MONTEROS, Carretera de Cadiz, Km. 194 Marbella

★ TELEPHONE: (52) 77-17-00
★ CABLES: Monteros
★ TELEX: 77059
★ IN OPERATION: since July 1962
★ RESERVATIONS: Distinguished Hotels Inc, New York/Hotels of Distinction Ltd, London
★ ROOMS: 152 doubles 16 singles
★ SUITES: 4
★ RESTAURANTS: 3 – La Cabane beach club, El Corzo grill and the main hotel
★ BARS: 4
★ DISCOTHEQUE: dancing nightly to a live band in the Bar Club. Also music in the El Corzo grill
★ SHOPS: 3 – ladies' and men's boutiques and drugstore with perfumery and beauty products
★ CONFERENCE ROOMS: 1 and also a conference room which is suitable for small, private functions
★ BANQUETING ROOMS: none
★ STANDARD BEDROOM SIZE: 30 m²
★ PRIVATE BALCONIES: yes

★ SWIMMING POOL: yes – 4, fresh water, 2 outdoor, 1 children's pool and a new indoor pool at La Cabane beach club
★ RECREATIONAL ACTIVITIES: 10 tennis courts and 5 squash courts; also Club Hipico with a choice of Andalusian ponies; table tennis, sauna and massage
★ GARDENS: yes – sub-tropical, small decorative pools with Japanese-style bridges and pink flamingoes roaming freely
★ NO. OF STAFF: 300
★ ROOM SERVICE: around the clock
★ ORIENTATION: rooms face north, south, east and west
★ CREDIT CARDS: American Express, Diners Club and Eurocard
★ OWNING COMPANY: Hotel los Monteros S.A.
★ GENERAL MANAGER: Gonzalo Lasso
★ DISTANCE TO BEACH: walking distance
★ DISTANCE TO SHOPS: 5 km
★ DISTANCE FROM AIRPORT: 50 km

Los Monteros is like an old friend whose company you have always enjoyed – a hotel so civilized, so affluently generous, so varied in its pleasures that you just slip in, unpack and take it all up where you left off last time. Of course, it's one of the best resort hotels in the whole of Europe, superbly run by a conservative management that does not know the meaning of razzmatazz. Bedrooms and suites are generally palatial, large, comfortable and beautifully designed and there are quite a few types to choose from. Then there are the villas down the road on the way to the La Cabane beach club where the tasty technicolour buffets seem to run for ever and ever and where the food, rich and international, manages to have that little touch of Spanish olé which makes all the difference. As for the El Corzo grill, it's one of the two or three best restaurants on the coast. Last time I was there, I discovered that Los Monteros smokes its own salmon. But of course. Los Monteros is what you would wish it to be at any time – quiet and peaceful, jumping and gay and always in the most perfect of tastes. The man who more or less 'made' Los Monteros recently left – one of the great hotel men of the world. I am keeping my fingers crossed that this splendid hotel will remain at the top.

MARBELLA CLUB HOTEL, Carretera de Cadiz, Marbella

★ TELEPHONE: 771300
★ CABLES: Clubhotel
★ TELEX: 77319
★ IN OPERATION: 30 years
★ RESERVATIONS: The Leading Hotels of the World/Relais et Chateaux, Paris
★ ROOMS: 28
★ SUITES: 22 and 5 bungalows
★ RESTAURANTS: 2

★ BARS: 2
★ DISCOTHEQUE: yes
★ SHOPS: 4
★ CONFERENCE ROOMS: 1 (40)
★ BANQUETING ROOMS: 1 (35 to 40)
★ STANDARD BEDROOM SIZE: 45 m²
★ PRIVATE BALCONIES: yes
★ SWIMMING POOL: yes – fresh water, two 150 m² and 220 m²

★ RECREATIONAL ACTIVITIES: sauna and massage, tennis; horse riding and golf nearby
★ GARDENS: yes
★ NO. OF STAFF: 153
★ ROOM SERVICE: around the clock
★ ORIENTATION: most rooms face the south
★ CREDIT CARDS: American Express, Diners Club and Eurocard
★ OWNING COMPANY: Marbella Club S.A.
★ GENERAL MANAGER: Tomas Carreras Costa
★ DISTANCE TO BEACH: on the beach
★ DISTANCE TO SHOPS: 3 km
★ DISTANCE FROM AIRPORT: 57 km

Everybody, but everybody, is asking the same question: Will the Marbella Club ever be the same now that Prince Alfonso has left? This book is not in the star-gazing business. All I know is that for the time being it is still one of the finest resort hotels in this part of the world. Age and maturity have given it a feeling of easy and elegant informality which is very difficult to achieve. It is still very private in the sense that it does not look like a hotel, more like a vast Andalusian garden with a few bits and pieces here and there. Those bits and pieces offer perfectly wonderful accommodation even in the more obvious buildings and if you are lucky enough to have a suite or better still one of the 'cottages' (Marie Antoinette would have liked them) you won't do better anywhere. The most apparent commodity is good taste – in furnishings, in colours, in everything. Privacy is a real and very valuable asset these days when false, cheery togetherness is so often the rule. The Marbella Club knows how to live well, graciously and intelligently. The food incidentally is very much better than it was. We would willingly hold up the Marbella Club as the 'right' kind of resort hotel – a place where People (upper-case P) congregate.

HOTEL PUENTE ROMANO, Carretera de Cádiz Km 184, Marbella

★ TELEPHONE: 77-01-00
★ CABLES: Hotel Puente Romano, Marbella
★ TELEX: 77399
★ IN OPERATION: since 1978
★ RESERVATIONS: The Leading Hotels of the World or directly
★ ROOMS: 150
★ SUITES: 45
★ RESTAURANTS: 3 – La Plaza, El Puente (Grill Room), La Tasca
★ BARS: 4 – La Cascada (with Piano Bar), Grill Bar, swimming pool snack bar and beach bar
★ DISCOTHEQUE: yes – Régine's
★ SHOPS: 4 boutiques, 1 hairdresser, 1 drugstore, 1 real estate agency
★ CONFERENCE ROOMS: 4 (20 to 150)
★ BANQUETING ROOMS: 1 (100)
★ STANDARD BEDROOM SIZE: 57 m^2
★ PRIVATE BALCONIES: yes
★ SWIMMING POOL: 3 – fresh water, 1 heated, 1 for children, main pool 25 × 8 m
★ RECREATIONAL ACTIVITIES: tennis (Puente Romano Tennis Club) aquatic sports, golfing facilities nearby
★ GARDENS: yes
★ NO. OF STAFF: 300
★ ROOM SERVICE: around the clock
★ ORIENTATION: south-east
★ CREDIT CARDS: American Express, Diners Club, Visa, Eurocard, Master Charge and Carte Blanche
★ OWNING COMPANY: Al Rima S.A.
★ GENERAL MANAGER: Willi Dietz
★ DISTANCE TO BEACH: on the beach
★ DISTANCE TO SHOPS: 3 km to Marbella town; 2 km to Puerto Banus
★ DISTANCE FROM AIRPORT: 57 km

Money without taste is money. Money with taste is shining success. Prince Alfonso (he who was Marbella) dreamt this one up in a moment of inspired recklessness – beginning with a tiny, old Roman Bridge in the centre and going on to build what one can only describe as an Andalusian village. No doubt you have seen developers' Andalusian villages before – but not one like this. I would call it one of the five most successful hotel creations I have ever seen. There are clusters of houses, vistas of sloping gardens, gurgling streams, an open-air amphitheatre, a Moorish restaurant (and others) and three swimming pools. But it is when one comes to the rooms and suites that one's eyes begin to open wide – everything is designed with such intelligent expertise that one wonders why it has not been done like this before. The furniture, much of it cane, is quite splendid and so are the extremely original colour schemes and the deceptive mirrors. Some rooms are split level, others straightforward but all are the kind of room you would like to have for yourself. It is all very, very clever with no false ostentation and not a single wrong note. The food seemed excellent for Spain.

Oviedo

HOTEL DE LA RECONQUISTA, Gil de Jaz, 16, Oviedo

- ★ TELEPHONE: 985/241100, 241200, 241300
- ★ CABLES: Reconquista
- ★ TELEX: 87328 – OASAE
- ★ IN OPERATION: 9 years
- ★ RESERVATIONS: direct or Keytel, S.A., Madrid and Barcelona
- ★ ROOMS: 123 doubles 14 singles
- ★ SUITES: 4
- ★ RESTAURANTS: 4
- ★ BARS: 2
- ★ DISCOTHEQUE: yes – and live music
- ★ SHOPS: 12
- ★ CONFERENCE ROOMS: 6 (50 to 800)
- ★ BANQUETING ROOMS: 5 (70 to 800)
- ★ STANDARD BEDROOM SIZE: 22 m^2

- ★ PRIVATE BALCONIES: yes
- ★ SWIMMING POOL: no
- ★ RECREATIONAL ACTIVITIES: sauna and gymnasium
- ★ GARDENS: no
- ★ NO. OF STAFF: 175
- ★ ROOM SERVICE: around the clock
- ★ ORIENTATION: main facade faces east
- ★ CREDIT CARDS: Diners Club, American Express, Visa, Master Charge and Carte Blanche
- ★ OWNING COMPANY: Hoteles Husa
- ★ GENERAL MANAGER: Rafael Vazquez
- ★ DISTANCE TO BEACH: 15 minutes
- ★ DISTANCE TO SHOPS: walking distance
- ★ DISTANCE FROM AIRPORT: 40 km

One of the trio of hotels in the smaller cities of Spain that always make foreign visitor catch their breath with surprise. This one is eighteenth century, built around a colonnaded square courtyard, and its austere beauty is undeniable. Most of the bedrooms have been planned, in a modern idiom, by some of Spain's greatest experts – lighting is fine, the atmosphere cool and calm and the furnishings and especially the carpets extremely beautiful. For Spain, the bathrooms are quite lovely and practical. Public rooms are vast, not too ornate this time and lined with great paintings and tapestries. Here and there, the modernity of a chair hits you where it hurts. I sometimes wonder if all modern chair designers are thin midgets. Service is calm and orderly and quite efficient and the food is remarkably authentic when it comes to the Spanish dishes and most of the country's good wines are available.

Santiago de Compostela

HOSTAL DE LOS REYES CATOLICOS, Plaza de Espana 1, Santiago de Compostela

- ★ TELEPHONE: 58 22 00
- ★ CABLES: Hostal
- ★ TELEX: 86004
- ★ IN OPERATION: 29 years
- ★ RESERVATIONS: Keytel International UK, London/Iberohotel System, Frankfurt Dusseldorf/Marketing Ahead U.S.A., Canada/Chico Int., Colombia
- ★ ROOMS: 157
- ★ SUITES: 3
- ★ RESTAURANTS: 3

- ★ BARS: 1
- ★ DISCOTHEQUE: no
- ★ SHOPS: 1
- ★ CONFERENCE ROOMS: 2 (50 to 200)
- ★ BANQUETING ROOMS: 3 (100, 150 and 250)
- ★ STANDARD BEDROOM SIZE: 18 m^2
- ★ PRIVATE BALCONIES: no
- ★ SWIMMING POOL: no
- ★ GARDENS: yes
- ★ NO. OF STAFF: 180

★ ROOM SERVICE: around the clock
★ ORIENTATION: faces main square
★ CREDIT CARDS: Diners Club, American Express, Bankamericard, Eurocard and Carte Blanche

★ OWNING COMPANY: Empresa Nacional de Turismo, S.A.
★ GENERAL MANAGER: Carlos de Luxan
★ DISTANCE TO SHOPS: 100 m
★ DISTANCE FROM AIRPORT: 15 km

In a previous edition we stated that we knew of two American tycoons who tried to buy this hotel. Now there have been at least three more bids. The enterprising company that runs Los Reyes Catolicos is not letting go this jewel of a place – surely one of the most beautiful and architecturally striking hotels in Spain. It was built by Ferdinand and Isabella as a hospital for pilgrims to the famous shrine of St. James. Now, just to stand looking at its facade you will be much moved. Of course, it is usually full, especially in the season since it is a destination in itself. Despite this tourist popularity, Los Reyes manages to remain a very good hotel indeed with unbelievably beautiful public rooms (especially the main restaurant) filled with many fine antiques and some great paintings and carpets. Rooms vary a lot in size – so ask to see them first. The best are imperial in both size and furnishings and even the marble floors in some of the bathrooms are heated. Whether you are a passing-through tourist or a proper resident, this hotel is where you must stay.

Seville

ALFONSO XIII, San Fernando, 2, Sevilla 4, Spain

★ TELEPHONE: (954) 22 28 50
★ CABLES: Alfonsotel
★ TELEX: 72725 HAS-E
★ IN OPERATION: since 1929
★ RESERVATIONS: Keytel International UK Ltd, London/Iberotel System, Frankfurt, Dusseldorf/Marketing Ahead Inc, New York/Chico International, Bogota
★ ROOMS: 129
★ SUITES: 19
★ RESTAURANTS: 1
★ BARS: 1
★ DISCOTHEQUE: no
★ SHOPS: 1 – boutique
★ CONFERENCE ROOMS: 1 (150 to 500)
★ BANQUETING ROOMS: 1 (500)
★ STANDARD BEDROOM SIZE: 20 m^2

★ PRIVATE BALCONIES: some rooms
★ SWIMMING POOL: yes – fresh water
★ RECREATIONAL ACTIVITIES: golf, tennis and excursions can be arranged
★ GARDENS: yes
★ NO. OF STAFF: 162
★ ROOM SERVICE: around the clock
★ ORIENTATION: rooms overlook the town
★ CREDIT CARDS: Diners Club, Visa, American Express and Carte Blanche
★ OWNING COMPANY: Empresa Nacional de Turismo, S.A.
★ GENERAL MANAGER: Carlos de Luxan
★ DISTANCE TO BEACH: 60 km
★ DISTANCE TO SHOPS: hotel is centrally located
★ DISTANCE FROM AIRPORT: 12 km

The bad old days of this famous hotel have, happily, come to an end. Over the past few years a great deal of money, plus good taste and *savoir-faire* have been lavished on it and Alfonso Treize is back in the top league. Really quite miraculous. This Moorish-Andalusian extravaganza shines again, with its caissoned ceilings in the dining room and its wall paintings, and its very good rooms have been modernized – but not too much so. The plumbing works and so does the service – with a smile and a Spanish grand gesture that is a pleasure to watch. Best of all are the interminable galleries, now beautifully furnished, and that superb Moorish lobby which is fit for a grand vizier. The food is Spanish-international and, in my opinion, lacks a little individuality. But taken as a whole this hotel is surely back among the great.

SRI LANKA
Colombo
LANKA OBEROI, 77 Steuart Place, Colombo

- ★ TELEPHONE: 20001/9 & 21171/9
- ★ CABLES: Obhotel
- ★ TELEX: Obhtel Ce 21201 & 21369
- ★ IN OPERATION: since 1975
- ★ RESERVATIONS: Loews Representation International, New York and London/Oberoi Hotels (India), Frankfurt/Odner Hotel Representatives Ltd, Hong Kong
- ★ ROOMS: 600
- ★ SUITES: 51
- ★ RESTAURANTS: 5 – the Supper Club, Ran Malu, London Grill, Coffee Shop and Araliya
- ★ BARS: 7
- ★ SHOPS: 30 – offering traditional Ceylonese specialities, gems, batiks, handloom textiles and handicrafts
- ★ CONFERENCE ROOMS: 9 (up to 1000)
- ★ BANQUETING ROOMS: 7 (up to 1000)
- ★ STANDARD BEDROOM SIZE: 20 m^2
- ★ PRIVATE BALCONIES: no
- ★ SWIMMING POOL: yes – fresh water 25 × 25 m

- ★ RECREATIONAL ACTIVITIES: tennis and fully equipped health club, 2 squash courts
- ★ GARDENS: yes
- ★ NO. OF STAFF: 800
- ★ ROOM SERVICE: around the clock
- ★ ORIENTATION: faces four directions
- ★ CREDIT CARDS: American Express, Diners Club, Bankamericard, Eurocard, Access and Master Charge
- ★ OWNING COMPANY: Asian Hotels Corporation
- ★ GENERAL MANAGER: Mr Azhar Siddiqi
- ★ DISTANCE TO BEACH: 8 km
- ★ DISTANCE TO SHOPS: 2 km
- ★ DISTANCE FROM AIRPORT: 30 km
- ★ ADDITIONAL FEATURES: The Club – an exclusive Businessman's club with separate dining and bar facilities, 2 meeting rooms, a library, Reuter News Service & full secretarial facilities. The hotel is also fully computerized.

If ever there was a city that deserved a good hotel, it was Colombo – that gentle exotic Bournemouth of the Orient. Colombo has the relics of high civilization aplenty – it just needed perking up and the Lanka Oberoi has done much towards this end. It is one of the original central atrium-style hotels. You go in and are greeted by an enormous tall central lobby, draped with huge batik hangings and splashed with tropical flowers. All rooms are approached through the corridors ringing this atrium and they are, as a result, extremely quiet. Here too, modern style has been softened by some nice local touches – rare woods, good hangings, lovely carpets and surprisingly good lighting for a new hotel. Wardrobes are huge and beautifully fitted by real joiners. There are verdant gardens and the grass grows right up to the edge of the original swimming pool built in the shape the old Kandy kings liked. The international food – always difficult in Sri Lanka – is very acceptable as is the service. Now there is more competition in Colombo but my feeling is that the Lanka is still ahead.

SUDAN
Khartoum
HILTON INTERNATIONAL KHARTOUM, P.O. Box 1910, Mogran, Khartoum

- ★ TELEPHONE: 74100 & 78930
- ★ CABLES: Hiltels – Khartoum
- ★ TELEX: KM. 250
- ★ IN OPERATION: 7 years
- ★ RESERVATIONS: Hilton Reservation Service

- ★ ROOMS: 271
- ★ SUITES: 34
- ★ RESTAURANTS: 3 – Ivory Club, Mogran Coffee Shop and Garden Restaurant
- ★ BARS: 2 – non-alcoholic

★ DISCOTHEQUE: no – live music in Ivory Club nightly
★ SHOPS: 6 – books, hairdressers, African handicrafts, leathergoods, duty-free goods and airways booking office
★ CONFERENCE ROOMS: 2 (5 to 500)
★ BANQUETING ROOMS: 2 (70 to 350)
★ STANDARD BEDROOM SIZE: 30 m^2
★ PRIVATE BALCONIES: no
★ SWIMMING POOL: yes – fresh water
★ RECREATIONAL ACTIVITIES: tennis, health club with sauna and massage, four-lane bowling alley and billiards
★ GARDENS: yes

★ NO. OF STAFF: 400
★ ROOM SERVICE: around the clock
★ ORIENTATION: rooms overlook either the Blue or the White Nile
★ CREDIT CARDS: American Express, Visa, Diners Club, Access, Master Charge, Eurocard, Air Canada and Lufthansa Courtesy Card
★ OWNING COMPANY: Sudan Kuwait Hotels Co
★ GENERAL MANAGER: Ulrich Wolffram
★ DISTANCE TO SHOPS: 3 km
★ DISTANCE FROM AIRPORT: 6.5 km

Strange as it may seem to some the Sudan – Africa's largest country – is one of my firm favourites and I'll go back to Khartoum at the drop of a credit card. Especially now that the Khartoum Hilton is there. And if this sounds like a bit of a joke, ask any old hand what it was like before this legendary city was Hiltonized. The hotel stands on a historic spot, the Mogran, where the Blue and White Niles meet and just across the great river is Omdurman where Young Winston – with some help from Kitchener – defeated the hellish plots of the Mahdi and you can still see the dancing dervishes there. The Khartoum Hilton has one thing in common with all its brothers and sisters – it works – which here, frankly, is nothing short of a miracle, especially in the bathrooms. Bedrooms, a trifle 'international', are nevertheless spacious and nicely equipped. There is a very good swimming pool – which one needs badly – and some sensational views of the two Niles. The food in the Ivory Club is better than one has any right to expect and as for the staff, the Sudanese have the widest smiles in Africa.

SWEDEN
Stockholm

GRAND HOTEL, P.O. Box 16424, S-103 27 Stockholm

★ TELEPHONE: 08/22 17 20
★ CABLES: Grand
★ TELEX: 19500
★ IN OPERATION: since 1874
★ RESERVATIONS: The Leading Hotels of the World
★ ROOMS: 166 doubles 184 singles
★ SUITES: 11
★ RESTAURANTS: 2 – French Dining Room and Grand Café
★ BARS: 1
★ DISCOTHEQUE: no – but dancing to live music Fri & Sat evenings
★ SHOPS: 1 – newspapers, books, souvenirs, jewellery, china, silk ties etc
★ CONFERENCE ROOMS: 15 (15 to 1000)
★ BANQUETING ROOMS: 15 (20 to 1200)
★ STANDARD BEDROOM SIZE: 28 m^2
★ PRIVATE BALCONIES: yes – some rooms

★ SWIMMING POOL: no
★ RECREATIONAL ACTIVITIES: sauna
★ GARDENS: no
★ NO. OF STAFF: 370
★ ROOM SERVICE: around the clock
★ ORIENTATION: facing the Royal Palace and by the River Strommen
★ CREDIT CARDS: American Express, Visa, Eurocard, Master Charge and Access
★ FURTHER DEVELOPMENTS: the Royal Winter Garden has been rebuilt to make it suitable for conferences and also for shows
★ OWNING COMPANY: AB Nya Grand Hotel
★ GENERAL MANAGER: Mr Sölve Persson
★ DISTANCE TO SHOPS: 300 m
★ DISTANCE FROM AIRPORT: 40 km

In Sweden where everybody is supposed to be both rich and equal, this unlikely double event has been achieved only at the Grand Hotel. It is better than any other and has been like that on and off for over a century. Right now, it is definitely on, one of those massive landmarks which the traveller would surely miss if someone turned it into the limpest member of an international chain. The Grand is what a big city hotel should be – all things to all men: good-looking, practical, very clean and beautifully laid out within the old shell and kept up to date in the tiniest detail. If you want to see the latest plumbing or the latest design it's bound to be here. Rooms and suites are large, but elegantly stark. One would call it restrained luxury. The only showpiece is the fantastic turn-of-the-century Mirror Hall – only slightly smaller than Versailles. Service is urbane, perhaps a little distant but very efficient and the food everywhere is worth a bank manager's frown, especially the smorgasbord in the riverside verandah.

SWITZERLAND

Basel

HOTEL DREI KOENIGE, Blumenrain 8, 4001 Basel

★ TELEPHONE: 061/25 52 52
★ CABLES: Troisrois Bale
★ TELEX: 62937
★ IN OPERATION: since 1026
★ RESERVATIONS: The Leading Hotels of the World
★ ROOMS: 48 doubles 35 singles
★ SUITES: 7
★ RESTAURANTS: 2 – Rotisserie des Rois and Restaurant Rhy-Deck
★ BARS: 1
★ DISCOTHEQUE: yes (private night club)
★ SHOPS: none
★ CONFERENCE ROOMS: 2 (6 to 200)
★ BANQUETING ROOMS: 2 (6 to 200)
★ STANDARD BEDROOM SIZE: 20 m²
★ SWIMMING POOL: no

★ PRIVATE BALCONIES: yes – some rooms, also terrace with seating equipment
★ GARDENS: no
★ NO. OF STAFF: 60
★ ROOM SERVICE: 06.30–24.00
★ ORIENTATION: most rooms overlook the river, some rooms overlook the city
★ CREDIT CARDS: American Express, Diners Club, Eurocard, Bankamericard, Carte Blanche
★ OWNING COMPANY: Société d'Exploitation et Gestion Hotelière
★ GENERAL MANAGER: P. Bougenaux
★ DISTANCE TO SHOPS: walking distance
★ DISTANCE FROM AIRPORT: 10 km (deluxe limousine service)

Forty years before William the Conqueror crossed to Hastings, there was already a hotel on this bank of the Rhine at Basel. It was called 'At the Sight of the Flower'. Then three crowned heads met there to put their seal on one of Europe's greatest carve-ups and The Three Kings it remained. They have stopped counting kings here now – so many have slept here, at this oldest hotel in Switzerland, that singling them out would be invidious. Some people have lately made rude comments about the hotel's modern improvements. I rather like them because, like so many things in Switzerland, they are in irreproachable taste and solidity. I still prefer the old period rooms, of which there are quite a few, all of them beautifully furnished and superbly cared for. The Three Kings is comfortable, beautifully run and one would be hard pressed to find fault. There certainly isn't any either in the service – in the finest Swiss tradition – or in the food which is spectacular and memorable.

Buergenstock

THE BUERGENSTOCK ESTATE (PALACE HOTEL, GRAND HOTEL), CH-6366, Buergenstock

★ TELEPHONE: Grand: 041/64 12 12, Palace: 041/64 11 22
★ CABLES: Freyhotel Buergenstock
★ TELEX: CH 78462

★ IN OPERATION: since 1874
★ RESERVATIONS: The Leading Hotels of the World
★ ROOMS: 152

★ SUITES: 11
★ RESTAURANTS: 6
★ BARS: 2
★ DISCOTHEQUE: live music
★ SHOPS: 5
★ CONFERENCE ROOMS: 8 (10 to 350)
★ BANQUETING ROOMS: 8 (10 to 400)
★ STANDARD BEDROOM SIZE: 25 m²
★ PRIVATE BALCONIES: yes
★ SWIMMING POOL: yes – fresh water
★ GARDENS: yes

★ NO. OF STAFF: 160
★ ROOM SERVICE: around the clock
★ ORIENTATION: rooms face north overlooking lake and south overlooking the Alps
★ CREDIT CARDS: American Express and Visa
★ OWNING COMPANY: (privately owned) Fritz Frey
★ GENERAL MANAGER: Rolf Schraegle
★ DISTANCE FROM AIRPORT: 75 km (Zurich)

For that top-of-the-world, nothing-but-the-best feeling, I know of nowhere that equals the Buergenstock Estate. It is mad, extravagant, totally unrealistic, obviously megalomaniac and at the same time so wonderful that it makes you feel better just being there. Sitting on top of a verdant mountain overlooking Lake Lucerne (you get there via Europe's fastest vertical transport) this is the private empire of the legendary Mr Frtiz Frey whom everybody knows because there is only one like him. There are three hotels – Palace, Park and Grand – plus a variety of private villas, very Swiss chalets and lots of little follies hidden away. Here you leave the ordinary world aside and enter a magnificent domain hung with Van Dycks and Tintorettos, Brueghels and Titians. Your room – palatial – may well show off a Gobelins tapestry but you won't get a refund if it does not because the room next door has a Sèvres table service. Priceless period furniture, finest silk Qum carpets, food that is of the highest order go with all that and, when you go out, there is at least half Switzerland at your feet. It is not the cheapest place in the world but one of the most unusual: the management are remarkably selective about who stays and who does not.

Geneva

LE RICHEMOND, Jardin Brunswick, 1201 Geneva

★ TELEPHONE: (022) 31 14 00
★ CABLES: Richotel
★ TELEX: 22 598
★ IN OPERATION: since 1875
★ RESERVATIONS: The Leading Hotels of the World, worldwide/Preferred Hotels, worldwide
★ ROOMS: 93
★ SUITES: 25
★ RESTAURANTS: 2 – Le Gentilhomme and Le Jardin
★ BARS: 2
★ DISCOTHEQUE: orchestra in restaurant Gentilhomme
★ SHOPS: hairdresser, newsagent and tobacconist
★ CONFERENCE ROOMS: 2 (50 to 300)
★ BANQUETING ROOMS: 4 (12 to 50)
★ STANDARD BEDROOM SIZE: 20 m²
★ PRIVATE BALCONIES: some rooms have balconies

★ SWIMMING POOL: no
★ RECREATIONAL ACTIVITIES: flowered terrace restaurant
★ GARDENS: public garden nearby – Jardin Brunswick
★ NO. OF STAFF: 280
★ ROOM SERVICE: around the clock
★ ORIENTATION: most rooms face lake and alps
★ CREDIT CARDS: American Express, Eurocard, Visa, Diners Club, Access, Master Charge
★ OWNING COMPANY: Mr Jean Armleder (Proprietor)
★ GENERAL MANAGER: Roland Klinger
★ DISTANCE TO BEACH: 200 m to lake
★ DISTANCE TO SHOPS: 500 m
★ DISTANCE FROM AIRPORT: 6 km (Geneva)

As hotels go, they do not come more aristocratic than this one.
The hotel has been owned and run by members of the same family since 1875 and they are known all over the world. Of course, Le Richemond should have been in this book

long ago but we make the usual excuse – we did not know it personally. Now that we do, we have no hesitation. It is suave, civilized, managed with great expertise and furnished with great distinction. There is nothing flashy about it – after all this time Le Richemond knows what is right and what is not. Public rooms are quiet and dignified, silent and serene. Bedrooms and suites are on the whole spacious, beautifully carpeted and curtained and agreeably furnished with style and with comfort in mind. We could not find a single detail that jarred on us. Service is Swiss, with a smile that is undoubtedly genuine – people are glad to see you and help you and do the latter swiftly and with superb, quiet efficiency. The food in the two restaurants is well above the standards of hotel food generally, delicate and well served. Obviously, Le Richemond is an extremely good address.

Gstaad

GSTAAD PALACE HOTEL, 3780 Gstaad

- ★ TELEPHONE: (030) 83131
- ★ CABLES: Palace
- ★ TELEX: 922222
- ★ IN OPERATION: since 1914
- ★ RESERVATIONS: The Leading Hotels of the World
- ★ ROOMS: 140
- ★ SUITES: 20
- ★ RESTAURANTS: 4
- ★ BARS: 2
- ★ DISCOTHEQUE: yes
- ★ SHOPS: 2
- ★ CONFERENCE ROOMS: 4 (10 to 200)
- ★ BANQUETING ROOMS: 2 (150 to 220)
- ★ STANDARD BEDROOM SIZE: 18 m²

- ★ PRIVATE BALCONIES: yes – in most rooms
- ★ SWIMMING POOL: yes – fresh water heated & indoor pool
- ★ GARDENS: yes
- ★ NO. OF STAFF: 220
- ★ ROOM SERVICE: around the clock
- ★ ORIENTATION: rooms face all directions
- ★ CREDIT CARDS: none
- ★ OWNING COMPANY: Royal Hotel Winter & Gstaad Palace A.G.
- ★ GENERAL MANAGER: Ernst A. Scherz
- ★ DISTANCE TO SHOPS: 300 m
- ★ DISTANCE FROM AIRPORT: 150 km (Geneva)

This castle-like hotel dominating one of Switzerland's best winter resorts is famous for many things and not the least of them is its guest list. They are all here – names that come straight from the Almanach de Gotha or have lots of zeros after the first digit – the rich, the influential, the beautiful and, oddly enough, the young. The Palace has been like this forever largely thanks to a management that knows how to attract clients and also how to entertain them. I don't like the main restaurant much but I do like the other

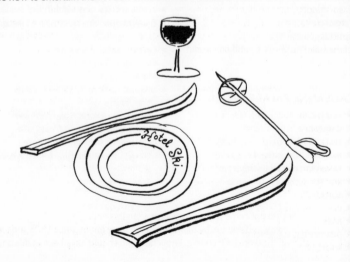

one that has a bar attached to it. The bedrooms vary a lot in size – some have super new bathrooms with his-and-hers – but what does not vary is the quality of the hotel and the service – very, very *soigné* and personalized. The swimming pool is truly one of the most beautiful in Europe and, with the high Alps outside during the day, the nights are filled with good-natured jollity. A very good place for a grand holiday.

Lausanne

BEAU-RIVAGE PALACE, 1000 Lausanne 6, Ouchy

★ TELEPHONE: (021) 26 38 31
★ CABLES: Beaurivage Lausanne
★ TELEX: 24 341 Boriv
★ IN OPERATION: since 1861
★ RESERVATIONS: The Leading Hotels of the World
★ ROOMS: 220
★ SUITES: 6
★ RESTAURANTS: 3
★ BARS: 2
★ DISCOTHEQUE: yes – dancing to live music six nights each week
★ SHOPS: 6
★ CONFERENCE ROOMS: 9 (50 to 500)
★ BANQUETING ROOMS: 10 (50 to 800)
★ STANDARD BEDROOM SIZE: 35 m^2
★ PRIVATE BALCONIES: yes
★ SWIMMING POOL: yes

★ RECREATIONAL ACTIVITIES: 18-hole golf course within 15 minutes of the hotel and all other outdoor sports facilities close by
★ GARDENS: yes – 10-acre private park
★ NO. OF STAFF: 250
★ ROOM SERVICE: 07.00–24.00
★ ORIENTATION: main facade faces south – also other directions
★ CREDIT CARDS: Eurocard, Master Charge, Access and American Express
★ OWNING COMPANY: Beau Rivage Palace S.A.
★ GENERAL MANAGER: Maurice R. L. Urech
★ DISTANCE TO SHOPS: 5 minutes by car
★ DISTANCE FROM AIRPORT: 60 km

Since the third edition of the guide, the Lausanne Beau Rivage has managed the impossible. Over a century old, it has refreshed itself and become young again. Don't ask me how they do it. Other things have changed too since at last it has successfully blended its three wings of different periods into one fantastic pad without losing any of its age-old charm, and what else would you expect from a hotel that was the original setting for Noël Coward's *Private Lives*? The Beau Rivage is one of the grand old hotels of the world. The huge wedding cake palace stands in its own ten-acre park facing the lake with a marvellously beautiful terrace, half in and half out of the hotel which is its great asset. Rooms are vast and quietly palatial without any ostentation and the service is so smooth that one hardly has time to aspirate for help. The food in the beautiful French restaurant with its fin de siècle decor is among the best in any Swiss hotel. Its famous general manager has gone now but his successor is also one of the great names of the hotel business around the world. The Beau Rivage is in good hands.

LAUSANNE PALACE HOTEL, 7–9 Grand Chene, 1002 Lausanne

★ TELEPHONE: (021) 20 37 11
★ CABLES: Palace Lausanne
★ TELEX: 24 171
★ IN OPERATION: since 1912
★ RESERVATIONS: Hotel Representative Inc
★ ROOMS: 175
★ SUITES: 25
★ RESTAURANTS: 1
★ BARS: 2
★ DISCOTHEQUE: nightclub
★ SHOPS: 7

★ CONFERENCE ROOMS: 4 (70 to 350)
★ BANQUETING ROOMS: 4 (70 to 260)
★ STANDARD BEDROOM SIZE: 26 m^2
★ PRIVATE BALCONIES: yes – terrace with seating equipment
★ SWIMMING POOL: no
★ GARDENS: yes
★ NO. OF STAFF: 180
★ ROOM SERVICE: around the clock
★ ORIENTATION: most rooms overlook the lake

★ OWNING COMPANY: Lausanne Palace
   S.A.
★ CREDIT CARDS: American Express,
   Diners Club, Carte Blance and
   Bankamericard

★ GENERAL MANAGER: André Hauri
★ DISTANCE TO SHOPS: walking distance
★ DISTANCE FROM AIRPORT: 60 km

In a small country where hotel standards are usually of the highest, the Lausanne Palace is no laggard – one of those old palace hotels that keeps renewing itself without disturbing anyone. The latest offering in the newly refurbished rooms (not all of them are) is a bedside control panel which adjusts almost everything around, the lighting, which by the way is far above the average, the curtains, the television, your life too, maybe. Bathrooms are the last word and you can choose music from three channels while you shave. Breakfast arrives, gleaming silver and immaculate napery, with a fresh red rose in a vase. The marbled, pillared lobby is so quiet that it is hard to realize one is in a public place – staff move with a noiseless glide which is a pleasure to watch. The great dining room is splendid *Belle Epoque*, the food quite perfect. The very experienced management is there to ensure that the highest standards never fall.

Lucerne
GRAND HOTEL NATIONAL, Haldenstrasse 4, CH-6002 Lucerne

★ TELEPHONE: 041/50 11 11
★ CABLES: National
★ TELEX: 868 135 Natlu-Ch
★ IN OPERATION: since 1871
★ RESERVATIONS: Steigenberger
   Reservation Service/Preferred Hotels,
   worldwide
★ ROOMS: 80 doubles 15 singles
★ SUITES: 4 Attika Suites, 2 Salons
★ RESTAURANTS: 5 – Promenade with Bar,
   Viennese Cafe, Restaurant Français,
   Von Pfyffer and Le Trianon
★ BARS: 1 – National Bar (in the lobby)
★ DISCOTHEQUE: no – but Night Club
   Hazyland opposite the Grand National
★ SHOPS: 1 – beauty salon
★ CONFERENCE ROOMS: rooms for 12 to
   350 persons
★ BANQUETING ROOMS: rooms for 12 to
   350 persons
★ STANDARD BEDROOM SIZE: 20 m^2

★ PRIVATE BALCONIES: yes – some rooms
★ SWIMMING POOL: yes – fresh water,
   72 m^2
★ RECREATIONAL ACTIVITIES: sauna,
   solarium in the hotel with tennis and golf
   nearby; horse riding 5 km away
★ GARDENS: no
★ NO. OF STAFF: 120
★ ROOM SERVICE: 06.30–24.00
★ ORIENTATION: facing the lake and the
   Alps
★ CREDIT CARDS: American Express,
   Diners Club, Visa, Eurocard and Master
   Charge
★ OWNING COMPANY: Grand Hotel
   National AG
★ GENERAL MANAGER: M. Windlin
★ DISTANCE TO BEACH: 1 km to Lido Beach
★ DISTANCE TO SHOPS: walking distance
★ DISTANCE FROM AIRPORT: 60 km

Cesar Ritz ran the Grand National for a dozen years while Escoffier devised ever new delights in the kitchen so the provenance could hardly be better. The hotel itself, standing like a statement of pride on the shores of Lake Lucerne, looks as if it has not changed for years – but study it carefully for here is one of those miracles of the hotel business – one that got better, and newer, and grander with age by the simple (but not inexpensive) process of taking the best from all periods. The result is luxury in the grand manner. Everything you see, everything you touch, is perfection – superb furnishings and carpets, beds so comfortable that no one needs sleeping pills and a service so smooth, so intelligently anticipating the guest's requirements that you only remember it afterwards. The Grand National's periodic face-lifts are just what they mean: you leave the bone structure and improve the rest but here you never see the telltale lines of a poor face-lift.

Montreux

LE MONTREUX PALACE, 100 Grand-rue, CH 1820, Montreux

★ TELEPHONE: (021) 63 53 73
★ CABLES: PALACEMTX
★ TELEX: 453 101 mpm ch
★ IN OPERATION: since 1906
★ RESERVATIONS: Steigenberger Reservation System, worldwide/Hotel Representative Inc (HRI), worldwide/Robert F. Warner, New York
★ ROOMS: 202 twins 28 singles
★ SUITES: 10 full and executive suites 25 junior suites
★ RESTAURANTS: 4 – Restaurant Français, Cave du Cygne, Le Grand Café, a Swiss coffee shop and a barbecue and snacks available at the swimming pool
★ BARS: 2 – the Golden Rose Bar and Le Tube
★ DISCOTHEQUE: no
★ SHOPS: various shops, including hairdresser, watch and jewellery shop, drugstore, Swiss embroideries, antiques
★ CONFERENCE ROOMS: 10 (20 to 1400)
★ BANQUETING ROOMS: 10 (10 to 1500)

★ STANDARD BEDROOM SIZE: 45 m^2
★ PRIVATE BALCONIES: yes
★ SWIMMING POOL: yes – fresh water, outdoor, 260 m^2
★ RECREATIONAL ACTIVITIES: tennis, mini-golf, mountain climbing, horse riding, sailing, swimming, 18-hole golf course nearby
★ GARDENS: yes
★ NO. OF STAFF: 250
★ ROOM SERVICE: 07.00–24.00
★ ORIENTATION: south with view of Lake Geneva and the Swiss Alps
★ CREDIT CARDS: American Express, Diners Club, Visa, Eurocard and Master Charge
★ OWNING COMPANY: Montreux Palace S.A.
★ GENERAL MANAGER: Alfred J. Frei, Administrator
★ DISTANCE TO SHOPS: 100 m
★ DISTANCE FROM AIRPORT: 80 km

How the Swiss manage to produce such hotel miracles we will never know. And the Montreux Palace is an excellent example of an old grand hotel, one of the most famous in the world, which, at every visit, seems to have been redecorated and refurnished yesterday. Everything is so fresh, so clean, so right that we think it is a very special genius. Now there is a new and impressive lobby but the plaster nymphs and angels still beautify other walls. The rooms are palatial – whatever their style – and we think that having breakfast on one's own terrace facing Lake Geneva and the French Alps beyond is one of the real pleasures left in one's travelling life.

Bathrooms are so elegant that one could spend a holiday in any of them, just for the sheer narcissistic enjoyment of so much good planning. In this hotel you will never see yesterday's flowers or a dirty ashtray and the minute you return from your stroll the receptionist gives you your key – without asking for your room number. As for the food, the only way to survive it is to go climb an alp.

St. Moritz

BADRUTT'S PALACE HOTEL, CH-7500, St. Moritz

★ TELEPHONE: (082) 2 11 01
★ CABLES: Palace
★ TELEX: 74 424 palsm ch
★ IN OPERATION: since 1896
★ RESERVATIONS: Hotel Representatives Inc
★ ROOMS: 260
★ SUITES: 15
★ RESTAURANTS: 5
★ BARS: 4
★ DISCOTHEQUE: yes – King's Club Disco

and Le Grand Bar Night Club with live combo
★ SHOPS: 12 – jewellery, fashion, antiques etc
★ CONFERENCE ROOMS: 3 (30 to 320)
★ BANQUETING ROOMS: 3 (30 to 450)
★ STANDARD BEDROOM SIZE: 30 m^2
★ PRIVATE BALCONIES: yes – most rooms
★ SWIMMING POOL: yes – fresh water, indoor 20 × 25 m, outdoor 8 × 25 m

★ RECREATIONAL ACTIVITIES: tennis, sauna, gym, ice rink in winter, Par T indoor golf; hotel has its own ski-school and own kindergarten; all summer and winter sports nearby

★ GARDENS: yes

★ NO. OF STAFF: 500

★ ROOM SERVICE: around the clock

★ ORIENTATION: most rooms face south facing Lake St. Moritz

★ FURTHER DEVELOPMENTS: 18 de luxe service flats, 4 indoor tennis courts, 1 squash court and additional meeting facilities

★ CREDIT CARDS: Amexo, Diners Club, Visa, Eurocard and Master Charge

★ OWNING COMPANY: The Badrutt Family

★ GENERAL MANAGER: Max Keller

★ DISTANCE TO SHOPS: own shopping arcade

★ DISTANCE FROM AIRPORT: 250 km (Zurich)

Should anyone still wonder which came first, the Badrutt dynasty or St. Moritz, the answer is the first. Four generations ago, it was Caspar Badrutt who took St. Moritz, a tiny village in the Engadine, and began transforming it into the stuff legends are made of. Since then, in the great and wonderful world of winter sports, this place has never really had any equals and of course Badrutt's Palace has been the focus of the chic, rich and beautiful people from January to April. To my way of thinking the hotel is the finest in Switzerland, one of the six best in Europe and a place at once so grand and so much fun that it has no real imitators. Its guest list reads like the Who's Who of the past eighty-odd years – anybody with any claim to fame, fortune or beauty has been there living it up. The place has such tradition, such aura that adjectives fail. Where else but at the Palace would you get *fraises des bois* in mid winter? Cartier and Vuitton are there of course together with all those little whatnot shops from the greatest city centres of the world. So is the Chesa Veglia, one of Europe's finest restaurants, and the Corviglia Club, the continent's most exclusive. I have not so far said anything about the hotel itself and neither do I intend to except to say that it is the best there is and a good deal of it. If you need convincing, go see for yourself though you'll have to be lucky with your booking.

CARLTON HOTEL, CH-7500 St. Moritz

★ TELEPHONE: 082 11 41

★ CABLES: Carltonotel St. Moritz

★ TELEX: 74 454

★ IN OPERATION: since 1913

★ RESERVATIONS: Steigenberger Reservation Service, New York/Ernest J. Newman Inc, New York/Robert F. Warner, New York

★ ROOMS: 85 doubles 30 singles

★ SUITES: 5

★ RESTAURANTS: 3 – Romanoff, Tschine Grill and Chalet Prueveda

★ BARS: 2

★ DISCOTHEQUE: live music in the bar

★ SHOPS: 1 – several showcases

★ CONFERENCE ROOMS: 4 (40 to 200)

★ BANQUETING ROOMS: 2 (up to 200)

★ STANDARD BEDROOM SIZE: 25–30 m²

★ PRIVATE BALCONIES: yes – 50% of the rooms

★ SWIMMING POOL: yes – fresh water, 8 × 15 m

★ RECREATIONAL ACTIVITIES: tennis courts, sauna, golf course, sailing, surfing, windsurfing, summer skiing, skating, hiking and mountain climbing

★ GARDENS: yes

★ NO. OF STAFF: 120

★ ROOM SERVICE: 07.00–24.00 and night service

★ ORIENTATION: south

★ CREDIT CARDS: American Express, Diners Club, Visa and Master Charge

★ OWNING COMPANY: Carlton Hotel St. Moritz AG

★ GENERAL MANAGER: B. Kilchenmann

★ DISTANCE TO SHOPS: 500 m

★ DISTANCE FROM AIRPORT: 250 km (Zurich)

The despair of those who run the Carlton must surely be that people the world over always make it their second choice in St. Moritz which is very unfair. If this hotel was situated anywhere else it would surely be number one and I have a special affection for it. A grand hotel in the grand Swiss manner, it is plush, dignified, extremely comfortable in every respect and beautifully situated. The minute one enters the panelled, thickly carpeted great hall, one has the feel of quality and as soon as one goes into the main restaurant it is obvious that dinner is going to be something of an event. Carlton food is renowned. Rooms are large and discreetly furnished and the bathrooms are superb. There is a beautiful indoor swimming pool and, apart from skiing, there are lots of interesting and convivial events. I have not been to the Carlton in the winter season but I am told that its clientele is younger and livelier than elsewhere.

Zurich

HOTEL BAUR AU LAC, Talstrasse 1, CH-8022 Zurich

★ TELEPHONE: 01/221 16 50
★ CABLES: Baurlac
★ TELEX: 813 567 bal
★ IN OPERATION: since 1844
★ RESERVATIONS: The Leading Hotels of the World/Preferred Hotels Association
★ ROOMS: 80 doubles 70 singles
★ SUITES: 15
★ RESTAURANTS: 3 – French Restaurant, Grill-Room and Pavillon Restaurant
★ BARS: 2
★ DISCOTHEQUE: yes
★ SHOPS: 1 newspaper stand
★ CONFERENCE ROOMS: 5 (10 to 180)
★ BANQUETING ROOMS: 5 (10 to 180)

★ STANDARD BEDROOM SIZE: 24 m^2 (single), 34 m^2 (double)
★ PRIVATE BALCONIES: yes
★ SWIMMING POOL: no
★ GARDENS: yes – private park
★ NO. OF STAFF: 350
★ ROOM SERVICE: 06.00–24.00
★ CREDIT CARDS: American Express
★ ORIENTATION: half the rooms face the lake or the canal
★ OWNING COMPANY: H. Kracht's Erben
★ GENERAL MANAGER: Michel Rey
★ DISTANCE TO SHOPS: 50 m
★ DISTANCE FROM AIRPORT: 14 km

If you hold petrodollars, gold bars from Dubai (or even sterling from North Sea oil) and you are business orientated, you will surely find kindred souls at the Baur au Lac, one of Switzerland's best-known hotels. Everything works with Swiss precision – laundry, telephone, messages, stock market news from everywhere and service so smooth one

does not even know it is there. A very handsome hotel, with good-sized rooms furnished with superb beds and good though predictable furniture. Public rooms are just right for those big deals and there is now a (happily) soundproofed discotheque. It had a superb private park, right in the middle of Zurich where one can actually hear birds singing, presumably to bank managers. The food of the Baur au Lac is justly celebrated, very substantial and handsomely served to people who know what is value for money. The management is one of the most experienced in Switzerland.

DOLDER GRAND HOTEL, Kurhausstrasse 65, 8032 Zurich-CH

★ TELEPHONE: (01) 251 62 31
★ CABLES: Doldergrand
★ TELEX: 816416
★ IN OPERATION: about a century
★ RESERVATIONS: The Leading Hotels of the World/Utell International Ltd/Preferred Hotels Association
★ ROOMS: 200
★ SUITES: 15 including Royal Suite with 2 beds and bathrooms and living room
★ RESTAURANTS: 2 – La Rotonde and in the bar
★ BARS: 1
★ DISCOTHEQUE: no – but piano music in the bar
★ SHOPS: 15 showcases (with purchasing at the news-stand)
★ CONFERENCE ROOMS: 6 (up to 250)
★ BANQUETING ROOMS: 6 (up to 250)

★ STANDARD BEDROOM SIZE: 28 m^2
★ PRIVATE BALCONIES: yes
★ SWIMMING POOL: yes – fresh water
★ RECREATIONAL ACTIVITIES: 9-hole golf course, 5 clay tennis courts, skating in winter, swimming in summer and horse riding nearby
★ GARDENS: yes
★ NO. OF STAFF: 260
★ ROOM SERVICE: around the clock
★ ORIENTATION: most rooms face the south overlooking the city, the lake and the distant Alps
★ CREDIT CARDS: Amexco, Master Charge, Visa and Eurocard
★ OWNING COMPANY: family-owned
★ GENERAL MANAGER: Raoul T. deGendre
★ DISTANCE TO SHOPS: 7 to 10 minutes
★ DISTANCE FROM AIRPORT: 18 km

Switzerland has many charms and Zurich only a few (one being money) and perhaps the best thing about the patrician Dolder Grand is that it is far enough from the city centre – ten minutes at most – for the noise of bulls and bears bellowing or computers and calculators ticking not to penetrate its august walls, surrounded as they are by vast cushions of parkland. Of course it is one of the great hotels of Switzerland – a fact one realizes at the first step inside. Apart from the size of the royal suite (only important crowned heads need apply), there is nothing at all flashy about the Dolder. It is solid, comfortable, beautifully and cleanly appointed and run like a Swiss timepiece. The staff are so expert at their job that one merely has to mention something for it to be done – instantly and without murmur. For exercise afterwards there is an interesting swimming pool with artificial waves, a very pretty 9-hole golf course and tennis courts. Though it is not cheap, you do not need a numbered bank account.

SYRIA

Damascus

HOTEL MERIDIEN, Av Choukry Kouatly, B.P. 5531, Damascus

★ TELEPHONE: 229200
★ CABLES: Homer Damas
★ TELEX: 11379 SY
★ IN OPERATION: 7 years
★ RESERVATIONS: Meridien Reservation International/Air France
★ ROOMS: 372

★ SUITES: 33
★ RESTAURANTS: 4 – Les Années Folles, Le Cafe des Deux Mondes, Walima and La Ghouta
★ BARS: 3
★ DISCOTHEQUE: yes – and live music

★ SHOPS: shopping arcade – 14 boutiques, including handicraft centre, barber shop, beauty salon etc
★ CONFERENCE ROOMS: 7 (25 to 1000)
★ BANQUETING ROOMS: 8 (25 to 650)
★ STANDARD BEDROOM SIZE: 25 m^2
★ PRIVATE BALCONIES: yes – all rooms
★ SWIMMING POOL: yes – fresh water, 32 × 12 m
★ RECREATIONAL ACTIVITIES: tennis, sauna and health club
★ GARDENS: yes – 2½ acres of park, planted with palm, pepper and eucalyptus
★ NO. OF STAFF: 380
★ ROOM SERVICE: around the clock
★ ORIENTATION: west
★ CREDIT CARDS: American Express and Diners Club
★ OWNING COMPANY: Meridien Hotels
★ GENERAL MANAGER: Gunther Schachtner
★ DISTANCE TO SHOPS: 5 minutes' walk
★ DISTANCE FROM AIRPORT: 23 km

Damascus is not yet lost to the tourist hordes but it soon will be and if you are going there go now and stay at the Meridien. The only place to stay, it is a French hotel cast in the American/international mould and managed by the very able Air France subsidiary. The bars are thriving, the laundry works such that a Russian grand duke could send his shirts here to be cleaned rather than Paris and your room is well up to big-city hotel standards anywhere, with the occasional touch of Franco-Arab decor. Bathrooms are excellent and the multilingual staff are very helpful and pleasant. Though the decor of the top floor restaurant is eminently forgettable it is even easier to forget when you have tried the food – Franco-Arab again – and seen far below the lights of Damascus, capital of the Ummayad caliphs, where the bazaar is still a bazaar and the tourist trapping is in close season all year round. Just to be able to call a cab and say 'Take me to The Street Called Straight' is sensation enough to match a chance encounter with St. Paul. And when you have seen the enormous mosque, the tomb of Saladin and all the rest, you will be glad the Meridien is there to welcome you back.

THAILAND

Bangkok

THE ORIENTAL HOTEL, 48 Oriental Avenue, Bangkok 10500

★ TELEPHONE: 234 8621-9
★ CABLES: Orienhotel
★ TELEX: TH 82997
★ IN OPERATION: 109 years
★ RESERVATIONS: The Leading Hotels of the World
★ ROOMS: 336 doubles 48 singles
★ SUITES: 22
★ RESTAURANTS: 5 – the Normandie, Lord Jim's, the Verandah, Riverside Terrace, D'Jit Pochanal
★ BARS: 2
★ DISCOTHEQUE: Diana's
★ SHOPS: 23
★ CONFERENCE ROOMS: 3 (50 to 800)
★ BANQUETING ROOMS: 6 (50 to 500)
★ STANDARD BEDROOM SIZE: 38 m^2
★ PRIVATE BALCONIES: yes – suites and de luxe rooms
★ SWIMMING POOL: yes – 2, fresh water, 25 × 12 × 2 m
★ RECREATIONAL ACTIVITIES: 2 tennis courts, 2 air-conditioned squash courts, 2 saunas, gym, jogging track, golf driving range
★ GARDENS: yes
★ NO. OF STAFF: 900
★ ROOM SERVICE: around the clock
★ CREDIT CARDS: American Express, Diners Club and Visa
★ OWNING COMPANY: Mandarin International Hotels Ltd
★ GENERAL MANAGER: Mr Kurt Wachtveitl
★ DISTANCE TO SHOPS: walking distance
★ DISTANCE FROM AIRPORT: 27 km

As a professional traveller, people often ask which is my favourite hotel. An impossible question to answer, but I would not dare leave the Oriental out of the first six. This miraculous hostelry is a monument to those who care for quality. The fact that it has lately received more international awards than any other establishment proves that (in this case at any rate) I am right.

It's really two hotels. One is the River Wing, towering and impressive, with rooms and suites which are among the most comfortable in the world with lovely views of the River of Kings on which, daily, the hotel's two boats – the Oriental Queen and the Orchid Queen – ply their trade. Down below is a truly magnificent lobby, chandeliered, sparkling and handsome. On top is the Normandie Grill, one of the two or three finest Western restaurants anywhere in the Far East. When I dined there, the little known French cheese I used to take with me to school just happened to be on the plateau.

Across the gardens is the period piece – the Oriental's Authors' Wing where, among others, Somerset Maugham and Joseph Conrad wrote and lived and listened, and where now there are suites named after them. Downstairs is a unique and quite splendid interior courtyard, with white cane furniture and exotic bamboos. Everything happens at the Oriental – Thai dancing, exotic shops, music, buffets by the river. As for service, with one of the highest staff-to-guest ratios in the east, it is also so good that one does not even notice it. Above it all reigns a subtle and infinitely intelligent management whose modesty is endearing. All those who love great hotels should stay at the Oriental at least once in a lifetime.

TUNISIA

Tunis

TUNIS HILTON HOTEL, Avenue Salambo, P.O. Box 1160, Tunis

- ★ TELEPHONE: 282 000
- ★ CABLES: Hiltel Tunis
- ★ TELEX: 12 372
- ★ IN OPERATION: 20 years
- ★ RESERVATIONS: Hilton Reservation Service, worldwide
- ★ ROOMS: 244
- ★ SUITES: 19
- ★ RESTAURANTS: 2 – Grill Room and Coffee Shop
- ★ BARS: 2 – Khema Bar and Oasis Pool Club Bar in swimming season
- ★ DISCOTHEQUE: no – but live music in the Grill Room
- ★ SHOPS: 9 – beauty shop, barber shop, Avis car rental, drugstore/pharmacy, news-stand, photo shop, souvenir/handicraft shop, bank, travel agency
- ★ CONFERENCE ROOMS: 3 (30 to 450)
- ★ BANQUETING ROOMS: 3 (30 to 350)
- ★ STANDARD BEDROOM SIZE: 21 m^2

- ★ PRIVATE BALCONIES: yes
- ★ SWIMMING POOL: yes – fresh water, 17.5 × 10 × 2 m
- ★ GARDENS: yes
- ★ RECREATIONAL ACTIVITIES: golf, tennis and horse riding nearby
- ★ NO. OF STAFF: 280
- ★ ROOM SERVICE: around the clock
- ★ ORIENTATION: main facade faces the city, the other facade overlooks the valley and the Bay of Tunis
- ★ CREDIT CARDS: American Express, Hilton, Diners Club, Eurocard, Master Charge, Access, En Route and Carte Blanche
- ★ OWNING COMPANY: operated by Hilton International Co
- ★ GENERAL MANAGER: Bernard Brack
- ★ DISTANCE TO BEACH: 16 km
- ★ DISTANCE TO SHOPS: 4 km
- ★ DISTANCE FROM AIRPORT: 4 km

Ever since the day I got back to Tunis from a rather mad, very dusty, muddy and mistaken Saharan adventure, I have never forgotten the Tunis Hilton – it gave exactly what was most wanted: courtesy and efficiency, cleanliness, practicality and an atmosphere that made me feel almost human again. In a charming country where, alas, most hotels have become package tour dormitories, this one is an exception. Unlike its bigger brothers in the chain, it is gently and intelligently decorated, with nice human touches and items that are not there just for show. A little away from the centre of town, it has peace and quiet, a lovely swimming pool and pleasant gardens.

Rooms are what one would expect but the care taken of them is above average because here is a management who cares and a staff who really do their smiling best. The food, one of Tunisia's better points, is very good – both French and Tunisian – and served with attention to detail. The wine waiters know their stuff and the head waiter in the main restaurant is a model of what that functionary should be.

TURKEY
Istanbul

HILTON INTERNATIONAL ISTANBUL, Cumhuriyet Caddesi, Harbiye, Istanbul

★ TELEPHONE: 46 70 50
★ CABLES: Hiltels Istanbul
★ TELEX: 22379
★ IN OPERATION: 30 years
★ RESERVATIONS: Hilton Reservation Services
★ ROOMS: 408
★ SUITES: 23
★ RESTAURANTS: 3
★ BARS: 4
★ DISCOTHEQUE: no – but live music
★ SHOPS: 14
★ CONFERENCE ROOMS: 2 (150 to 450)
★ BANQUETING ROOMS: 3 (50 to 600)
★ STANDARD BEDROOM SIZE: 25 m^2
★ PRIVATE BALCONIES: yes – all rooms
★ SWIMMING POOL: yes – fresh water
★ RECREATIONAL ACTIVITIES: four tennis courts

★ GARDENS: yes – 13 acres of lawn and private garden
★ NO. OF STAFF: 650
★ ROOM SERVICE: around the clock
★ ORIENTATION: rooms face Bosphorus and gardens
★ CREDIT CARDS: American Express, Diners Club, Carte Blanche, TWA Getaway and Ambassador, Eurocard, Master Charge, Hilton Credit ID Cards and Hilton Preferential Cards
★ OWNING COMPANY: Turkish Republic Pension Fund
★ GENERAL MANAGER: Norbert Spichtinger
★ DISTANCE TO BEACH: 20 minutes by car
★ DISTANCE TO SHOPS: walking distance
★ DISTANCE FROM AIRPORT: 24 km

A quarter of a century is quite a long lifetime for a Hilton hotel. Too long for some I know but not for the Istanbul variety which I still rate among the two or three best in this worldwide chain. To be here, facing the beautiful Bosphorus and knowing that behind you the wheels are turning with high American efficiency seems to present the best of both worlds. Down below, the Grand Bazaar is not far away as are St. Sophia and Topkapi. What counts here is the very high standard of hotel-keeping. Charmingly decorated, in a Hilton-Islamic manner with lots of green plants and fresh flowers, the rooms are the usual Hilton size – very acceptable, and the bathrooms work like a dream. As in most countries with high unemployment the services such as laundry are more or less instant and room service most efficient. In the top floor grill, the food is by far the best of any Istanbul hotel.

UNITED ARAB EMIRATES
Fujairah

HILTON INTERNATIONAL FUJAIRAH, P.O. Box 231, Fujairah

★ TELEPHONE: 22411
★ CABLES: Hiltels Fujairah
★ TELEX: 89018FU
★ IN OPERATION: 7 years
★ RESERVATIONS: direct or Hilton Reservation Service

★ ROOMS: 99
★ SUITES: 7
★ RESTAURANTS: 3 – Coffee Shop, Siji Restaurant, Pool Terrace Cafe
★ BARS: 1

* DISCOTHEQUE: yes and occasional live music
* SHOPS: 2 – 1 newsagent/pharmacy and 1 clothes/sports equipment
* CONFERENCE ROOMS: 5 (up to 25)
* BANQUETING ROOMS: 1 (up to 200)
* STANDARD BEDROOM SIZE: 24 m^2
* PRIVATE BALCONIES: all rooms
* SWIMMING POOL: yes – fresh water
* RECREATIONAL ACTIVITIES: swimming, tennis, badminton, fishing, water skiing, land surfing, mini-golf, playground and 200 m beach

* GARDENS: yes
* NO. OF STAFF: 150
* ROOM SERVICE: around the clock
* ORIENTATION: facing east over Gulf of Oman
* CREDIT CARDS: all major credit cards
* OWNING COMPANY: operated by Hilton International
* GENERAL MANAGER: Emanuel Matsakis
* DISTANCE TO BEACH: on the beach
* DISTANCE TO SHOPS: 1.5 km
* DISTANCE FROM AIRPORT: 128 km (Dubai)

If you have never heard of Fujairah, you are forgiven – neither have millions of other people. I discovered it some years ago and thought it was like one of those places one reads about in books about the French Foreign Legion: reddish-brown mountains, very spectacular belts of palms, blue seas and a sheikh's palace with a flag on top. Nobody there, except the Sheikh and his subjects of course though it is only an hour's drive away from those nasty oil wells on the Gulf. Imagine my surprise a while later coming back and finding a Hilton in Fujairah! And not just any Hilton, but a charming baby-sized one, right on the beach, built with imagination and wit, with an interior garden and rooms that are superbly equipped, fresh and ideally suited to this often ferocious climate. A beach hotel à la Hilton. That's new and in my opinion well worth going to because it is the only one of its kind and its location is worth the journey – you drive over moonish mountains and deserts to the point where you think this must indeed be the end of the world. But there, on the free and clear Indian Ocean side is Fujairah, with its 119 varieties of fish, its dates and its ancient ways. I even had Greek food at the Fujairah Hilton. I also had total peace and quiet in a country one normally associates with banks, gold bars and unbearable jazziness. Good for Hilton – they can do anything when they set their minds to it.

UNITED STATES
Amelia Island, Florida
AMELIA ISLAND PLANTATION, Amelia Island, Florida 32034

* TELEPHONE: (904) 261-6161
* CABLES: no
* TELEX: 56-8424
* IN OPERATION: 10 years
* RESERVATIONS: direct
* ROOMS: 1000 in 500 rented villas and over 100 oceanfront hotel rooms
* RESTAURANTS: 5
* BARS: 4
* DISCOTHEQUE: yes
* SHOPS: several including grocery, bicycle rental, ladies' apparel, crafts, hairdressers, plants and gifts
* CONFERENCE ROOMS: 23 (15 to 500)
* BANQUETING ROOMS: 16 (32 to 480)
* STANDARD BEDROOM SIZE: 30 m^2
* PRIVATE BALCONIES: yes
* SWIMMING POOL: yes – 14, fresh water, I Olympic size at Beach club

* RECREATIONAL ACTIVITIES: 27 holes of Peter Dye golf, 19 Har Tru tennis courts (3 floodlit), 2 deco-turf tennis courts, bicycling, jogging trails, health spa, horse riding, sailing, fishing, paddleboats, electric cars, playgrounds, tours and youth programme
* GARDENS: yes
* NO. OF STAFF: 600
* ROOM SERVICE: yes – throughout the property
* ORIENTATION: buildings face all directions, amongst the trees, behind the sand dunes and beside lagoons
* FURTHER DEVELOPMENTS: Courtside village – a tennis village comprising 48 condominiums located near Racquet Park Tennis Centre. Linkside – 50

low-rise condominiums on the 27th fairway of Amelia Links Golf Course
★ CREDIT CARDS: all major credit cards
★ OWNING COMPANY: Amelia Island Plantation Co

★ GENERAL MANAGER: James M. Rester
★ DISTANCE TO BEACH: on the beach
★ DISTANCE TO SHOPS: small village located on property
★ DISTANCE FROM AIRPORT: 47 km

Amelia Island is the 1800-acre tip of a wild and breezy island off the coast of Florida – virtually untouched, untamed, completely natural and just right for all those who are tired of conventional resorts – it is partly tidal, the home of freewheeling seabirds. Beaches are vast and totally uncluttered and there is no hotel as such – only the centrepiece of the Amelia Island Beach Club. Most of the rooms are individual villas – some by the beach, some by the lagoon and others by the golf course. Each villa has between one and four bedrooms – very spacious indeed, most of them privately owned and decorated to satisfy a personal taste. There is maid service but no room service – everybody walks or usually cycles to one of four restaurants where all the good things of the sea await the gourmet. There is conviviality if you want it and perfect, but perfect solitude if that is what you are seeking.

Beverly Hills, California

BEVERLY WILSHIRE HOTEL, 9500 Wilshire Blvd, Beverly Hills, Ca. 90212

★ TELEPHONE: 213-275-4282
★ CABLES: Bevshire
★ TELEX: 698-220
★ IN OPERATION: since 1926
★ RESERVATIONS: Preferred Hotels Association/The Leading Hotels of the World, worldwide
★ ROOMS: 450 – including suites
★ RESTAURANTS: 4 – La Bella Fontana, El Padrino Bar and Rotisserie, Hernando's Hideaway and the Pink Turtle Cafe
★ BARS: 3 – Hideaway Bar, Zindabad Pub and El Padrino Bar
★ DISCOTHEQUE: dancing Thursday to Saturday nights in Hernando's Hideaway
★ SHOPS: 10
★ CONFERENCE ROOMS: 8 (25 to 1000)
★ BANQUETING ROOMS: 8 (25 to 1000)
★ STANDARD BEDROOM SIZE: 50 m^2

★ PRIVATE BALCONIES: yes – in 50% of the rooms
★ SWIMMING POOL: yes – fresh water, 14×17.5 m
★ RECREATIONAL ACTIVITIES: sauna and gymnasium
★ GARDENS: no
★ NO. OF STAFF: 750–800
★ ROOM SERVICE: around the clock
★ ORIENTATION: rooms face all four directions
★ CREDIT CARDS: American Express, Bankamericard, Carte Blanche, Master Charge, Visa and Diners Club
★ OWNING COMPANY: Courtright Co
★ GENERAL MANAGER: George White
★ DISTANCE TO BEACH: 15 km
★ DISTANCE TO SHOPS: walking distance
★ DISTANCE FROM AIRPORT: 35 km

One European traveller who arrived at the Beverly Wilshire looked at the place and asked: 'Who built this place – Nero?' In a city devoted to show, to ostentation, it is right that there should be nothing shy about the Beverly Wilshire – it is an overstatement of almost everything: money (lots of it), good taste and good manners, superb management skills and the tremendous impresario-like personality of the man who owns it – a legend everywhere. Built into and overflowing the shell of an old building once described as 'Rudolph Valentino baroque or Theda Bara regency', the Beverly Wilshire has simply everything – marble from Italy, carpets from Persia, chandeliers from France and indeed entire decor schemes imported in toto from all parts of the world. Even staircases and corridors are fantastic – there must be an emperor at least, if not Sam Goldwyn behind it. Rooms and suites are palatially vast and beautifully appointed and you can have them in any style you like – French, Spanish, Mexican, Californian, Italian and so on. The hotel entrance is a private driveway and the swimming pool is large enough for a water ballet. Two of its restaurants – the Grand Trianon and La Bella Fontana – are probably the most beautiful hotel eating places anywhere and what is more, both food and wine reflect the decor – the cellar being one of the owner's great joys. Service, altogether, is matchless in efficiency and know how, performed without effort or fuss in a hundred different ways.

Boca Raton, Florida

BOCA RATON HOTEL AND CLUB, Boca Raton, Florida 33432

★ TELEPHONE: (305) 395-3000

★ CABLES: no

★ TELEX: 803936 Boca Club

★ IN OPERATION: since 1926

★ RESERVATIONS: The Leading Hotels of the World, worldwide/K & K, Frankfurt

★ ROOMS: 912 doubles, singles – rates available

★ SUITES: 39

★ RESTAURANTS: 8 – Top of the Tower, Patio Royale, Cathedral, The Club, Espresso House, Court of the Four Lions, Cabana Club, Boca West; The Court House (at tennis courts) and Halfaway House (at golf course)

★ BARS: 10

★ DISCOTHEQUE: no – but live music and dancing

★ SHOPS: 11 – boutique, menswear, children's shop, cosmetics, flowers, news-stand

★ CONFERENCE ROOMS: 29 (10 to 1500)

★ BANQUETING ROOMS: 20 (10 to 1100)

★ STANDARD BEDROOM SIZE: 35 m^2

★ PRIVATE BALCONIES: yes – some

★ SWIMMING POOL: yes – 4, fresh and salt water

★ RECREATIONAL ACTIVITIES: 5 18-hole golf courses, 47 tennis courts, jogging trail, bicycle riding, marina, fishing, sailing, athletics club and health spa

★ GARDENS: yes

★ NO. OF STAFF: 1450

★ ROOM SERVICE: 07.00–02.00

★ ORIENTATION: all directions

★ CREDIT CARDS: American Express, Master Charge and Visa

★ OWNING COMPANY: The Arvida Corporation

★ GENERAL MANAGER: George Roy

★ PRESIDENT: L. Bert Stephens

★ DISTANCE TO BEACH: directly

★ DISTANCE TO SHOPS: 1 km

★ DISTANCE FROM AIRPORT: Miami 60 km; Palm Beach 40 km; Fort Lauderdale 40 km

This hotel was built back in the mad twenties as a kind of American Moorish castle on the Florida shore – a kind of Citizen Kane place with only slightly less exuberance – great salons with caisson ceilings, a magnificent jumbo-sized lobby and a restaurant designed like a European cathedral. Then it grew and grew, millionaires still came but so did many other affluent Americans because Boca Raton, forever changing, never changed its standards – the highest in the land, rated today by America's most prestigious judges as one of the ten best. Four splendid golf courses and over forty tennis courts; eight restaurants and so many bars that one never need go thirsty; and if you like a resort not to bore you, try this one – it is guaranteed to give you something different to do every hour of the day if you so wish. It also gives you an enormous choice of accommodation – so many that I can't list them here. I rather fancy the grand suites and lovely, spacious rooms of the central Cloister Inn – but there is a pad somewhere for every taste. What is most surprising is that it works like a dream, with regiments of staff, superb management and chefs that certainly know a Bearnaise. Also worth mentioning is the new Boca Raton Beach Club – latest and mostest.

Boston, Massachusetts

THE RITZ-CARLTON HOTEL, 15 Arlington Street, Boston, Massachusetts 02117

★ TELEPHONE: (617) 536-5700

★ CABLES: Ritzboston

★ TELEX: 94-0591

★ IN OPERATION: 57 years

★ RESERVATIONS: The Leading Hotels of the World

★ ROOMS: 288
★ SUITES: 48
★ RESTAURANTS: 4
★ BARS: 1
★ DISCOTHEQUE: no – but live music in cafe and dining room
★ SHOPS: 7 – dress shop, florist, barber shop, jeweller, drugstore etc
★ CONFERENCE ROOMS: 11 (10 to 300)
★ BANQUETING ROOMS: 22 (5 to 250)
★ STANDARD BEDROOM SIZE: 32 m^2
★ PRIVATE BALCONIES: no
★ SWIMMING POOL: no
★ GARDENS: no

★ NO. OF STAFF: 465
★ ROOM SERVICE: 06.30–01.00
★ ORIENTATION: rooms face east, north and south
★ CREDIT CARDS: Master Charge, Visa, American Express, Ritz-Carlton and Diners Club
★ OWNING COMPANY: W. B. Johnson Properties Inc
★ GENERAL MANAGER: Henry E. Schielen
★ DISTANCE TO BEACH: 5 km
★ DISTANCE TO SHOPS: walking distance
★ DISTANCE FROM AIRPORT: 4 km

Hotel-fanciers the world over all have their favourites in the great cities and many of them name the Ritz-Carlton as one of the great hotels of our era. From short acquaintance I cannot disagree. This is a noble, elegant, well-bred house which is sensationally comfortable – vast rooms, superb bathrooms and a kind of ageless grace which is quite remarkable combined with a gay, light look. Most bedrooms have a real fireplace with a real logfire in it of an evening if you so wish. The food is real too, a circumstance so rare in the U.S.A. that some visitors never get farther than the Ritz-Carlton. Urbane without being pompous, once they know you and remember you life has the pain quickly removed. One French lady we sent there recently came back rapturous: '*Un vrai grand hotel*,' she said.

Chicago, Illinois

RITZ-CARLTON, 160 East Pearson at Water Tower Place, Chicago, IL 60611

★ TELEPHONE: (312) 266 1000
★ CABLES: RITZCGO
★ TELEX: 20-6014
★ IN OPERATION: 8 years
★ RESERVATIONS: Four Seasons Hotels, Toronto, New York, London/The Leading Hotels of the World/Utell International, worldwide/Air Canada Reservations, worldwide/American Airlines (Sabre), worldwide
★ ROOMS: 322
★ SUITES: 82
★ RESTAURANTS: 3 – The Dining Room, The Cafe, The Greenhouse
★ BARS: 2 – The Bar, The Greenhouse
★ DISCOTHEQUE: yes
★ SHOPS: 1 – gifts, flowers, sundries
★ CONFERENCE ROOMS: 6
★ BANQUETING ROOMS: 6
★ STANDARD BEDROOM SIZE: 41 m^2

★ PRIVATE BALCONIES: no
★ SWIMMING POOL: yes – fresh water
★ RECREATIONAL ACTIVITIES: spa, indoor pool, outdoor sundeck (seasonal), sauna, steam, gym, massage, tanning facilities
★ GARDENS: no
★ NO. OF STAFF: 600
★ ROOM SERVICE: around the clock
★ ORIENTATION: some have partial views of Lake Michigan
★ CREDIT CARDS: American Express, Diners Club, Visa, Master Charge, Carte Blanche, En Route
★ OWNING COMPANY: Four Seasons Hotels Ltd (operator)
★ GENERAL MANAGER: Antoine Corinthios
★ DISTANCE TO BEACH: 8 km
★ DISTANCE TO SHOPS: hotel located in city
★ DISTANCE FROM AIRPORT: 30 km

A very distinguished hotel indeed in a city not generally known for its taste. It's modern and, because of its location, perhaps a little odd – the lobby is on the twelfth floor but the rest is Grand hotel, American-style. Beautifully planned and decorated with intelligence and wit, the Ritz-Carlton does justice to the distinguished company that owns it. I especially like the charming 'Greenhouse' with its cane furniture and lovely plants and the super-stylish dining room where, from the tableware to the food, nothing is too good. Food is in fact well above normal hotel standards, rich but well balanced, beautifully cooked and presented, and it is one of this hotel's best features. Bedrooms are majestic in style and the bathrooms are imperial. There is no noise, no bustle. Doors close quietly, ceilings are much higher than in most modern hotels and you can even open the windows for fresh air which, this being Chicago, is both hot and cold. A very fine hotel indeed.

Colorado Springs, Colorado

THE BROADMOOR, Box 1439, Lake Avenue & Lake Circle, Colorado Springs Co. 80901

★ TELEPHONE: (303) 634-7711
★ CABLES: no
★ TELEX: no
★ IN OPERATION: since 1918
★ RESERVATIONS: BB & H Hotels Inc, New York/Mr Robert L. Pfeiffer, Silver Spring/Great Resorts Inc, Chicago
★ ROOMS: 510
★ SUITES: 50
★ RESTAURANTS: 9
★ BARS: 9
★ DISCOTHEQUE: live music
★ SHOPS: 15 – clothing, gifts, antiques, leather goods, drugs etc
★ CONFERENCE ROOMS: 37 (up to 2400)
★ BANQUETING ROOMS: 4 (300 to 1600)
★ STANDARD BEDROOM SIZE: 32 m^2
★ PRIVATE BALCONIES: yes

★ SWIMMING POOL: yes – 3, fresh water, 30 m long, 22 m long and kidney-shaped Golf Club Pool
★ RECREATIONAL ACTIVITIES: tennis, golf, saunas, skiing, ice skating, boating, skeet and trap
★ GARDENS: no
★ NO. OF STAFF: 1150
★ ROOM SERVICE: 07.00–22.00
★ ORIENTATION: rooms face mountains, lake and city
★ CREDIT CARDS: none
★ OWNING COMPANY: El Pomar Investment Co
★ GENERAL MANAGER: G. Russell Freymuth
★ DISTANCE TO SHOPS: 10 minutes
★ DISTANCE FROM AIRPORT: 8 km

A hotel with everything? Well, I really cannot think of what else the Broadmoor could have except a name with a happier allusion. This is one of the first of all American self-contained resort hotels and for years visiting foreigners have marvelled at how much could be packed into one place. It is the only hotel I know where indoor tennis courts are actually beautiful as are the three swimming pools. There are three golf courses too, all beautifully combed and manicured. There are nine restaurants, each with its speciality and its own atmosphere. Rooms are vast and the suites are large enough for family and friends too – there is plenty of everything. Broadmoor offers so many activities that one is never bored. It is so vast that it is a full-time job just finding your way around. Service is exceedingly good and very friendly. One tends to stay in after one's arrival which is a mistake because the Colorado Rockies are all around and not to be missed.

Dallas, Texas

FAIRMONT HOTEL, Akard at Ross, Dallas, Texas, 75201

★ TELEPHONE: (214) 748-5454
★ CABLES: Fairmont
★ TELEX: (810) 961 9051
★ IN OPERATION: since 1970
★ RESERVATIONS: The Leading Hotels of the World
★ ROOMS: 600

★ SUITES: 50
★ RESTAURANTS: 3
★ BARS: 2
★ DISCOTHEQUE: Supperclub/Showroom
★ SHOPS: 9
★ CONFERENCE ROOMS: 24 (20 to 2500)
★ BANQUETING ROOMS: 24 (20 to 1900)

★ STANDARD BEDROOM SIZE: 35 m^2
★ PRIVATE BALCONIES: no
★ SWIMMING POOL: yes – fresh water, heated
⋆ GARDENS: yes
★ NO. OF STAFF: 1000
★ ROOM SERVICE: around the clock
★ ORIENTATION: all directions

★ CREDIT CARDS: American Express, Master Charge, Diners Club and Carte Blanche
★ OWNING COMPANY: Fairmont Hotel Corporation
★ GENERAL MANAGER: Peter Baekkelund
★ DISTANCE TO SHOPS: walking distance
★ DISTANCE FROM AIRPORT: 30 km

Thanks, or perhaps no thanks, to television, everybody the world over knows what Dallas is like. Well, the Fairmont isn't like that and this is a compliment. In this often brash, raucous city with, admittedly, a stunning profile, the Fairmont is elegant, superbly run, very sophisticated and not at all vulgar. It has style. Every one of the king-sized beds has two pillows – one hard and one soft. Towels are best Irish linen and sheets so new one would swear they buy them for each guest. The rooms are among the largest in any American hotel and the whole of Dallas rises around you like some modern fugue. This hotel has probably the highest staff-to-guests ratio in America and it shows, from the minute you step into the lobby to be greeted with the traditional champagne. From then on it's champagne all the way. Decor is ultra modern but carried out with great taste and the food in the three restaurants ranges from American-traditional to the finest Paris can offer.

THE MANSION ON TURTLE CREEK, Turtle Creek Boulevard, Dallas, Texas 75219

★ TELEPHONE: 214-559-2100 (tollfree within Texas 800-442-3408) (tollfree outside of Texas in U.S.A. 800-527-5432)
★ TELEX: 794 946 MANSION DAL
★ IN OPERATION: 3 years
★ RESERVATIONS: direct
★ ROOMS: 145
★ SUITES: 7 executive suites 3 master suites 2 terrace suites
★ RESTAURANTS: 1 + Promenade
★ BARS: 1 and 1 lounge
★ DISCOTHEQUE: no
★ SHOPS: none
★ CONFERENCE ROOMS: 4 (10 to 200)
★ BANQUETING ROOMS: 4 (10 to 200)
★ STANDARD BEDROOM SIZE: 35 m^2
★ SWIMMING POOL: outdoor, heated
★ RECREATIONAL ACTIVITIES: pool, jogging,

President's health club and spa within one mile of hotel
★ GARDENS: 1.4 acres of landscaped gardens with courtyard, fountain, oak trees
★ NO. OF STAFF: 300
★ ROOM SERVICE: around the clock
★ ORIENTATION: faces north, residential
★ CREDIT CARDS: American Express, Diners Club, Mastercard, Visa and Carte Blanche
★ OWNING COMPANY: Rosewood Hotels Inc, Dallas, Texas
★ GENERAL MANAGER: Mr Alexander de Toth
★ DISTANCE TO SHOPS: ¾ km
★ DISTANCE FROM AIRPORT: Dallas/Ft Worth 30 minutes; Love Field approximately 5 miles

Surprising anyone in the hotel field in the United States is getting rather difficult since this great country now has some of the very finest hostelries in the world. But the arrival on the scene of The Mansion on Turtle Creek did cause a stir – even in Dallas. I recall being on hand shortly after its opening when I saw one well-known American personality (trying to slip past incognito) leaving the hotel shaking his head with a mixture of sadness and envy. And well he might. The Mansion is the latest and the mostest – a superb, smallish hotel centred around what remains of one of those 1920s private palaces of which there are so many in America and the fact that it is run by the '21' people from New York helps. But what matters is the sheer, extravagant beauty of the place – magnificent and often understated decor, superb marble floors and caisson ceilings, furniture made with love, and colours planned by a genius. I especially liked the marvellous Terrace Dining Room but everywhere one's eye is caught by some tiny detail of sheer perfection. Rooms and suites are palatial and quiet and the food, when I was there, was extremely good. Inevitably, only time will tell since hotels, like wine, take a little of that to mature properly. But the first impression is one of delight at seeing what is undoubtedly one of the most beautiful hotels in America.

Hawaii

KAPALUA BAY HOTEL, One Bay Drive, Maui, Hawaii

★ TELEPHONE: 669-5656

★ CABLES: Kapotel

★ TELEX: 6696516

★ IN OPERATION: since October 1978

★ RESERVATIONS: (US) 1-800-367-8000

★ ROOMS: 194

★ SUITES: 3

★ RESTAURANTS: The Garden, Plantation Veranda, Bay Club and Grill & Bar, Market Cafe

★ BARS: 6

★ DISCOTHEQUE: no – but piano and dance music

★ SHOPS: 20 – clothing, sundries, art gallery, sports clothing, men and women speciality shops, 3 jewellery shops, shell shop, artifact shop, realty office, deli and children's shop

★ CONFERENCE ROOMS: 4

★ BANQUETING ROOMS: 2

★ STANDARD BEDROOM SIZE: 39 m²

★ PRIVATE BALCONIES: yes

★ SWIMMING POOL: yes – fresh water, 23 × 12 m

★ RECREATIONAL ACTIVITIES: 10 tennis courts, 2 golf courses, snorkelling, windsurfing, lei making, quilt making and exercise classes

★ GARDENS: yes

★ NO. OF STAFF: 450

★ ROOM SERVICE: 06.45–22.30

★ ORIENTATION: all directions

★ CREDIT CARDS: American Express, Diners Club, Visa and Master Charge

★ OWNING COMPANY: Maui Land and Pineapple Co

★ GENERAL MANAGER: Brian A. McLaughlin

★ DISTANCE TO BEACH: on ocean front

★ DISTANCE TO SHOPS: adjacent

★ DISTANCE FROM AIRPORT: 6.5 km

Undoubtedly one of the finest resort complexes in the whole Pacific, it is not surprising that it should be the brainchild of Laurence Rockefeller (though in this case not owned by him) which is recommendation enough. One is constantly amazed by the American genius for creating resorts that are so well planned, so spacious and so carefully tended that they have no equal in this department. Here, on this superb plantation island of Maui, away from the meretricious glitter of Honolulu, is a haven of rest and good living. There is so much room, both inside and out, that one feels in a special world – green, blue and gold horizons wherever you look and not a hint of speculative building. Apartments are spacious in the extreme, beautifully furnished in a cool and fresh manner and every room has its own ceiling fan – just in case you prefer it to air-conditioning. I most certainly do. Public rooms are vast, peopled with graceful and artistic little touches and the service is charmingly polite and attentive. Everything you want is here – golf, tennis, water sports, interesting excursions and, of course, a beach to end all beaches. Everything is quiet and well ordered and that includes the food and drink, specially planned to make you feel good and not greedy.

KONA VILLAGE RESORT, P.O. Box 1299, Kaupulehu-Kona, Hawaii 96745

★ TELEPHONE: (808) 325-5555/(800) 367-5290
★ CABLES: COCONUT
★ TELEX: 325-6114 KVR
★ IN OPERATION: since 1966
★ RESERVATIONS: tollfree to Hawaii from U.S. mainland (800) 367-5290
★ ROOMS: 95
★ RESTAURANTS: 2 – Hale Moana Hale Ho'okipa
★ BARS: 3 – Shipwreck Bar at poolside, Hale Samoa Longhouse, Talk Story Bar on beach
★ DISCOTHEQUE: no – but nightly live entertainment
★ SHOPS: 2 – Island Copra & Trading Company, general store and village goldsmith
★ CONFERENCE ROOMS: 1 – Hale Ho'okipa (up to 100)
★ BANQUETING ROOMS: 1 – Hale Ho'okipa
★ STANDARD BEDROOM SIZE: 31–57 m^2
★ PRIVATE BALCONIES: most rooms
★ SWIMMING POOL: yes – fresh water

★ RECREATIONAL ACTIVITIES: sailboats, outrigger canoes, snorkelling gear, glass-bottom boat, tennis courts, shuffle-board, guided historical walks, hammocks, weekly Luau, weekly Manager's Cocktail Party – all at no charge. Optional sports: deep-sea fishing, scuba diving, tennis lessons
★ GARDENS: yes
★ NO. OF STAFF: 150
★ ROOM SERVICE: no
★ ORIENTATION: individual thatched bungalows (*hales*) overlook gardens, ocean or lagoons
★ CREDIT CARDS: American Express, Diners Club, Bankamericard, Master Charge
★ OWNING COMPANY: AIRCOA
★ GENERAL MANAGER: Fred Duerr
★ DISTANCE TO BEACH: resort surrounds natural, sandy beach
★ DISTANCE TO SHOPS: 24 km
★ DISTANCE FROM AIRPORT: 8 km

Like they used to say about Los Angeles, it's so nice to know that people who like Honolulu live there or go there! For the rest of us, the much-maligned Hawaiian islands have other treasures – like Kona Village for instance. It is what every Pacific island resort should be like and so often is not: beautiful, simple but practical, gentle and reflective and absolutely natural. The management insists that the speciality of the house is leaving you alone in your own thatched cottage. A few are even built on the water. Others line the magnificent beach and there is no way you can overhear your neighbours. You are on your own. Of course, Kona Village is on what Americans call the Big Island of Hawaii – not Oahu – and just about as far from Waikiki as you could be without swimming home. In addition to this, being American-owned and run, Kona Village has one great plus which is so often lacking in Pacific islands – the bathrooms work, the tableware is clean and if you have to drink water, you can. The food is technicolour, prepared by people who really know how varied and eye-popping Pacific food can be. As for the place itself, it is built on or close to the site of some ancient Hawaiian sacred grounds. I am full of praise for Kona Village – there are too few places like it.

MAUNA KEA BEACH HOTEL, P.O. Box 218, Kamuela, Hawaii 96743

★ TELEPHONE: (808) 882-7222
★ CABLES: Maunakea Hawaii
★ TELEX: (743) 882-7090
★ IN OPERATION: 19 years
★ RESERVATIONS: Westin Hotels, worldwide
★ ROOMS: 310
★ SUITES: 10
★ RESTAURANTS: 6
★ BARS: 5

★ DISCOTHEQUE: no – live music
★ SHOPS: 7
★ CONFERENCE ROOMS: 2 (20 to 300)
★ BANQUETING ROOMS: 9 (50 to 400)
★ STANDARD BEDROOM SIZE: 21 m^2
★ PRIVATE BALCONIES: yes
★ SWIMMING POOL: yes – fresh water
★ RECREATIONAL ACTIVITIES: golf, putting, tennis, snorkelling, surfing, sailing, 2-mile jogging and exercise course and

scuba diving are just some of the activities. There is also horse riding nearby at the hotel's stables

★ GARDENS: yes
★ NO. OF STAFF: 700
★ ROOM SERVICE: 07.00–22.00
★ ORIENTATION: rooms face beach, sea and mountains

★ CREDIT CARDS: none
★ OPERATING COMPANY: Westin Hotels
★ GENERAL MANAGER: Adi W. Kohler
★ DISTANCE TO BEACH: located on beach
★ DISTANCE TO SHOPS: shops in hotel
★ DISTANCE FROM AIRPORT: 71 km (Kowa)

The legendary Laurence Rockefeller dreamt this one up about twenty years ago and I have the greatest respect for his intelligent vision. The fact that Mauna Kea is now run by another – though very expert company – has not put off the customers and it remains the prototype of the American leisure way of life out there on one of Hawaii's nicer islands. When it comes to beach resorts, Americans should be copied by others – they have the right ideas. In this case, it's 10,000 acres of parkland, planted with half a million tropical plants, beautifully landscaped and next to a superfine white sand beach. There is a golf course (Robert Trent Jones, of course) and so many things to do that you can't possibly get bored. In such a monolith, rooms tend to be rather similar but are very handsomely furnished and with good terraces. The food in the six restaurants has variety enough to please anybody (only the coffee is rather awful). What pleases me most about Mauna Kea above all is the intelligent use it makes of Pacific art forms – there are over 1000 beautiful artifacts from all over – well chosen, well displayed and of great curiosity value.

Hot Springs, Virginia

THE HOMESTEAD, Hot Springs, Virginia 24445

★ TELEPHONE: (703) 839-5500
★ CABLES: no
★ TELEX: no
★ IN OPERATION: since 1894
★ RESERVATIONS: direct
★ ROOMS: 600
★ SUITES: 82
★ RESTAURANTS: 7
★ BARS: 2
★ DISCOTHEQUE: yes
★ SHOPS: 15
★ CONFERENCE ROOMS: 26 (25 to 1500)
★ BANQUETING ROOMS: 20 (25 to 1100)
★ STANDARD BEDROOM SIZE: varying
★ PRIVATE BALCONIES: yes

★ SWIMMING POOL: yes – 3, fresh water
★ RECREATIONAL ACTIVITIES: 3 18-hole golf courses, 19 tennis courts, bowling, riding and fishing
★ GARDENS: yes
★ NO. OF STAFF: 1200
★ ROOM SERVICE: around the clock
★ ORIENTATION: south-east, north and south
★ CREDIT CARDS: all major credit cards
★ OWNING COMPANY: Virginia Hot Springs Inc
★ PRESIDENT: W. Dan Reichartz
★ DISTANCE FROM AIRPORT: 45 km

Parts of this vast hotel go back to George Washington's time and other bits and pieces have been added by whichever generation of owners felt rich enough to entertain that certain *folie de grandeur*. The result is without a doubt one of the finest and grandest country resorts in the United States – a place of immense beauty and great charm, with great vistas of colonnades, patios and terraces – all this in 17,000 acres of absolutely gorgeous Virginia countryside. Apart from one new wing whose architecture does not appeal much, The Homestead is one of those places you fall in love with at first sight. What is more (and often rare in North America) the service carried out by a staff who outnumber guests two to one is matchlessly efficient and the food served in any of the four restaurants is good. Breakfasts are a legend. You can play golf (three courses) or just get lost in that splendid landscape of Virginia. The Homestead ought to be a national monument.

Houston, Texas

THE REMINGTON ON POST OAK PARK, 1919 Briar Oaks Lane, Houston, TX 77027

★ TELEPHONE: (713) 840 7600
★ CABLES: no
★ TELEX: 765 536
★ IN OPERATION: since November 1982
★ RESERVATIONS: The Leading Hotels of the World, worldwide
★ ROOMS: 248
★ SUITES: 27
★ RESTAURANTS: 1 restaurant with 3 dining areas
★ BARS: 1
★ DISCOTHEQUE: pianist in the bar from 17.00 to 24.00
★ SHOPS: yes – boutique and beauty salon
★ CONFERENCE ROOMS: 6
★ BANQUETING ROOMS: 6
★ STANDARD BEDROOM SIZE: 37 m^2
★ PRIVATE BALCONIES: 12 rooms and 2 suites have balconies

★ SWIMMING POOL: yes – fresh water, heated
★ RECREATIONAL ACTIVITIES: jogging track in park next to hotel, privileges at the Houstonian Health Club
★ GARDENS: hotel located in Post Oak Park
★ NO. OF STAFF: 400
★ ROOM SERVICE: around the clock
★ ORIENTATION: east and west
★ CREDIT CARDS: all major credit cards
★ OWNING COMPANY: Rosewood Hotels Inc
★ GENERAL MANAGER: Guenter H. Richter (Managing Director), Paul Zuest (Manager)
★ DISTANCE TO BEACH: 80 km
★ DISTANCE TO SHOPS: nearby
★ DISTANCE FROM AIRPORT: 48 km

Three years ago, when we first saw The Mansion at Turtle Creek in Dallas, we decided that the Lone Star State must have changed while we were not looking. It had. That hotel made news all over the world and hoteliers are still visiting it – just to see if what everybody says is true. It is, and to prove that it can be done, here is the Mansion's sister in Houston. Bigness is no longer everything – beauty is, and good taste, and hotel knowhow and, if we are not careful we are going to overdo it. So why don't you go and see for yourself and see what a really great modern hotel can be like if only they try (and have the Hunt oil money behind them). The Remington, middle-sized, makes you feel good the minute you enter. One would say that Americans have recently discovered that the real understatement is what counts. Everything is quite simply beautiful – vast rooms, softly furnished and softly lit, great and happily mixed furniture, an obvious liking for the green things of life, the right pictures, the totally perfect doorway. One feels that the chairs have been made with the sitter in mind. So it is with the beds, the luxurious bathrooms and the often marvellous decor of the public rooms – we just loved the conservatory (every hotel should have one . . .). Service is silent and urbane. Yes, there is no doubt about it – the American way of life is changing. And if you hang on a while, a dozen more of these are coming along – each different, each man-sized. Congratulations.

Little River, California

HERITAGE HOUSE, Little River, California 95456

★ TELEPHONE: (707) 937 5885
★ CABLES: no
★ TELEX: no
★ IN OPERATION: 35 years
★ RESERVATIONS: direct
★ ROOMS: 59
★ SUITES: 8
★ RESTAURANTS: 1
★ BARS: 1
★ DISCOTHEQUE: no

★ SHOPS: 1 art gallery and 1 gift shop (antiques) on grounds
★ CONFERENCE ROOMS: none
★ BANQUETING ROOMS: none
★ STANDARD BEDROOM SIZE: 37 m^2
★ PRIVATE BALCONIES: yes, some rooms
★ SWIMMING POOL: no
★ RECREATIONAL ACTIVITIES: beautiful grounds for walks
★ GARDENS: yes – total of 35 acres

★ NO. OF STAFF: 100
★ ROOM SERVICE: no
★ ORIENTATION: most rooms have ocean view
★ CREDIT CARDS: none
★ OWNING COMPANY: Mr & Mrs L. D. Dennen (owners)

★ GENERAL MANAGER: Mr L. D. Dennen
★ DISTANCE TO BEACH: small cove reached from grounds of hotel
★ DISTANCE TO SHOPS: 8 km (Mendocino)
★ DISTANCE FROM AIRPORT: 240 km (San Francisco)

Heritage House is absolutely charming and I am glad to welcome it among the new listings since there can be few similar hostelries in the United States. It was recommended to me by one prominent British hotelier whose judgment I respect but, alas, I only had time to pass by for lunch and a quick visit. Both were highly enjoyable. Here, in the great redwood country, near the majestic Pacific cliffs and in utter seclusion, is this unique little inn – some of it dates back to the 1870s – which makes you feel glad you are alive. Guests stay in a gaggle of quite beautiful little timbered cottages, each one different from the next and furnished with love and care. There are even some old pot-bellied stoves (but no television or telephones . . .). Fine bathrooms of course, since this is America! The atmosphere of total peace is shattering and I am told that one has to be up early to catch a reservation since city people in the know make a beeline for Heritage House. Food is fine, simple and, for a change, completely American.

Los Angeles, California

HOTEL BEL AIR, 701 Stone Canyon Road, Los Angeles, California 90077

★ TELEPHONE: 213-4721211
★ CABLES: no
★ TELEX: 674151
★ IN OPERATION: since 1930
★ RESERVATIONS: The Leading Hotels of the World, worldwide
★ ROOMS: 59
★ SUITES: 33
★ RESTAURANTS: 1 restaurant and Alfresco terrace
★ BARS: 1
★ DISCOTHEQUE: vocalist and pianist in bar
★ SHOPS: none
★ CONFERENCE ROOMS: 2 (50 to 200)
★ BANQUETING ROOMS: 2 (50 to 200)

★ SWIMMING POOL: yes – fresh water, heated
★ RECREATIONAL ACTIVITIES: jogging trails, tennis and golf nearby
★ GARDENS: yes – 11.5 acres of grounds
★ ROOM SERVICE: 06.00–24.00
★ ORIENTATION: east and west
★ CREDIT CARDS: American Express, Diners Club, Mastercharge and Visa
★ OWNING COMPANY: Rosewood Hotels
★ GENERAL MANAGER: Geoffrey A. Gelardi (Managing Director)
★ DISTANCE TO SHOPS: 5 minutes' walk to Beverly Hills
★ DISTANCE FROM AIRPORT: 25 km

If you were, are or will be a millionaire, this hotel is for you. Nothing flashy, you understand, but the kind of quiet luxury and relaxed atmosphere that go with the knowledge that you don't have to worry about anything – least of all money. Now that the Bel Air has been taken over by America's most recent and best grand hotel pioneers, it is bound to suit you, right down to the swans on the pond, the Bougainvillaea, the peaceful gardens and the admirable, understated decor of both public and private rooms. Service, at one time a little offhand, is now back on course – polite, efficient and totally discreet. Food is great and served with confidence but no razzmatazz. The bedroom we inspected was the way home should be: intimate, superbly clean and fresh and, thankfully, one did not sink into the carpets right up to the knees. If you have what it takes, there is little need for offensive vulgarity. A very up-and-up hostelry that gives you the instant feeling that this is how life should be lived.

Montecito, California

SAN YSIDRO RANCH, 900 San Ysidro Lane, Montecito, California 93108

★ TELEPHONE: (805) 969-5046
★ CABLES: no
★ TELEX: no
★ IN OPERATION: since 1893
★ RESERVATIONS: direct or Mark Allen Travel, London
★ ROOMS: 14
★ SUITES: 24
★ RESTAURANTS: 1 – The Plow & Angel
★ BARS: 1 – The Plow & Angel. Guests can make their own drinks in the Honor Bar until 6.00 p.m. Bar open at pool during busy season
★ DISCOTHEQUE: no – but live entertainment in bar
★ SHOPS: no – but some items available at front desk
★ CONFERENCE ROOMS: 2 – 54 m² (up to 30), 72 m² (up to 50)
★ BANQUETING ROOMS: 1 (up to 30)
★ STANDARD BEDROOM SIZE: 36 m²
★ PRIVATE BALCONIES: most rooms have patios; deluxe rooms have private jacuzzis

★ SWIMMING POOL: yes – fresh water, heated, 15 m long
★ RECREATIONAL ACTIVITIES: 3 tennis courts, 540 acres of hiking trails, riding and badminton; croquet available; golf nearby. Barbecue at poolside on Saturdays
★ GARDENS: flower garden and orange groves
★ NO. OF STAFF: 115
★ ROOM SERVICE: 08.00–10.00, 11.30–14.00 and 18.00–21.00
★ ORIENTATION: rooms overlook gardens, creek or ocean
★ CREDIT CARDS: Visa, Mastercard and American Express.
★ OWNING COMPANY: SYR Corporation. Owners: Susie and Jim Layenson
★ GENERAL MANAGER: Bob DeCock
★ DISTANCE TO BEACH: 3 km (Santa Barbara); 6 km (boat harbour)
★ DISTANCE TO SHOPS: 8 km
★ DISTANCE FROM AIRPORT: 144 km (international); 32 km (local)

This book does not name-drop. It drops hotels. But we had known for a long time that San Ysidro had a guest list second to none, since 1893, too: Galsworthy, Laurence Olivier and Vivien Leigh, Winston Churchill, the Kennedys, etc. And when I got around to visiting it (the world's a big place . . .) I began to understand why. San Ysidro is one of the most private of all private places. The cottages are so remote and hidden away that, as the management says: 'We have to give our room service waiters a compass and a map . . .'. It's no joke either – since you get the feeling here that if a guest does not leave his cottage it is because he does not want to meet anyone. How nice. The so-called cottages are nice too – I would have had another word for them maybe since they are all superbly comfortable, all different and very individual, spread across 500 acres of glorious Southern California countryside and well away from noise and bustle. Lots of famous writers have written here and you know what writers are – they do like some choice eating between paragraphs and I suppose even I could write a great novel at San Ysidro where the food, and the wine, are quite superb. They even give you brandy-soaked French toast as breakfast. If you want it, that is. Yes, I definitely liked the place – it offers the kind of living you deserve if only the world would let you.

New Orleans, Louisiana

THE PONTCHARTRAIN HOTEL, 2031 St. Charles Avenue, New Orleans, La. 70140

★ TELEPHONE: (504) 524-0581
★ CABLES: no
★ TELEX: 266068 PONT
★ IN OPERATION: 57 years

★ RESERVATIONS: Preferred Hotels Association, worldwide/Robert F. Warner, Inc
★ ROOMS: 53 doubles 10 singles

★ SUITES: 20
★ RESTAURANTS: 2 – Cafe Pontchartrain and Caribbean Room
★ BARS: 1 – The Bayou Bar
★ DISCOTHEQUE: no – but two pianists in The Bayou Bar
★ SHOPS: none
★ CONFERENCE ROOMS: yes
★ BANQUETING ROOMS: 3 (12 to 65)
★ STANDARD BEDROOM SIZE: 30 m^2
★ PRIVATE BALCONIES: no
★ SWIMMING POOL: no
★ RECREATIONAL ACTIVITIES: tennis and golf nearby
★ GARDENS: no

★ NO. OF STAFF: 225
★ ROOM SERVICE: 07.00–21.00
★ ORIENTATION: on fashionable St. Charles Avenue, two blocks from the Garden District
★ CREDIT CARDS: American Express, Diners Club, Master Charge, Carte Blanche and Bankamericard
★ OWNING COMPANY: Albert Aschaffenburg (President)
★ GENERAL MANAGER: Honoré Aschaffenburg
★ DISTANCE TO SHOPS: within walking distance
★ DISTANCE FROM AIRPORT: 15 km

As a one-time Frenchman in voluntary exile on this side of the English Channel for over forty years, I must frankly admit that I have never cared overmuch for New Orleans – a little too much like *l'ancienne France*. But, as I wrote in the last edition, I am quite willing to return just to stay at the Pontchartrain.

This is a very great hotel indeed because it is itself – individual, the result of having belonged to the same gifted family for near on sixty years. It all shows in the rooms and suites, almost all different, and in the quiet good taste of the smallest item. Nothing jars, nothing shocks and one haughty German count I met there accidentally had to admit that they could not do better back home. Service is faultlessly quiet and attentive – people seem to know what you want or are looking for before you have had time to ask. The lobby is old world in the grand manner but the plumbing, thank goodness, is American. Food in the Caribbean Room turned out to be a very pleasurable experience. In my opinion, this smallish hotel is one of the crown jewels of the American hotel industry. Long may it flourish.

Newport, Rhode Island

INN AT CASTLE HILL, Ocean Drive, Newport, Rhode Island 02840

★ TELEPHONE:(401) 849-3800
★ CABLES: no
★ TELEX: no
★ IN OPERATION: 13 years
★ RESERVATIONS: direct
★ ROOMS: 17 (summer), 10 (winter)
★ SUITES: 1
★ RESTAURANTS: 1
★ BARS: 3
★ DISCOTHEQUE: piano in lounge, summer Sunday afternoons on lawn
★ SHOPS: none
★ CONFERENCE ROOMS: 1 (up to 20)
★ BANQUETING ROOMS: 2 (20 to 55)
★ STANDARD BEDROOM SIZE: 112 m^2
★ PRIVATE BALCONIES: summer rooms have front porch

★ SWIMMING POOL: no
★ RECREATIONAL ACTIVITIES: 32 acres of private shoreline for walking, skin diving, beaches
★ GARDENS: no
★ NO. OF STAFF: 90
★ ROOM SERVICE: no
★ ORIENTATION: overlooking bay or ocean
★ CREDIT CARDS: Visa and Master Charge
★ OWNING COMPANY: Inn at Castle Hill Inc
★ GENERAL MANAGER: Paul McEnroe (owner)
★ DISTANCE TO BEACH: 50 m
★ DISTANCE TO SHOPS: 8 km
★ DISTANCE FROM AIRPORT: 35 km

I am told that Newport people (very 'iffy-sniffy' as everyone knows . . .) call this sort of place a 'cottage'. Well, well, if it is, I would not mind paying rent for it to the lord of the manor. As it is, all one can do is to spend a night or two there and, as a European, realize once again that there is a good deal more to the American way of life than hamburger stands.

The Inn is absolutely delicious — very grand but not overpowering, filled with quite lovely period pieces often of rare wood and very old vintage and panelled in gleaming chestnut. Floors positively glow when they turn on the Tiffany lamps at night and, quite quickly, you get the feeling that you are going to like this place. That's before you have tasted the food. For myself, it is only in later years that I have come to the conclusion that New England seafood is absolutely tops — sharing Neptunish honours with France's Atlantic coast, and here that seafood is refined into a kind of art form. You just have to taste it to believe it. Outside, the bracing (if that's what they call it . . .) Atlantic roars away and inside the Inn, beautifully managed and serviced, you don't care: let the forces of nature do their worst since you are cocooned in comfortable security.

New York City, New York

THE CARLYLE HOTEL, 35 East 76th Street, New York, N.Y. 10021

★ TELEPHONE: 212-744-1600
★ CABLES: The Carlyle New York
★ TELEX: 620692
★ IN OPERATION: 54 years
★ RESERVATIONS: direct
★ ROOMS: 110
★ SUITES: 70
★ RESTAURANTS: 2
★ BARS: 1
★ DISCOTHEQUE: no – but jazz pianist in the bar
★ SHOPS: 3 – florist, beauty salon and barber shop
★ CONFERENCE ROOMS: 2 (50 to 150)
★ BANQUETING ROOMS: 2 (30 to 120)
★ STANDARD BEDROOM SIZE: 30 m²

★ PRIVATE BALCONIES: yes – some rooms
★ SWIMMING POOL: no
★ GARDENS: no
★ NO. OF STAFF: 400
★ ROOM SERVICE: around the clock
★ ORIENTATION: facing both east side and Central Park from upper floors
★ CREDIT CARDS: American Express, Diners Club, Carte Blanche, Visa and Master Charge
★ OWNING COMPANY: Hotel Carlyle Management Corp
★ GENERAL MANAGER: George Markham
★ DISTANCE TO SHOPS: walking distance
★ DISTANCE FROM AIRPORT: 20 km

The Carlyle was ever a hotel of great distinction, long tradition and a gay and charming decor which is bound to please the most fastidious. Of New York's hotels, it is probably the most intimate and simpatico – people are there to help whatever time of day or night and they are pleased to see you which, even though the guests are among the world's most civilized, is not easy. Service is truly impeccable and nowhere more so than in the two restaurants where the lightness of the decor gives the pleasing appearance of a stage set. Rooms and suites are vast, extremely well and tastefully furnished and so well equipped that one tends to go around to see what could possibly be missing. Food is distinguished and intelligently French and international and the wines are well chosen. The famed Café Carlyle has been a notable New York rendezvous for a long time. This is a hotel of style, elegance and great quality.

THE MAYFAIR REGENT, 610 Park Avenue, New York, N.Y. 10021

★ TELEPHONE: (212) 288-0800
★ CABLES: Mayrege
★ TELEX: 236257
★ IN OPERATION: 56 years
★ RESERVATIONS: The Leading Hotels of the World, worldwide/Regent International Hotels, New Mexico, Tel: 1-800-545-4000
★ ROOMS: 199

★ SUITES: 143
★ RESTAURANTS: 1 – Le Cirque
★ BARS: 1 – The Mayfair Lobby Lounge
★ DISCOTHEQUE: no
★ SHOPS: none
★ CONFERENCE ROOMS: 1 (100)
★ BANQUETING ROOMS: 1 (80)
★ STANDARD BEDROOM SIZE: 86 m²
★ PRIVATE BALCONIES: no

★ SWIMMING POOL: no
★ GARDENS: no
★ NO. OF STAFF: 210
★ ROOM SERVICE: around the clock
★ ORIENTATION: Park Avenue at 65th Street
★ CREDIT CARDS: American Express, Master Charge, Visa and Diners Club

★ OWNING COMPANY: Regent International Hotels
★ GENERAL MANAGER: Dario Mariotti
★ DISTANCE TO SHOPS: walking distance
★ DISTANCE FROM AIRPORT: 20 km

We all have our weaknesses of course, and our idiosyncrasies – this book is full of the latter. And without denigrating any of the other great New York hostelries, I have a personal confession to make: the Mayfair Regent is the hotel I would choose for myself in this great city. Don't ask me why because the reasons are buried somewhere deep in my subconscious. I just like it, that's all. It's quiet, dignified, comfortable, noiseless and superbly run by a genial management. It also happens to be on Park – for me the only New York avenue worth living on. Rooms here are more like suites, and with closets which in some hotels would pass for bedrooms. Everything is spacious, good-looking, fresh. The new lobby lounge is an absolute delight. As for its restaurant, Le Cirque, one has to make an appointment weeks ahead in order to lunch or dine there on some of the finest French food New York has to offer, served in the grand manner. Nothing is too good or too difficult for this hotel.

One is even given a choice of soap in the bathroom and if it's raining, an umbrella is provided for the foreign visitor who arrived without one – though it must be said that Britishers carry their own to New York (as they do to Khartoum . . .).

THE PIERRE HOTEL, Fifth Avenue and 61st Street, New York, N.Y. 10021

★ TELEPHONE: (212) 838 8000
★ CABLES: Pierreotel
★ TELEX: 12 7426
★ IN OPERATION: 55 years
★ RESERVATIONS: Four Seasons Hotels
★ ROOMS: 235
★ SUITES: 60
★ RESTAURANTS: 2 – Café Pierre and Rotunda
★ BARS: 1
★ SHOPS: 5 – barber shop, beauty salon, florist, news-stand and jewellery
★ CONFERENCE ROOMS: 4 (20 to 750)
★ BANQUETING ROOMS: 4 (20 to 850)
★ STANDARD BEDROOM SIZE: 28 m^2

★ PRIVATE BALCONIES: no
★ SWIMMING POOL: no
★ GARDENS: none
★ NO. OF STAFF: 550
★ ROOM SERVICE: around the clock
★ ORIENTATION: main facade faces Central Park
★ CREDIT CARDS: American Express, Carte Blanche, Diners Club, Master Charge, Visa
★ OWNING COMPANY: 795 Corporation
★ GENERAL MANAGER: George D. Schwab (Managing Director)
★ DISTANCE TO SHOPS: walking distance
★ DISTANCE FROM AIRPORT: 20 km

Nothing is ever wrong with the Pierre that I can see. It is perfection itself when it comes to big city hotels and of course it is a New York landmark – the Big Apple would not be the same without it. People know the kind of person you are when you are booked in at the Pierre. Since the last edition, the hotel has improved further, mostly in decor – it is now gentle and totally non-flash and seems to have recaptured most of its old-time glory. Like most good American hotels, the Pierre has bedrooms where one could hold a convention and the suites are fit for any president of anything. In everything, the Pierre has atmosphere, cachet and a splendid sophistication which appears to come naturally. Service is great – they even remember how you like your breakfast from your last visit. As for the celebrated Café Pierre – long may it survive.

THE REGENCY HOTEL, 540 Park Avenue (at 61st Street), New York, N.Y. 10021

★ TELEPHONE: (212) 759-4100
★ CABLES: Regency NYK
★ TELEX: 147180
★ IN OPERATION: 23 years
★ RESERVATIONS: Loews Representation International, New York, California, London, Rio de Janeiro, Frankfurt, Tokyo and Toronto
★ ROOMS: 496
★ SUITES: 95
★ RESTAURANTS: 1 – Le Restaurant
★ BARS: 1 cocktail bar
★ DISCOTHEQUE: no
★ SHOPS: 1 news-stand
★ CONFERENCE ROOMS: none
★ BANQUETING ROOMS: 3 (10 to 180)

★ STANDARD BEDROOM SIZE: 25 m^2
★ PRIVATE BALCONIES: some rooms
★ SWIMMING POOL: no
★ RECREATIONAL ACTIVITIES: none
★ GARDENS: none
★ NO. OF STAFF: 325
★ ROOM SERVICE: around the clock
★ ORIENTATION: mostly south and east
★ CREDIT CARDS: American Express, Carte Blanche, Diners Club, Visa and Master Charge
★ OWNING COMPANY: Loews Corporation
★ MANAGING DIRECTOR: Richard Garland
★ DISTANCE TO SHOPS: located in middle of city
★ DISTANCE FROM AIRPORT: 20 km

If only all big-city hotels were like this one. New York is indeed fortunate in having a few of them and the Regency shines among the brightest – a hotel that charms you the minute you walk into its distinguished lobby. This is not one of these built-yesterday-and-awful-tomorrow kind of places but a hotel of great distinction and I am told on good authority that most New York tycoons living on that side of town make it their meeting place. Having partaken of only one dinner (alas) in its restaurant, I can understand why – the food is elegant, very fresh and beautifully served. The same praise goes to the rooms which are among the nicest in New York – rooms without gimmicks but filled with good, solid, well-chosen furniture, extremely good beds and decorated in a civilized, timeless manner which is a pleasure to see. Everything is pin-clean and fresh looking and the service is immediate and silently friendly, especially at breakfast time when one needs all the ego-building one can get. I have known the Regency for a fair long time but it is only now that numerical changes have allowed me to do it justice. It belongs here.

Palm Beach, Florida

THE BREAKERS, South Country Road, Palm Beach, Florida 33480

★ TELEPHONE: 305-655-6611
★ CABLES: no
★ TELEX: 80-3414
★ IN OPERATION: 58 years
★ RESERVATIONS: Morris Associates, London/Hans Regh Associates, Frankfurt
★ ROOMS: 534
★ SUITES: 34
★ RESTAURANTS: 3
★ BARS: 3
★ DISCOTHEQUE: no – but entertainment and dancing nightly
★ SHOPS: 13 – barber shop, beachware beauty shop, drug store, florist, furs, gifts, jewellery and gown shop, menswear, photography, sports, etc
★ CONFERENCE ROOMS: 17 (75 to 1200)
★ BANQUETING ROOMS: 17 (20 to 900)

★ STANDARD BEDROOM SIZE: 33 to 44 m^2
★ PRIVATE BALCONIES: yes – some rooms
★ GARDENS: yes
★ SWIMMING POOL: yes – outdoor, 18.5 × 14.5 m, and indoor fresh water, 8 × 14 m
★ RECREATIONAL ACTIVITIES: tennis, golf, health club and sauna, putting green, driving range, cycling, lawn bowling, shuffleboard, croquet, horse-shoes, children's playground; fishing, sailing, water skiing and snorkelling all arranged nearby
★ NO. OF STAFF: 1200
★ ROOM SERVICE: 07.00–23.30
★ ORIENTATION: directly on the ocean to the east with the main façade facing west

★ CREDIT CARDS: Master Charge,
Bankamericard, Visa and American
Express
★ OWNING COMPANY: Flagler System Inc

★ PRESIDENT: Stayton Addison
★ DISTANCE TO BEACH: on the beach
★ DISTANCE TO SHOPS: 1.5 km
★ DISTANCE FROM AIRPORT: 6 km

In olden days American tycoons used to arrive at The Breakers in their own railroad cars. Now all you need is the wish to arrive, a Cadillac or Lincoln, and there you are, in one of America's oldest and most elegant resort hotels because that is what The Breakers is. It's been around so long – by American standards – that it no longer has to advertise. Everybody wants to come here but only a few need apply because Palm Beach is Palm Beach and not for the common herd. If you are feeling at all common give it a miss. There are Florentine ceilings, Venetian arches, Roman courtyards, Flemish tapestries and excellent American bedrooms that are attractively periodless. There are magnificent vistas of well-upholstered corridors and terraces with moulded ceilings and antique American furniture which does not seem at all out of place. It is a beachside hotel with all the sophistication of a grand hotel. There is so much to do – swimming pools, golf, tennis and beachsports – that you end up doing just what you like. One dresses for dinner in some truly splendiferous restaurants where the food sometimes matches the decor and, all in all, this is a hotel for civilized people. It is a mere credit card's throw away from Worth Avenue where Cartier, Tiffany and the rest are waiting for you.

San Antonio, Texas

FOUR SEASONS HOTEL, 555 South Alamo, San Antonio, Texas 78205

★ TELEPHONE: (512) 229-1000
★ CABLES: no
★ TELEX: 767-381
★ IN OPERATION: since 1979
★ RESERVATIONS: Central Reservations for Four Seasons Hotels Ltd, New York, Toronto, London, etc
★ ROOMS: 250
★ SUITES: 8
★ RESTAURANTS: 2 – The Anaqua Restaurant and Restoration Bar and Grill located in courtyard area
★ BARS: 2 – Lobby Bar and Palm Terrace Cocktail Lounge
★ DISCOTHEQUE: no – but live music
★ SHOPS: 1 – gift shop
★ CONFERENCE ROOMS: 11 – 54 m² to 126 m² (30 to 400)
★ BANQUETING ROOMS: 1 – divides into 3 of 180 m² (30 to 400)

★ STANDARD BEDROOM SIZE: 24 m²
★ PRIVATE BALCONIES: most rooms
★ SWIMMING POOL: yes – heated, fresh water
★ RECREATIONAL ACTIVITIES: 2 tennis courts, well-equipped exercise rooms with saunas. Golf packages available by special arrangement with local country club. Complimentary bicycles
★ GARDENS: yes
★ NO. OF STAFF: 240
★ ROOM SERVICE: around the clock
★ CREDIT CARDS: American Express, Diners Club, Carte Blanche, Visa, Mastercard and Four Seasons
★ OWNING COMPANY: Four Seasons Hotels Ltd, of Toronto, Canada
★ GENERAL MANAGER: John Indrieri
★ DISTANCE TO SHOPS: walking distance
★ DISTANCE FROM AIRPORT: 13 km

With due respect to all those who live there, J.R. can keep Dallas – I'll have San Antonio, the nicest, most friendly and most civilized city in Texas. And if I get back there, my address will be the Four Seasons. Having had my share of great American hotels, I was amazed to see how different this one could be: a gently palatial place, full of lovely indoor vegetation, a most unusual and graceful lobby and the whole place obviously furnished by someone who decided that this piece would look good here, that piece there, and so on. None of your computer-planned decor here. It is nicely Hispanic (after all, the Alamo is only down the street) but it also seems to have that Tex-Mex mixture which happens to be so successful in San Antonio, a place where people have time to live and time to stroll along their city-bound river. Rooms are ample, fresh and beautifully kept and service is smiling and quick. Since San Antonio is food-conscious, so is this hotel – the menus I had were beyond reproach. They also shine your shoes, give you a newspaper and are ready day and night to help you with any odd wish. That's nice.

San Francisco, California

FOUR SEASONS-CLIFT HOTEL, 495 Geary, San Francisco, California 94102

★ TELEPHONE: (415) 775-4700
★ CABLES: no
★ TELEX: 340647
★ IN OPERATION: 68 years
★ RESERVATIONS: direct
★ ROOMS: 379
★ SUITES: 84
★ RESTAURANTS: 1 – the French Room
★ BARS: 2 – the Redwood Room and Lobby Bar
★ DISCOTHEQUE: pianist in the Redwood Room, classical guitarist in Lobby Bar
★ SHOPS: none
★ CONFERENCE ROOMS: 5 (20 to 225)
★ BANQUETING ROOMS: 5 (20 to 150)

★ STANDARD BEDROOM SIZE: 81 m^2
★ PRIVATE BALCONIES: no
★ SWIMMING POOL: no
★ GARDENS: no
★ NO. OF STAFF: 350
★ ROOM SERVICE: around the clock
★ ORIENTATION: faces west
★ CREDIT CARDS: Amexco, Visa, Master Charge, Bankamericard and Diners Club
★ OWNING COMPANY: Four Seasons
★ GENERAL MANAGER: Paul M. G. Astbury
★ DISTANCE TO BEACH: 5 km
★ DISTANCE TO SHOPS: walking distance
★ DISTANCE FROM AIRPORT: 20 km

I have long had two firm favourites in this lovely city of San Francisco and when one very well travelled hotel man told me that he always stayed elsewhere, I decided on my last visit to try 'elsewhere' – the Four Seasons-Clift – and I must admit that, in a different way, it compares favourably with my other two friends. It is an exceedingly refined and elegant hotel – good taste going right through from the furniture to the silver. Rooms and suites are very large indeed – an ordinary room here would be called an apartment elsewhere – and they are all delightfully furnished with good, solid, unpretentious items – good sofas, nice carpets, immaculate curtains. Everything is in pleasing pastel shades, restful and pleasant, with an occasional flash of brilliant colour, and in general, like most good American hotels, it pays great attention to design-cum-practicality. One is never short of storage space or bathroom space. Service is quiet, efficient and totally unflappable, and I thought that the food in the French Room was of the highest standard and served with an appropriate quiet elegance.

THE STANFORD COURT HOTEL, 905 California Street, San Francisco, California 94108

★ TELEPHONE: (415) 989-3500
★ CABLES: Stancourt
★ TELEX: 34-0899
★ IN OPERATION: 12 years
★ RESERVATIONS: Preferred Hotels Association, Illinois
★ ROOMS: 402
★ SUITES: 34
★ RESTAURANTS: 2 – Fournou's Ovens and Cafe Potpourri
★ BARS: 2

★ DISCOTHEQUE: no
★ SHOPS: 6
★ CONFERENCE ROOMS: 2 (30 to 150)
★ BANQUETING ROOMS: 2 (60 to 450)
★ STANDARD BEDROOM SIZE: 25 m^2
★ PRIVATE BALCONIES: no
★ SWIMMING POOL: no
★ RECREATIONAL ACTIVITIES: golf and tennis close by
★ GARDENS: no
★ NO. OF STAFF: 375

★ ROOM SERVICE: 06.30–24.00
★ ORIENTATION: facing California Street and San Francisco Bay
★ CREDIT CARDS: American Express, Diners Club, Master Charge, Bankamericard, Visa and Carte Blanche
★ OWNING COMPANY: Royal Stanford Hotel Co
★ GENERAL MANAGER: William F. Wilkinson (Vice President); John Cameron (Managing Director)
★ DISTANCE TO SHOPS: 5 minutes' walk
★ DISTANCE FROM AIRPORT: 25 km

Like people, hotels grow, change, mature, develop a very particular personality. Stanford Court is the pride and joy of every discriminating traveller passing through that lovely city of San Francisco and, in its first few years (about the lifetime of this guide), it has attracted more praise, more awards and more bouquets than almost any other hotel in North America and, what is more, it is always changing in small but subtle ways. Corseted in one of those massive Nob Hill mansions of bygone years, Stanford Court is virtually peerless, without reproach. Here you don't even pay for your local telephone calls and while the management don't encourage you to steal their coathangers, they really don't mind all that much. You enter through a discreet courtyard and immediately you know that one man's genius created this place – there are entire walls of Portuguese azulejos, a French provincial restaurant, Fournou's Ovens which even chauvinistic Frenchmen respect, great Baccarat chandeliers and acres of shining marble. Bedrooms are immaculately maintained, very practical and beautifully conceived down to the minutest details. When you eat there you discover that in this department too, intelligence and wit reign as well as good taste – nothing is overdone. Service is the same – they brush your clothes, replace buttons and even get you a new tube of toothpaste when it appears you need it. And when, as the odd Briton, you return around mid-afternoon, the concierge greets you by name, gives you your key and asks whether you would like China or Indian tea.

Santa Fe, New Mexico

RANCHO ENCANTADO, Rt. 4, Box 57C, Santa Fe, New Mexico 87501

★ TELEPHONE: (505) 982-3537
★ CABLES: no
★ TELEX: no
★ IN OPERATION: 15 years
★ RESERVATIONS: direct
★ ROOMS: 36 rooms and suites
★ RESTAURANTS: 1
★ BARS: 1
★ DISCOTHEQUE: no
★ SHOPS: supplies obtainable from Club House
★ CONFERENCE ROOMS: 1 (137 m²)
★ BANQUETING ROOMS: 1 (137 m²)
★ STANDARD BEDROOM SIZE: 121 m²
★ PRIVATE BALCONIES: most rooms
★ SWIMMING POOL: yes – fresh water, heated, 295 m²
★ RECREATIONAL ACTIVITIES: tennis, billiards, riding and a clubhouse with cocktail lounge; golf available nearby
★ GARDENS: yes
★ NO. OF STAFF: 55
★ ROOM SERVICE: none
★ ORIENTATION: most rooms are south/south-west
★ CREDIT CARDS: American Express, Master Charge, Visa, Diners Club and Carte Blanche
★ OWNING COMPANY: Betty Egan (owner)
★ GENERAL MANAGER: John T. Egan
★ DISTANCE TO SHOPS: 12 km
★ DISTANCE FROM AIRPORT: 112 km

I have not yet met anyone who, having been to Santa Fe, did not fall in love with it at first sight – surely the most charming and most unusual state capital in the United States: American and yet Spanish, traditional and yet venturesome and absolutely beautiful, right there in the middle of Indian America. As for the Rancho Encantado, its long list of return guests shows its pedigree. It is a cheerful, often amusing place run by a very gifted family and you feel that you are a guest in some kind of Western house party. It's mostly traditional adobe cottages and buildings, all of them decorated in genuine Indian-Spanish-American style with beautiful tiles and superb Indian rugs, all in very good taste. There are lovely gardens, lots of let's-go land around it and a magnificent swimming pool. The food at Rancho Encantado is well known to most American gourmets as being well above the average and is often innovative and different. All around are some of the greatest Indian pueblos of America and, over it all, the noble profile of the Sangre de Cristo mountains. A marvellous place to be in if you want to get to know that glorious South West.

Saranac Lake, New York

THE POINT, Star Route, Saranac Lake, New York 12982

★ TELEPHONE: (518) 891-5674
★ CABLES: no
★ TELEX: no
★ IN OPERATION: 4 years
★ RESERVATIONS: direct
★ ROOMS: 8
★ SUITES: none
★ RESTAURANTS: 1
★ BARS: there is no bar – this is a private house
★ DISCOTHEQUE: no
★ SHOPS: no
★ CONFERENCE ROOMS: 1 (up to 20)
★ BANQUETING ROOMS: no
★ STANDARD BEDROOM SIZE: 30–55 m^2
★ PRIVATE BALCONIES: some rooms have terraces
★ SWIMMING POOL: no – but private beach on lake

★ RECREATIONAL ACTIVITIES: canoe trips, boating, hiking, tennis, skiing (downhill and cross-country), golf, sailing, skating, badminton, billiards, ping-pong and croquet
★ GARDENS: yes
★ NO. OF STAFF: 9–11
★ ROOM SERVICE: none
★ ORIENTATION: views of mountains in all directions
★ CREDIT CARDS: no
★ OWNING COMPANY: privately owned
★ GENERAL MANAGERS: Edward G. L. Carter and James W. Myhre
★ DISTANCE TO SHOPS: 15 km
★ DISTANCE TO BEACH: on the property
★ DISTANCE FROM AIRPORT: domestic 15 km; international 100 km

This is undoubtedly one of the two or three oddest places listed in this book. It is not a hotel (heaven forbid) and not even a guesthouse since the only guests there are people whom the owner, Ted Carter, actually likes. It's really like being invited to a very special house party by a man who insists on keeping Armagnac in his boathouse and Vuitton suitcases in the closets. Originally The Point was what they call here in the Adirondacks a 'camp'. A log-cabin if you like, except that in this one, having been built by William Rockefeller in the early thirties, one suspects that the only thing that held the logs together were the French Impressionists. The feeling has not changed much – only the people. It's way up New York State on the shores of Upper Saranac Lake – a jewel if ever there was one – and you arrive in a kind of Cleopatra's barge well stocked with liquids and little titbits and you sail right into the boathouse where sleek speedboats have come to rest. Then come the surprises: The Point is absolutely, but absolutely, lovely, a place in which everything you see is total perfection of taste with priceless pieces scattered about in glorious extravagance. The Great Hall is so 'great', with its massive fireplace and vast couches, that you can't stop looking. Bedrooms are vast, and just the same as the rest of the place – deliciously odd, amusingly grand and yet intimate because this is a lived-in place. One eats with one's host and his co-owner, James Myrhe, a young man who is one of the finest cooks I have ever met, who produces great food like a conjurer, and everything comes on Carter's own family Meissen (eighteenth century and worth 500 dollars a plate . . .). The talk is great, the wine superb and the whole place sparkles with wit and charm. Outside, the great dark green woods on the Adirondacks frame a lake of pure silver and the air is like vintage Pommery. Some of the time you sail, trek, go canoeing or just sit and reflect on your good fortune at just being there.

Scottsdale, Arizona

MARRIOTT'S CAMELBACK INN RESORT & GOLF CLUB, P.O. Box 70, 5402 E. Lincoln Dr, Scottsdale, Arizona 85252

★ TELEPHONE: 602 948 1700
★ CABLES: no
★ TELEX: 910 950 1198
★ IN OPERATION: since 1935
★ RESERVATIONS: Marriott Tollfree Reservations, U.S.A./Supranational, London, Paris, Rome and West Germany
★ ROOMS: 400
★ SUITES: 25
★ RESTAURANTS: 3 – Chaparral Dining Room, North Pool Buffet, Camelback Golf Club
★ BARS: 2 – Oasis and The Chaparral Lounge
★ DISCOTHEQUE: live music nightly
★ SHOPS: 3
★ CONFERENCE ROOMS: 20 (10 to 1500)
★ BANQUETING ROOMS: 20 (10 to 1500)
★ STANDARD BEDROOM SIZE: 46 m^2

★ PRIVATE BALCONIES: yes
★ SWIMMING POOL: yes – 2 fresh water
★ RECREATIONAL ACTIVITIES: 10 tennis courts (5 floodlit), 2 18-hole golf courses, 9-hole pitch and putt course, 2 whirlpools, ping pong, shuffleboard, putting green, bicycling, hiking, horse riding and Exer-Trail
★ GARDENS: yes
★ NO. OF STAFF: 600
★ ROOM SERVICE: around the clock
★ ORIENTATION: all rooms face gardens
★ CREDIT CARDS: American Express, Visa, Carte Blanche, Diners Club and Master Charge
★ OWNING COMPANY: Marriott Hotels Inc
★ GENERAL MANAGER: Jim Buckley
★ DISTANCE TO SHOPS: 5–8 km
★ DISTANCE FROM AIRPORT: 30 km

In my not very humble opinion, anyone who has not seen Arizona has not lived. And anyone who has not tried the grandeur that is Scottsdale is missing something. You must visit this amazing hostelry which combines the best of the West's free and easy life with civilized luxury – a very rare mixture. Camelback Inn is spread out over unending acres of lush gardens, with the desert in the background, and its Mexican-type casas are very large indeed, often with a living room and a patio and own entrance. They are delightfully cool, very clean and, though furnished *en serie* the apartments are practical and attractive. Considering the distance, service is remarkably good. What impresses about Camelback Inn is that instead of providing simply wholesome but plain American fare, its food is amazingly varied, served with the touch of the expert on superb table settings. Then there are all the things you can do – swim, sunbathe, play golf, tennis, hiking and riding in the desert and the famous 'Camelback Caravans' which although somewhat showbiz do recapture some of the old adventurous spirit.

Tucson, Arizona

ARIZONA INN, 2200 E. Elm Street, Tucson, Arizona 85719

★ TELEPHONE: (602) 325-1541
★ CABLES: Az Inn-Tuc
★ TELEX: 165523
★ IN OPERATION: 54 years
★ RESERVATIONS: direct
★ ROOMS: 86
★ SUITES: 7
★ RESTAURANTS: 1 main dining room, pool dining room (winter season)
★ BARS: 1 main bar, pool bar (winter season)
★ DISCOTHEQUE: pianist only
★ SHOPS: 1

★ CONFERENCE ROOMS: 5
★ BANQUETING ROOMS: 5 (60 to 205)
★ STANDARD BEDROOM SIZE: all rooms are different but spacious
★ PRIVATE BALCONIES: 40 with patios
★ SWIMMING POOL: yes – outdoor, fresh water and heated
★ RECREATIONAL ACTIVITIES: tennis courts, putting green, croquet and table tennis; riding and golf nearby
★ GARDENS: 14 acres of lawns and gardens
★ NO. OF STAFF: 100
★ ROOM SERVICE: 07.00–21.00

★ ORIENTATION: 60 rooms on the ground floor
★ CREDIT CARDS: American Express, Master Charge and Visa
★ OWNING COMPANY: family owned

★ GENERAL MANAGER: Robert Minerich
★ DISTANCE TO SHOPS: 3 km
★ DISTANCE FROM AIRPORT: 16 km

Anyone who follows the fortunes of the distinguished magazine I serve knows that I am crazy about Arizona – though some still ask me where it is! This one state has three hotels listed in this guide and as far as I am concerned that's it. What makes me glow with pleasure is the receipt of a letter recently from one Swedish lady who wrote: 'What you said about the Arizona Inn is absolutely true. . . . My American husband did not know there were such places left in his own country. . . .' Arizona Inn is one of the nicest pads in the West – not like a hotel at all – but a cluster of Indian-Spanish-Mexican adobe buildings ranged around a manicured lawn and a gorgeous swimming pool. As for the bar, with its Audubons on the walls, it even makes tequila drinkable. Yet, however informal it may look at first, Arizona Inn is deceptive on this point since it is really a very civilized, very high class hotel, where good taste and fine service dominate. If you like the South West but don't like the hustling and the razzmatazz, this is the place for you.

TANQUE VERDE RANCH, RT8 Box 66, Tucson, Arizona, 85748

★ TELEPHONE: 602-296-6275
★ CABLES: no
★ TELEX: no
★ IN OPERATION: since 1860
★ RESERVATIONS: direct
★ ROOMS: 60
★ SUITES: 15
★ RESTAURANTS: 3 – main dining room, Mexican Room and Pinata Room
★ BARS: 1
★ DISCOTHEQUE: no
★ SHOPS: 1
★ CONFERENCE ROOMS: 3 (25 to 125)
★ BANQUETING ROOMS: 3 (25 to 125)
★ STANDARD BEDROOM SIZE: 75 m^2
★ PRIVATE BALCONIES: yes
★ SWIMMING POOL: yes – fresh water, 1 indoor and 1 outdoor

★ RECREATIONAL ACTIVITIES: tennis, jacuzzi, saunas and exercise room, horse riding, pack trips, nature hikes and bird banding
★ GARDENS: yes
★ NO. OF STAFF: 65
★ ROOM SERVICE: at special request
★ ORIENTATION: desert and mountain views
★ CREDIT CARDS: none
★ OWNING COMPANY: Arizona Sunshine Ranches
★ GENERAL MANAGER: Bob Cote
★ DISTANCE TO SHOPS: 6 km
★ DISTANCE FROM AIRPORT: 40 km

When general manager Bob Cote and I met again last year, we compared notes. Yes, he too had had letters from people suggesting that this travel fellow in lil' ole' England had taken leave of his senses by putting a dude ranch among the best hotels in the world. . . . Well, neither of us has changed his mind. Bob still runs one of the fun-most places in the West and I still think Tanque Verde is a winner. As I wrote in a previous edition, this is part of our folk memory: 25,000 acres of absolutely virgin Arizona open range, a genuine and original Western ranch with horses everywhere, chuck wag-gons, saddle rooms, sing-songs and bar-b-cues, fellows in checked shirts and wide hats, the swish of leather boots and bedrooms one could hold a convention in. All this and Tombstone a pistol shot away – what more could one want? It is guaranteed to turn the shyest city gent into Bill Cody in a short while and even the horses know a dude bottom when they feel one. And yes, people still slap me on the back and say 'Howdy, pardner'. I wish they would not. Makes my teeth rattle. Tanque Verde? Just take me back there.

Washington D.C.

THE RITZ-CARLTON, 2100 Massachusetts Avenue, N.W.,
Washington D.C. 20008

★ TELEPHONE: 293-2100
★ CABLES: no
★ TELEX: TWX 7108229228
★ IN OPERATION: 55 years
★ RESERVATIONS: The Leading Hotels of
the World
★ ROOMS: 165
★ SUITES: 16
★ RESTAURANTS: 1
★ BARS: 1
★ DISCOTHEQUE: no – but piano music in
bar
★ SHOPS: none
★ CONFERENCE ROOMS: 3 (10 to 60)
★ BANQUETING ROOMS: 3 (10 to 100)
★ STANDARD BEDROOM SIZE: 28 m²

★ PRIVATE BALCONIES: no
★ SWIMMING POOL: no
★ GARDENS: no
★ NO. OF STAFF: 200
★ ROOM SERVICE: 07.00–23.00
★ ORIENTATION: north-west
★ FURTHER DEVELOPMENTS: the addition of
105 rooms and 5 banqueting rooms
★ CREDIT CARDS: American Express,
Master Charge, Bankamericard, Diners
Club and Visa
★ OWNING COMPANY: John B. Coleman Co
★ MANAGING DIRECTOR: Eric Ewoldt
★ DISTANCE TO SHOPS: 2 blocks
★ DISTANCE FROM AIRPORT: 16 km

Even when it was operated by a different company under a different name, this hotel
always was one of our favourites. Now that Ritz-Carlton run it, it is even better and
ranks even higher. It is one of those solid, no nonsense, no flash American hotels and
always looks as if it were truly lived in. There is even a wintertime logfire going in the
oak-panelled bar and furnishings everywhere are quite spotless, beautifully co-
ordinated and a pleasure for the eye. Bedrooms are standard-sized for America, which
means big everywhere else, are quiet and have great charm. They change the flowers
every day and your messages follow you until you've been found. Under the new
management the food is better than ever, international-American and served with
quiet competence and a sureness of touch that are a pleasure to watch.

White Sulphur Springs, West Virginia

THE GREENBRIER, White Sulphur Springs, West Virginia 24986

★ TELEPHONE: (304) 536-1110
★ CABLES: no
★ TELEX: no
★ IN OPERATION: 206 years
★ RESERVATIONS: direct
★ ROOMS: 588 doubles 27 singles
★ SUITES: 51
★ RESTAURANTS: 6
★ BARS: 5
★ DISCOTHEQUE: yes – and live music for
dancing
★ SHOPS: 27
★ CONFERENCE ROOMS: 30 (10 to 2000)
★ BANQUETING ROOMS: 20 (26 to 1200)
★ STANDARD BEDROOM SIZE: 22 m²
★ PRIVATE BALCONIES: yes – some rooms
★ SWIMMING POOL: yes – fresh water,
indoor 30 × 12 m and outdoor
36 × 14 m

★ GARDENS: yes
★ RECREATIONAL ACTIVITIES: twenty tennis
courts, three 18-hole golf courses,
paddle tennis, bowling, horse riding,
carriage rides, spa, jogging and hiking
trails, fishing, trap and skeet, putting,
shuffleboard, billiards, table tennis,
bicycling, ice skating and cross-country
skiing
★ NO. OF STAFF: 1400
★ ROOM SERVICE: 07.00–24.00
★ ORIENTATION: rooms face all directions
★ CREDIT CARDS: Master Charge, Visa and
American Express
★ OWNING COMPANY: CSX Inc
★ GENERAL MANAGER: William C. Pitt
(President and Managing Director)
★ DISTANCE FROM AIRPORT: 15 km

This hotel, one of America's grandest resorts, has won the country's prestigious hotel
award no less than sixteen times. I have visited it twice and greatly admire it as being

the perfect blend of the old world and the new. Here are 6500 acres of marvellously green Allegheny mountainscape, trails galore, riding, ice skating, bowling, tennis courts and swimming pools both inside and out. It's a vast place and it certainly takes an army to run it. Decor is traditional Southern American furnishings that are quite perfect everywhere both in quality and in upkeep. Originating as a spa, it still runs a health farm side as well as a quite famous school of cookery. Despite its size, Greenbrier has tranquillity and intimacy and is in such a healthy situation that one feels better just being there. Rooms and suites are quite large and very well designed and some have marvellous breakfast balconies overlooking the peaceful green hills. There is so much variety in restaurants and bars that if you stay a week your experiences will all be different. You can also play golf by the way – three 18-hole courses.

YEMEN ARAB REPUBLIC

Sana'a

SANA'A SHERATON HOTEL, P.O. Box 2467, Sana'a, Yemen Arab Republic

* TELEPHONE: 221000-237500/8
* CABLES: no
* TELEX: 2222 SHSAN YE
* IN OPERATION: since February 1981
* RESERVATIONS: Sheraton Hotels or Sheraton Reservation Offices
* ROOMS: 300
* SUITES: 6
* RESTAURANTS: 4 – Coffee Shop, Night Club, Poolside Restaurant, Speciality Restaurant
* BARS: 1
* DISCOTHEQUE: no – but live music
* SHOPS: 4 – sports, boutique, travel agent, pharmacy
* CONFERENCE ROOMS: 5 – multi-function rooms accommodating from 40 to 550 persons with multi-lingual translation facilities and projector booth
* BANQUETING ROOMS: 5 (40 to 550)

* STANDARD BEDROOM SIZE: 24 m^2
* PRIVATE BALCONIES: no
* SWIMMING POOL: yes – fresh water, Olympic size
* RECREATIONAL ACTIVITIES: 2 tennis courts (floodlit), sports and health centre with separate gymnasiums, sauna and massage
* GARDENS: yes
* NO. OF STAFF: 338
* ROOM SERVICE: around the clock
* ORIENTATION: all rooms have mountain view
* CREDIT CARDS: all major credit cards
* OWNING COMPANY: Arab Hotels Company, Kuwait
* GENERAL MANAGER: Adriano Severi
* DISTANCE TO SHOPS: 5 km
* DISTANCE FROM AIRPORT: 10 km

The first time I travelled to that little-known and yet amazingly beautiful country, North Yemen, I spent some of my time in a tent and the rest of the time in ancient Arabian caravanserais whose roofs leaked abominably. I did not mind so much – after all the Queen of Sheba wasn't far away. Henceforth, whenever people tell me that hotel chains don't really look after travellers in strange places I shall point with some pride to the Sheraton Corporation's pluck in building a modern hotel on the outskirts of Sana'a, that sand-coloured Chicago of Arabia. A more unlikely place I cannot imagine but this is, for me, the acceptable face of travel capitalism. What's more the hotel works. Bedrooms are international and, thank goodness, so are the bathrooms. Public rooms are handsomely decorated with the odd touch of the country. Service works like a clock. In the main restaurant, you can have escargots, foie gras and shashlik as well as American rib-eye steak. Well, well. How is that for enterprise? And don't say you don't care, because you do. Down the road is the superb Wadi Dhar valley with the former Imam's splendid tower palace. North Yemen? Now you can really go and see for yourself.

YUGOSLAVIA

Belgrade

HOTEL JUGOSLAVIJA, Bul. Edvarda Kardelja 3, 11181 Beograd-YU

- ★ TELEPHONE: 011/600-222 & 609-444
- ★ CABLES: Hotel Jugoslavija
- ★ TELEX: 11777 & 11349 yu hotju
- ★ IN OPERATION: since 1969
- ★ RESERVATIONS: Steigenberger Reservation Service, worldwide
- ★ ROOMS: 186 doubles 308 singles
- ★ SUITES: 29
- ★ RESTAURANTS: 3 – Panorama, Derdap and Zlatan Ovan
- ★ BARS: 2
- ★ DISCOTHEQUE: live music
- ★ SHOPS: 4 – barber's shop and beauty parlour, souvenirs, newspapers, tobacco, etc
- ★ CONFERENCE ROOMS: 5 (30 to 1800)
- ★ BANQUETING ROOMS: 5 (110 to 1370)
- ★ STANDARD BEDROOM SIZE: 23 m^2
- ★ PRIVATE BALCONIES: yes – all rooms

- ★ SWIMMING POOL: yes – fresh water, 12 × 5 m
- ★ RECREATIONAL ACTIVITIES: sauna, exercise room and massage
- ★ GARDENS: yes
- ★ NO. OF STAFF: 600
- ★ ROOM SERVICE: around the clock
- ★ ORIENTATION: rooms overlook the River Danube, park and residential area
- ★ CREDIT CARDS: Diners Club, American Express, Carte Blanche, Master Charge, Eurocard, Access and Barclaycard/Visa
- ★ OWNING COMPANY: Hotel Group Metropol
- ★ GENERAL MANAGER: Mr Bogoljub Starcevic
- ★ DISTANCE TO BEACH: by the hotel
- ★ DISTANCE TO SHOPS: 5 km
- ★ DISTANCE FROM AIRPORT: 16 km

No one can miss the Jugoslavija – it's that long grey battleship of a place along the banks of the Danube and, although some of the indoor corridors do bear a resemblance to a freeway interchange and the hotel is as modern as tomorrow, I would forgive it all this for the fact that, as big city hotels go, it is extremely efficient, practical, very clean and suprisingly personal in some little ways. Breakfast arrived with an English-language newspaper and the floor waiter asked me if this was the way I liked the toast – otherwise he'd go away and get another lot. Yugoslavs are very cheerful people, anxious to please, and I never saw a sour face. Rooms tend to be a little mass-produced and homogenous but clean and bright. It is a hotel for visiting politicians and businessmen and as such it works very well – with messages taken and delivered promptly and accurately. As for the food, I soon discovered that the hotel's local dishes were infinitely superior to what passes for international cuisine.

ALTERNATIVE TOURISM

One of the occupational hazards of being a travel writer is created by the lady who sits next to you at a dinner party. Eventually, inevitably, she asks you what you do for a living. You tell her and immediately she goes into adjectival rhapsodies mixed with the various green tinges of envy. Her second question is where the hazard lies. Confidentially, she whispers: 'Tell me something – which country do you like best?'

That is when my eyes take on a kind of glazed look. I sit back in my chair and try to give her the answer she really wants: a secret place, a bit of private and invaluable information about where the real experts go for their holidays. Some little place in Southern Italy maybe? Or the gardens of the Taj Mahal? Or that unforgettable island tucked away in a wine-dark sea?

Although I have now visited 102 countries (some of them many times) this is where I come unstuck, and my answer always disappoints my dinner companion. As the United States Marines used to sing, I have seen the world from the halls of Montezuma to the shores of Tripoli. I have seen the sun rise over Serengeti, the ebbtide spreading its white lace tablecloth of froth over countless West Indian beaches, the wonders of the Nile, both white and blue. I have felt the earth shake with the stamping of a Zulu *impi* in Natal, watched Tahitian girls dancing, and listened to the call of the Australian kookaburra. I have crossed the Sahara Desert twice, started climbing the Himalayas and thought better of it and I have also sat on the edge of a live volcano. I can remember, as clearly as yesterday, the divine luminosity of so many Greek mornings and when it comes to the past of man I still go frothing at the mouth at the thought of Ephesus or Palmyra, Jericho or Madurai.

It's no good. How can I tell this dear lady about my favourite place? How can I explain that my kind of travel isn't her kind, that it is a state of mind, a kind of perpetual motion geared to going out and seeing and imbibing things, of meeting man of a different colour on the other side of the world and suddenly discovering that he is my brother?

This is where I see many of you alert and critical readers and travellers pursing your lips and saying: 'All stuff and romantic nonsense. How do you square that up with reality? What do you do when you get up at five a.m. to have the Acropolis all to yourself and find that three thousand Japanese (with their cameras) have got there before you?' Indeed. Last year, 314 million tourists cavorted around the world – 100 million of them on the Mediterranean shores alone, making Europe collapse gently into the polluted waters. The floating market in Bangkok does not float any more (too many tourists) and for all I know the great Nile might soon stop flowing because of the waterborne traffic jams. Like Patrick Leigh Fermor, 'I lament this gregarious passion which destroys the object of its love. . . .' Tourism pollutes and more tourism pollutes absolutely. One might like one's fellow men but there is no doubt about it: they make a mess of the travelling environment. Anyone who has been to Torremolinos or La Manga de Mar Menor, or Miami Beach, or Tolon in Greece, or Mykonos, where there are now more discotheques than windmills, will know this.

I do not believe that this can be stopped. What is more, to stop it would be extremely anti-social and selfish. For centuries, ever since Marco Polo walked to China and the conquistadores began talking about El Dorado, the imagination of mankind has been geared to dreaming about travel. For a long time it was all in the mind, of course – think how long it took the Crusaders to reach the Holy Land. Then, suddenly, things changed. Society gave man the jet engine, extra leisure, more disposable income more widely spread, and of course credit cards. What would one expect him to do? Stay at home? Why should *you*, because you were born with more perception, a better chance of education or simply more money, think that the world belongs to you as a kind of private preserve? No, the masses will continue to visit the great clichés of the travel world and one cannot stop them. But it is perfectly possible to avoid them, or have a good try and this is what this article is all about – alternative tourism – the deliberate avoidance of the obvious. I am constantly amazed at the number of intelligent, reasonably affluent people who fall for it. When they buy a car they make quite sure it is the car they want and the same with a house. But give them the travel picture and they are the softest touch. There is not enough consumerism in this matter of travel choice.

It is my contention that, even now, it is possible to travel happily ever after (or almost ever) without falling into the trap of following your leader. One must be discriminating, coldly calculating, well informed and well read, very demanding and totally dedicated. It's rather like collecting pictures: you would wish to acquire the finest paintings you can afford to buy. Would it ever occur to you to buy prints instead of originals? Of course not. The same goes for travel: don't collect a coffee-table kind of world – look for the real thing.

Let us put it another way. I believe (in fact I know) that for every travel cliché there is a genuine alternative – perhaps not so famous, not so immortalized but much more personal and rewarding. How many wonders of the world are there? The ancients used to say seven. Travel agents have now made it more like seventy. But let's keep it to seven – possibly the Parthenon, the Taj Mahal, the Grand Canyon, the Pyramids, the Tower of London, Chartres Cathedral, Venice. An arbitrary choice which you might well question.

There is no doubt in my mind about at least one aspect of these places. Each must be seen at least once in a lifetime because they are all so unique and the sight and feel of them is our heritage. This is where we come back to our Japanese friends crawling all over the Acropolis – what does one do? One of the easiest ways is to make sure that you are there at the wrong time of year. Yes, the wrong time. I can swear to the fact that the Parthenon, seen on a chancy winter morning, with patches of blue in the sky and a sharp little Aegean wind blowing the smog off Athens can be very much more meaningful and dramatic. The same goes for the Taj Mahal. Contrary to all guidebook advice, I once insisted on visiting this most perfect of monuments in the middle of the Indian monsoon season and I got my reward – the pure, incredibly white dome changing its tinge every half hour, being polished by a sudden downpour or emerging from the mist like some poetic dream. The Grand Canyon? Go there in the summer and what do you see apart from thousands of tourists? The biggest ditch in the world, so big that it leaves you with your mouth open. Go there in early spring when the year's weather has not yet weighed the world down and it is a revelation – you can see the colours, the strata, the shape and the bones of this incredible place. The Pyramids? In the travel agent's 'right season' one can hardly see them for the touts. Again, choose an off-season morning. The Tower of London? Go and see it in the pouring rain, close to a grey Thames, and you will get much closer to William the Conqueror. As for Chartres Cathedral, I know what I do first of all – I never even get into the place. I choose a hillock in the fields of waving corn, stop the car, get out my biggest telephoto lens and just sit there to contemplate this Bach fugue in stone flying off into the sky. Venice, notoriously difficult to avoid since there is nowhere quite like it, also repays time and trouble. Here, too, forget the sunshine and the obvious charms of the Italian summer prints. Looking at the Piazza San Marco as it lies under a foot of water and with gaggles of umbrellas crossing it, you will get a new dimension.

So forget the clichés. Are you a serious traveller or a collector of Kilroy-Was-Here postcards? Another thing. Although the places listed above are unique and must be seen at least once in a lifetime, do remember this: for every one of them there is an alternative, perhaps not as great or special a place but one that will give you a very special feeling of personal discovery. While all the Japanese tourists are clicking their Nikkons at the Parthenon, travel a hundred miles south through the Peloponnese to the Temple of Apollo at Bassae. If there are more than five sight-seers there when you arrive, please send me a note and I will refund you the cost of this book. Yet Bassae is just as sensationally beautiful as the Parthenon though on a smaller scale, and Iklerios built it before the Parthenon – maybe as a model. The Taj Mahal – well, it too is unique but for every 10,000 people who go to see it, possibly ten go to see the mausoleum of Itma-ad-Daulah in the same city. Of course they are not the same, but that Indian-Moghul feeling will be there. As for the Grand Canyon (and I hope my Arizona friends will forgive me . . .) let us say that if I have not seen better I have inspected earthly chasms that were more my size. The Blyde River in South Africa for instance, the Great Rift Valley in East Africa or even the more humble Gorges du Tarn in France – all of them easier to take in when you have seen the original. The Tower of London? As a symbol of Norman power, I would rather have Caernarvon Castle in North Wales.

What this means is quite simple: if you see yourself as a connoisseur of travel, don't go in for the obvious or, if you must, go and see it at a non-obvious time.

This philosophy goes for every facet of travel: there is always something equal, or better, or different. It goes for beaches, too. Everybody, it sometimes seems, goes to Barbados. There is nothing wrong with Barbados (some of my best friends run hotels there . . .) but I can think of a hundred places where the beach will be just as good and the weather just as brilliant – but who thinks of the Maldives or the east coasts of Sri Lanka or Malaysia? Even nearer the Barbados prototype there are many islands where holiday buyers never really go. Not long ago, searching through the brochures of tour operators in Britain, I found that only two had something going on Tobago and only one appeared to know where the Grenadines, those heavenly microdots, were located. And if you now throw the argument back at me and say that I am the one who is creating tourist pollution tomorrow by extending the invitation today, I am sorry to say that you are wrong. If I am still around in ten years' time, I shall certainly find places to visit that mass tourism does not touch. Think of it – Indonesia, one country, has 11,000 islands and yet everyone goes to Bali. The beauty of the world is inexhaustible if only you care to open the package.

Another rule of my alternative tourism game has to do with the duration of a holiday. I am constantly amazed at the millions of people who buy a pre-digested holiday, say to the Orient, in seventeen days from door to door with six stops on the way. Do they know what they are doing? Or are they collecting visas and airports? Travel – good, rewarding, unforgettable travel – takes time. If all you want to do is to see another airport check-in desk, you can do so easily by travelling anywhere in the shortest possible time. That is what airplanes are for. But take the man who spends three days in Bangkok as part of his Instant Asia whirlwind, what is he going to learn about Thailand that he cannot find in the guidebooks? What is he going to meet up with except another venal taxi driver or a tout for the traditional Bangkok 'massage'? My point is that it is better to see one good-sized country in two weeks than six in fourteen days. So the rule of alternative tourism is this: decide what it is that really interests you, deep down, give yourself time and go. You will never regret it.

There are quite a few other rules in this game and one is called 'How to Avoid Travel Agents'. Use the travel agent as a fixer-upper, not as a motivator. Americans, especially those living in smallish, well-heeled cities, are better off than most in this respect. Quite often their travel agent is still a friend and counsellor. Not so elsewhere. In Europe, particularly in Britain and Germany, we suffer at the hands of a business zombie called a tour operator. Over the years he has made it easier, and cheaper for us to travel. Now he only sends us to the places he *thinks* we would like and he is almost always wrong.

His job is not to open new windows on the world. On the contrary – it is to make the windows bigger so that more people go to the same places. Like a supermarket chain selling breakfast cereals, he first of all limits the choice (he does not have to chase his tail all over the place . . .), then he increases the size of the packet of cereal to make you feel that it is good value for money and then, when you are hooked, he puts up the price and his profit. The tour operator does not promote travel or the idea of travel – he hinders it.

He serves you up with the kind of meal he thinks is good for you. You wonder what Italy south of Naples is like? He says that you would not like it and sends you to Rimini instead (see Rimini and die). He is a master of the obvious, the shop-soiled, the tired and tatty. He is happiest, and richest, when he can shoehorn more people into the same place, preferably near an international airport so that he can cut down on transfer costs. Mention any part of the world you fancy to the tour operator and what do you find? The adjectival emphasis is on what a beautiful place it is, how happy you will be etc. Everywhere, this dead hand of the tourism organizer is there, permanently tipping the scales.

Pick anywhere out of the blue. Sicily for instance. All travel agents want to take you to Taormina. Very nice too. 'And every day,' they say, 'you will look out of your bedroom window and see Mount Etna . . . .' But please don't look around because every tourist in the place is doing exactly the same thing – looking at Mount Etna over breakfast. Has your travel agent or tour operator ever heard of Monreale, or the great Hellenistic temples of Segesta and Agrigento? He does not know where they are. 'But you told me you wanted a beach,' he says plaintively, 'so I gave you a beach . . . !' But what about all the other beaches in Sicily? It is after all an island and there are beaches everywhere. Try those on the south coast – there is nobody there.

'India,' says your travel agent in a kind of ecstatic whisper. He has got the Moghuls all wrapped up in ten days. What if you want to see something else in India? He shrugs his shoulders and replies: 'Nobody wants to go there . . .' He is wrong – you do and you are the one who is paying for the fulfilment of your dream. I have been going to India every year for the past fifteen years and I have hardly touched the starting gate.

Take another aspect of the great rip-off. Unless he is a very special fellow, your tour operator is sooner or later going to lie to you. You want a tropical island but would like to get away from the Caribbean? 'Right,' he says thumbing his way through the tropical islands gaudies. 'The Seychelles . . . out there in the Indian Ocean. Marvellous. Super beaches. Just as good as the Caribbean and cheaper, too. That's what you want for your winter holiday!' Now, hold on a minute: a winter equivalent to Jamaica or Barbados? If you go to the Seychelles in January you will find that the rainfall is sixteen inches for the month and you won't be able to get out between the showers.

Readers might conclude that I am violently anti-travel agent. Not at all. I just want him to stay where he is, behind his counter, making up my tickets and shuffling timetables. I do not want him to come out and lead me off by the hand. There are of course some good travel agents. A few. Most of them will be small and specialized or else operating in the long haul market where they still have a part to play. After all it is a little difficult to get off for Bolivia or Bhutan without reasonable certainty that you will get there. Long haul people are not yet after the mass market and so they have more time for you.

Time and again, especially over the past few years, I have come across people who have successfully and rewardingly travelled the world without the help of an organized holiday. Once, I met a man in France's Loire Valley who told me that he had come specially to see all the châteaux that never seemed to appear in the guidebooks. My heart warmed to him – he had over fifty of them on his list. I added one more, Montpoupon, down in the Indre area. He shook my hand and was off like a streak of lightning. Another time, in a taverna overlooking a very good beach in the Peloponnese, I met a French couple who seemed to know the area. Did they know such and such a beach? I asked. The husband looked at me and replied: 'Yes, we do know it but there was someone on it when we passed this morning . . . !'

The happiest travellers I have ever met have been people who did their own thing. Once, in a tiny airport in the jungly heart of Papua New Guinea, I suddenly heard a rapid flow of Spanish and turned around to find a dozen Spaniards, very chic in bush clothes and complete with super luggage from Loew's. Spaniards in

Papua New Guinea – what in Hades were they doing there? One of them told me that once a year their greatest pleasure was to escape to a really rough, little-known country, look at the locals, go upriver by canoe and never see a telephone. I much admired their courage.

One day in the Maldive Islands quite a few years ago, I looked through my binoculars at the intense pale blue of the lagoon and there, right in the middle, was a man wearing rubber boots, a floppy straw hat and a pair of very floppy shorts. He had to be British – only the British wear this sort of garment. In those days, the hotel was the only one, with only twelve rooms and inevitably we met that night in what passed for the bar. Of course he was British – a High Court judge at that. He explained that he loved lagoons, went around with a stick, dug up all the stones to look at the marine life and had a whale of a time. That man knew every tropical lagoon I had ever heard of between Cancer and Capricorn and he went to a different one each year. 'What does your wife think about it?' I asked. 'Doesn't she get bored being all by herself?' He replied that she did not. She read novels and played patience on the terrace and once a year, without him, she went back to visit all the great museums of Italy. I admired these people tremendously: they had come to terms with just what they enjoyed and did it. Without a travel agent of course.

At this stage, dear readers, I can almost hear you protesting: 'It's all very well for you – you are a professional traveller and you know how to find your way about. I could not begin to fix it all up . . . .' You could. If you know the mechanics of travel in your own country and have due regard for national and seasonal difference and the modalities of price, it is not at all difficult to arrange a trip to France from Kansas, Birmingham or Düsseldorf. All you need is imagination, patience and to make sure that you are well informed. Read all you can about the destination of your choice and then go, go, go. This kind of freelance travel is coming, as sure as little apples. The more hidebound, mass-oriented and institutional tour operators become, the more their would-be clients will become aware of alternative tourism. Already the ingredients are there.

Air fares, once almost invisible behind the barbed wire of bureaucracy, are coming down. The gap between short haul and long haul is closing and I can now go to India for not much more than the airline would have charged me to Athens. What we, in Britain, call the 'bucket shops' – places that sell discounted tickets – are becoming respectable. You can book your own hotel and the people there will be delighted to hear from you – the individual client – whether you come from Wagga Wagga or Memphis, Tennessee. Some agents even offer discounted accommodation at certain times of year and if you can't be bothered with telephoning or telexing, most big cities around the world have an agent for the hotel you are trying to book in. Airlines don't mind either – in fact they are often delighted to find a man who knows what he wants and how much it is going to cost him. Instead of being ripped off by travel agents, they are dealing with a real, live human being. Almost certainly, car rental is at least one third cheaper when you look for it at your arrival airport and the man will be perfectly happy with your credit card.

Alternative travel is coming. I can foresee the time, not all that far away, when you will be buying a holiday (with or without the help of your TV information service) just the way you used to buy a jigsaw puzzle – fitting all the pieces together. This piece is the blue sky, that piece is the cost of the air ticket, that one goes for unpolluted sea, another is a Roman temple or a jazzy resort or a cruise up the Amazon. Even a trip to Las Vegas taking in Bryce Canyon on the way to clear the alcoholic fumes . . .

Then, alone and at peace, you will sit down, spread them on the carpet and fit them together and construct your holiday the way you want it. When that happens, the world will once again become a great, big, wonderful place in which your own leisure personality emerges triumphant and there will be no talk of tourist pollution. Let those who want togetherness have it. They are welcome. I intend to go the other way.

HOW
TO TRAVEL
HAPPILY

All I can do is to try to help you with a few general tips I have found useful in many years of travelling all over the world.

CLIMATE AND TRAVEL SEASONS

It is impossible to generalize accurately. My bedside reading is the British Meteorological Office statistics covering the last thirty years month by month in 982 places around the world from Aarhus to Zumbo. But not even that respected publication could tell that it would rain in Greece in September when the cradle of Western Civilization looked like a suburb of Manchester or Cincinnati.

The thing to remember is that what makes the high season is not necessarily the glorious weather in the place you are planning to visit, but the terrible climate in your own country which forces the likes of us to emigrate. It is the demand which creates a high season – not the climate. Even the national tourist offices' statistics are open to debate. Naturally they want you to visit their country and many of them are not above doing some creative editing with the facts and figures. If you want to be as sure as you can be, consult your own government's meteorological statistics for the world and if you work out a fair average you can't go too far wrong. The first and obvious thing to remember is that the seasons are reversed whether you go North or South of the Equator – ie while Scotland freezes in winter, Australians are having a sunny Christmas. This can be confusing.

Here are a few generalities about the main parts of the world.

EUROPE AND THE MEDITERRANEAN

The right time to travel in this temperate continent is between May and October – and that's the time when Europe is overrun with tourists. The weather depends on your luck but you cannot expect to be truly warm in the Mediterranean in the winter – from Spain to Cyprus, the daily average may be around ten or eleven degrees centigrade though it can be much higher due to micro-climate conditions which affect certain parts because of orientation, mountain protection, etc. You can swim quite happily off a beach in Rhodes in early November and there are climatically favoured places like Almeria (Spain), the Algarve (Portugal), Taormina (Sicily), Southern Crete and Cyprus where the weather is likely to be better than average in the winter months.

It is sensible to give careful study to the orientation of the resort of your choice. If it faces south and is protected from the north by a range of mountains, it is likely to be temperate in winter. Winds like the *mistral* and the *sirocco* (Western Mediterranean), the *bora* (Adriatic) and the *meltemi* (Aegean Sea) must be taken into account. These have their seasons of greater or lesser force.

AFRICA AND THE INDIAN OCEAN

Again it is difficult to generalize but north of the Tropic of Capricorn, it is likely to be drier in our winter than south of the Equator. Avoid inland areas in high summer. The East African coast is affected by the 'big rains' (April/May) and the 'little rains' (October/November). In islands like the Seychelles, the monsoon strikes in December/January/February and to a lesser extent it is the same in Mauritius, but average temperatures will remain around twenty-six degrees centigrade and the islands are likely to be less humid than the continental coast.

NORTH AMERICA

As every New Yorker knows to his cost, the sub-tropical climate in summer of his own city makes life well-nigh unbearable. Californians know that there is a vast difference between, say, San Diego and San Francisco. The most equable climate is in Florida and the South Western States (not in summer) and further south where, unfortunately, the climate can be turned upside down by Mexico's vertical geography, ie you could be chilly in Mexico City and swelter in Acapulco.

THE CARIBBEAN AND SOUTH AMERICA

Together with some Pacific islands, the Caribbean (though not Bermuda) has the most equable climate in the world – hovering around the twenty-six to thirty degrees centigrade mark all the year round though the rainfall tends to be heavier in the summer months. In South America, apart from altitude factors which can alter things considerably, the further North you go the warmer and rainier it is and the other way around, bearing in mind the fact that because of hemispheric factors, the Rio winter is our summer. I have suffered from heat stroke in Manaos after nearly freezing solid in Sao Paulo the day before.

SOUTHERN ASIA AND THE FAR EAST

This is monsoon country and if you wish to go to India you'd better stay at home from May to September – though the monsoon comes later in the South and differs in timing between the east and west coast. In Singapore, it rains most from November to January while in Hong Kong the big rains come from May to September – though winter temperatures in the two cities can vary by as much as eight or ten degrees centigrade, Hong Kong being the cooler. Japan has a temperate climate fairly similar to Europe.

CLOTHING

When travelling in hot or tropical countries, there are only two words in your vocabulary – cotton and wool. Reject all synthetic materials, particularly nylon. Wearing them can create serious health hazards, starting with heat rash. The only synthetic material I carry is a plastic shower-coat bought in Japan. It folds down as small as a pack of cards and has repaid the investment a thousand-fold.

Wear loose clothing if you can – nothing restricting – and never start on your travels with new shoes – you'll regret it. Men should take plenty of shirts (hotel laundries are expensive, unpredictable and addicted to eating shirt buttons . . .) and women should take as many light dresses as possible, especially those that fold flat. Remember also that if you are travelling to a tropical country you will find, nine times out of ten, that the locals have long ago designed the most comfortable wear – imitate them and buy some (this applies especially to Africa, India and the East).

I mention wool because a little wool will go a long way when you need it and you never know whether you will or not. My long-time favourite is an alpaca cardigan – light but warm and easy to pack. Alas, it is expensive and fairly delicate. My wife swears by cashmere.

LUGGAGE

There are two schools of thought here – some take as little as possible and others take as much as possible. I confess to belonging to the latter group for two reasons. The first is that I am an eternal optimist and usually hope that there will be porters around (there aren't). The second reason is more important and concerns the number of times I have had to meet Presidents or Prime Ministers or other VIPs in shirtsleeves and I now like to be ready for anything – from climbing the Himalayas to meeting African chiefs or going out on the town. All this is a matter of personal choice.

When it comes to the choice of luggage, watch out: the best is not always the most practical. I love the 'weekend in Monte Carlo' type of leather cases and indeed Gucci or St. Laurent bags but I have become convinced over the years that all airlines share a luggage-mangling mafia that delights in tearing off handles, bashing in corners and breaking the locks – the more beautiful the luggage the greater the temptation. On the whole, I find that moulded cases are still the best and most durable.

HOTEL ROOMS

All the hotels listed in this book are – I think – good ones but that should certainly not prevent you from being inquisitive and asking questions. Here are a few tips:

★ Don't feel shy at asking to see your room before you sign in – hotel people may raise an eyebrow but they will respect you; one does not buy a refrigerator sight unseen.

★ Have a good look around, count the coathangers, inspect the bath and washbasin overflow outlets – if they are clean that's a good sign. Trail a finger inside drawers for dust. Make sure you have the pillows or bolsters you like. Try the shower. Make sure the curtains work. Many hotels are *very* bad at room lighting – so inspect your bedside lighting and if it is not sufficient for you to read by, ask for another lamp. Test the beds for comfort. If you are alone in a double room, *never* choose the bed nearest the telephone: a long succession of guests have been sitting on the edge of this bed to telephone and made it as sway-backed as a camel.

★ Watch out for room service and especially for room service breakfast in any country like the United States where labour is expensive. Charges can be exorbitant. Many good hotels nowadays have adopted the American method of giving you a breakfast order to fill up and hang on your doorknob. I approve of this since it saves time and limits linguistic difficulties at a time of the morning when you can do without them.

★ Tipping. As far as possible, if you can find out, adopt the custom of the country. I have always used a method once explained to me by the late Aga Khan – no mean traveller himself. It's quite simple if a trifle unfair: you tip heavily when you arrive and fairly lightly when you leave. The hotel bush telegraph soon gets going and everybody knows what you are up to and you'll get good service.

★ Most grand hotel *concierges* or head porters are vastly knowledgeable, multi-lingual, helpful and thoroughly familiar with the minor details of travel and tourism. Consult them but try to judge your man. Many are the well-paid end of a mafia which extends to taxi-drivers, car hire companies, restaurants, guides, etc. I always arrive forewarned, that is with the right guidebooks and the right information since this is always handsomely repaid in practice. One of the best I know because of its frankness and lucidity is the Fodor series.

★ Languages. Nobody can expect you to become fluent in Swahili or Serbo-Croat overnight. English is universal and a little French helps quite a bit. Besides this do try to make an effort to master simple words like 'Good morning', 'Good night', 'Thank you', 'Where', 'How much', 'Please', in the local language. People of all nations without exception will be pleased that you have tried. If you are in a country where you cannot even read the alphabet (Arab lands, Japan, etc), ask your hotel porter to write down addresses, etc for your taxi-driver.

★ Be fair, frank and open. If you have any prejudices, leave them at home. Whether a man is red, white, black, yellow or blue, give him a smile and a firm handshake and take him for what he is – not what you would like him to be. Treat people as equals – you'd be surprised how much more fun you will get out of travelling.

HEALTH

I must be lucky for all I ever suffered in two-and-a-half decades of travelling – even in remote countries – was a dose of 'Montezuma's Revenge' in Mexico and another of 'Delhi Belly' in India.

Inquire about the 'jabs' you need if any. Vaccination against smallpox (almost eradicated), yellow fever and cholera are more often than not compulsory. I also

lieve very strong in TAB – anti-typhoid vaccination – and rarely travel without
sect-repellents, stomach-upset remedies advocated by my doctor (they vary
om country to country), and water sterilization tablets for those countries where
nuine mineral water may be hard to get.

an we drink the water? That's a question most readers always ask and, alas,
ere is no hard-and-fast rule but over the years one has developed a sixth sense in
is – I never drink the water in tropical or backward countries and even in some
uropean countries I have my own particular habits. In Italy, for instance, I will
ink the water north of Rome but not south of it. I will drink it in Portugal but not
Spain, in Greece but not in Turkey. It is irrational but all I can say is that it has
orked for me – so far.

part from accidents, one is convinced that no hotel listed in this book will serve
ou food that will make you ill. But it is when eating out that you should observe
e simplest basic rules: no peeled fruit, no shellfish in polluted areas, no food
at you cannot recognize or inquire about. Beware of exotic food. For every ten
avellers who are upset by tainted food, at least one hundred become ill through
surfeit of strange food. So do beware of all those curries and other very hot
shes from India down to Indonesia. Your stomach is simply not used to them.

s for circadian dysrythmia, or jet lag to most of us, habitual travellers are used to
these days. North to south and south to north journeys don't affect anyone, but
ast to west and vice versa do, and the best physicians recommend a more or less
ng period of physical rhythm re-adjustment in each case, i.e. don't rush off to a
ightclub when your body cycle is still on breakfast time. Be sensible and if you
re not sure, ask your airline.

While in the air, make yourself at home – take off your shoes, relax, wear
omething loose and warm, go to the loo as often as possible and drink lots of
quids but never fizzy drinks – everything from champagne to cokes; try to give
em up and stick to fruit juices, wine or whisky. Fizzy 'soft' drinks are the worst
ffenders, yet people keep asking for them on airplanes. It is the worst thing they
ould do.

nally, I can't give you any advice about the final hurdle – the customs man. His
enre varies in every country and I have met quite a few. All I can say is this: don't
ke him for an idiot. Most customs men are very good psychologists and can
istinguish at a glance between the holidaymaker who has splashed out a bit on
aubles and the professional smuggler. Let discretion be your guide.

IR TRAVEL

ou may well ask: 'That's all very well but after all that how do I avoid all the
ggravations connected with air travel?' I sympathize. Having flown well over
vo million miles I believe that air travel as it is today is one of the most
ehumanized and degrading forms of transport imaginable. But one can't have it
oth ways. One cannot have the benefit of being able to reach Outer Mongolia
uickly and then blame the airlines for getting you there. Most airlines, alas,
ersistently refuse to take the human element into account. All, but really all
abitual travellers know that air travel could be simplified, made more comfort-
ble and interesting. No one listens – except another traveller. One can only
uggest a few ways – some of them obvious – which will minimize your trauma.

* If Concorde is going where you are going – take it. Despite its bad press (mostly
  among those who have never experienced it) it still gets you there twice as fast
  (and with half the aggravation), your luggage is security-banded and you don't
  wait around so much.

* Travel first class if you can. As in everything else, the best costs more and for
  some of us it is worth it – more legroom, more moving-about room, better food
  and drink, less herding and an opportunity to complain bitterly if something
  goes wrong. More loos too – and that makes a great difference on a long flight.
  First class is supposed to be anti-social but how long is it since you last carried a
  pack on your back?

★ Take fares, now. Or leave them because the chances are you will neve
understand them. Even airline people don't and on one occasion recently
was quoted *seven* different fares by the same airline for the same journey. It is
measure of the airlines' giddy death-wish that they will offer you a seat at an
price and in the end you'll find that this only works on Wednesdays or c
January 2. Take my advice: go shopping for the most awkward, most tiresom
most argumentative travel agent you can find (someone you would *hate* to c
business with . . .) and give him your custom. The chances are high that h
will get you the best deal.

★ However complicated your journey is – stopover, side trips, etc – any worl
airline should be able to issue you with a valid ticket. In principle. But it do
not work, despite all the computers and the gizmos. So check it and then chec
it again because only you know where you want to go and when. Not lor
ago, one world-famous airline issued me with a ticket for several shor
inter-island flights in the Caribbean. When I got to my first take-off point,
discovered that the ticket was based on a two-year-old timetable. Whateve
you do, examine your ticket carefully, turn it upside down if you like but neve
take anyone's word that it's all OK.

★ Despite the booking girl's pretty smile, don't believe anything she says whe
she assures you that you are on the 'waiting-list' unless you can see your nam
on that list at different times during the waiting period. The girl does not mea
to lie but she does, or she is over-ruled by her bosses. Maybe the President
aunt wants to go your way at the last minute and, believe me, she will and yo
won't. So only accept a firm, OK booking and if you are travelling with, sha
we say, an esoteric airline, insist on seeing your name on the passenger lis
You won't be popular but you'll take off.

★ Don't be taken in by the airlines' special classes, the businessmen's special
the club-this and VIP-that. At the time of writing I have counted up to 4
promotional gimmicks of this kind and most of those I have experienced ar
not worth it. I once reluctantly paid an extra $187 for a system that had bee
boosted to the skies. I discovered that the only thing I received which econom
passengers did not receive was a free drink. A very expensive free drink.

★ If you must travel economy, find out which type of aircraft you will be flying o
and ask the airline or the travel agent *in advance* to show you the seating pla
adopted by this particular airline. There *are* differences. Make a note of th
seat numbers nearest the emergency exists – they always have more legroom

★ Make up your mind once and for all that there aren't any *good* airports – onl
bad ones and not-so-bad ones. Reconcile yourself to the fact that when you ge
to one airport or another, something nasty will happen: air-conditionin
breakdown, a strike, a power failure and so on. You'll never be disappointec
If you can, especially in Southern Europe, avoid the obvious 'holiday' airpor
(Gerona, Barcelona, Alicante, Malaga, Venice, Pisa, Nice, Athens, etc
Arrival and departure are guaranteed to put you off air travel for ever. Th
worst international airports I know are Los Angeles, Kennedy, Mexico City
Cairo, Khartoum, Kingston, Dar-es-Salaam, Conakry, Dakar, Kinshasa
Damascus, Baghdad, Delhi, Bombay, Calcutta, Heraklion, Rome an
Palermo. I will not name the *next* worst since that would cover all the rest.

★ If you are on a short flight – say anything under three hours – leave the airline
food alone. It will be a good miss. If you think that you really will get hungr
do what a friend of mine does – take your own picnic with you.

★ Avoid airport food and drink at all costs. You are more likely to get foo
poisoning in an airport than anywhere else in the world.

★ Make up your mind – once and for all – never to buy *anything* in an airpor
unless you happen to know that the duty free shop is really what it says. Ai
ports are the world's biggest emporiums of rubbish and in all my travels I hav
been able to count on the fingers of one hand the items that were worth buying
Apart from that, flying is fun. Getting there is even better.